ORIGO

STEPPING STONES 2.0

COMPREHENSIVE MATHEMATICS

AUTHORS

James Burnett
Calvin Irons
Peter Stowasser
Allan Turton

PROGRAM CONSULTANTS

Diana Lambdin
Frank Lester, Jr.
Kit Norris

CONTRIBUTING WRITER

Beth Lewis

STUDENT BOOK B

ORIGO EDUCATION

CONTENTS

CONTENTS

Step In **What do you know about one hundred?**

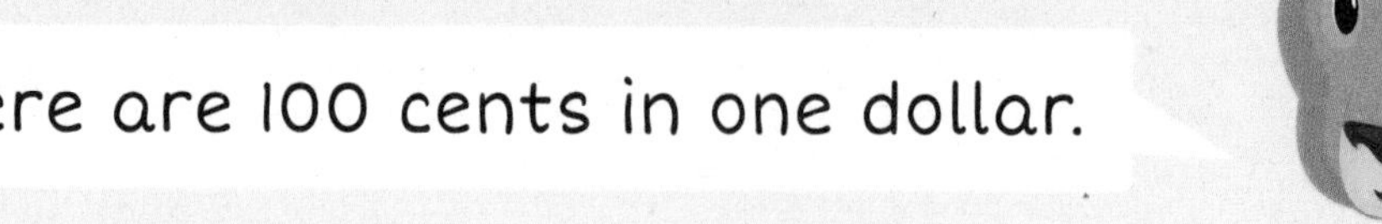

I have seen 100 miles on signs.

Where have you seen **100** written?

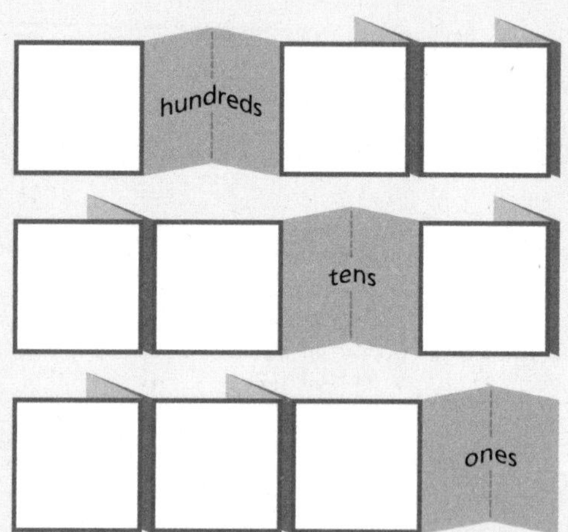

How would you write 100 on this expander?

Write **100** on this expander.
What do you notice?

Write **100** on this expander.
What do you notice?

Step Up 1. Use the number chart to help you answer the questions.

61	62	63	64	65	66	67	68	69	70
71	72	73	74	75	76	77	78	79	80
81	82	83	84	85	86	87	88	89	90
91	92	93	94	95	96	97	98	99	100

a. What number is **one less** than 100? 

b. What number is **ten less** than 100? ______

2. Circle the number. Then write the number of ones left over.

a. Circle 70 fingers.

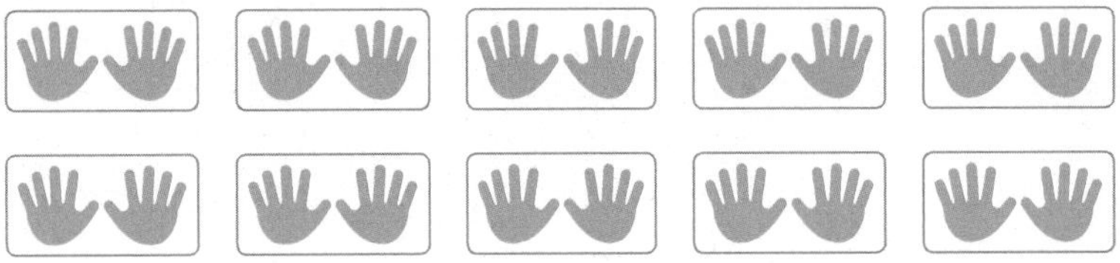

☐ not circled

b. Circle 50 fingers.

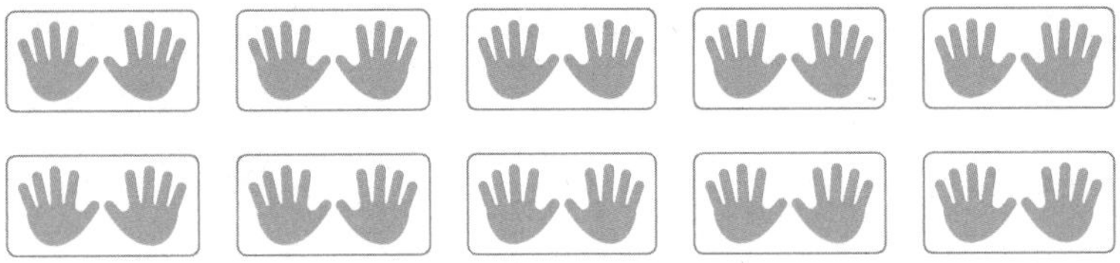

☐ not circled

c. Circle 90 fingers.

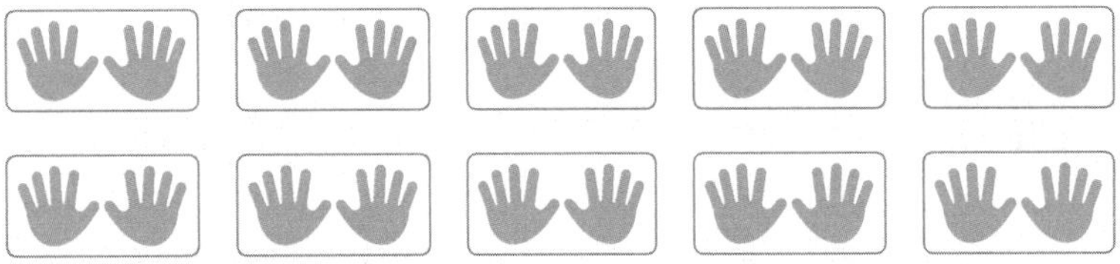

☐ not circled

3. Color the blocks. Then write the number of ones left over.

a. 25 ones

☐

b. 85 ones

☐

c. 65 ones

☐

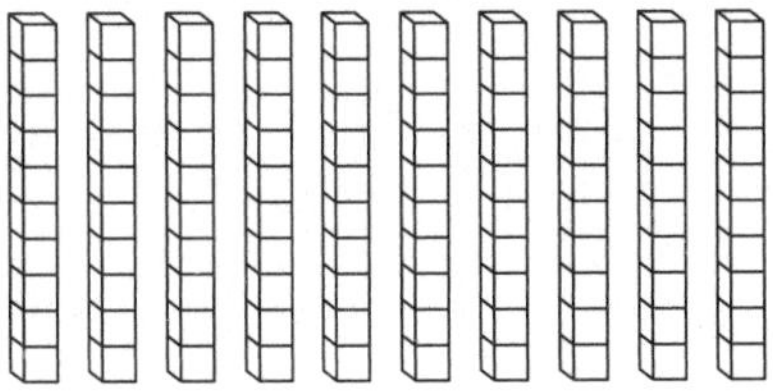

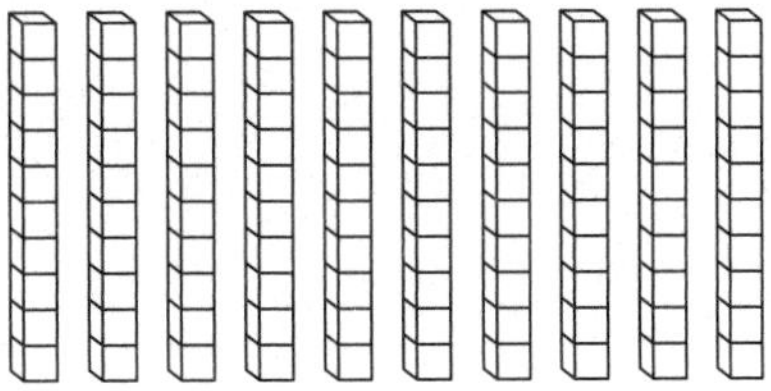

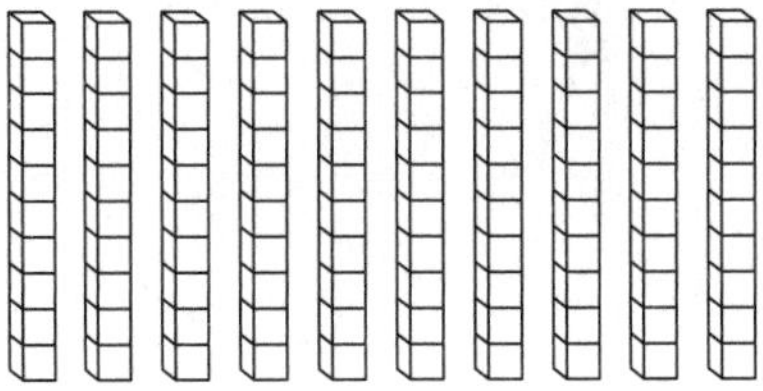

Step Ahead

Complete these to show other pairs of two-digit numbers that make 100.

a. ☐0 and ☐0

b. ☐5 and ☐5

c. ☐5 and ☐5

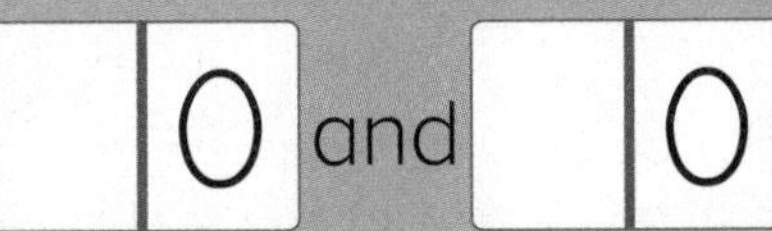

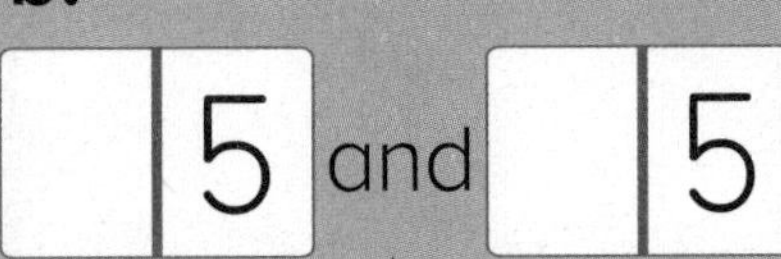

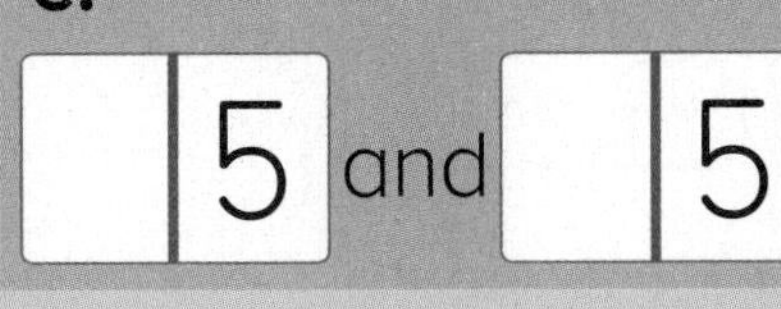

7.2 Number: Writing three-digit numbers to 120 (without teens)

Step In What number does this picture of blocks show?

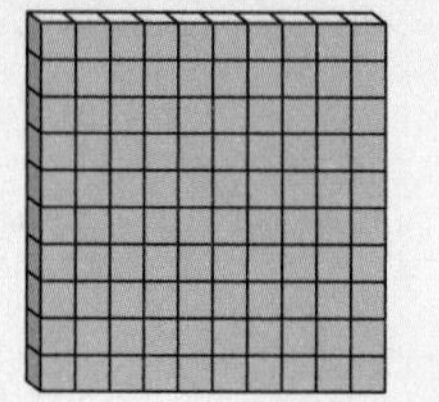

How would you write this number on an expander? How do you know?

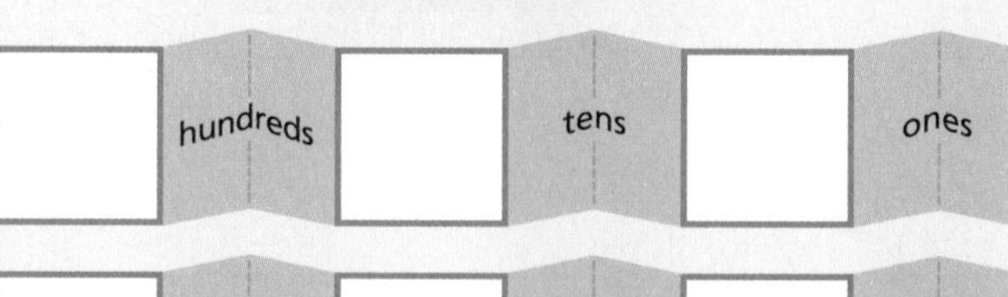

Look at the number on this expander. What does each digit mean?

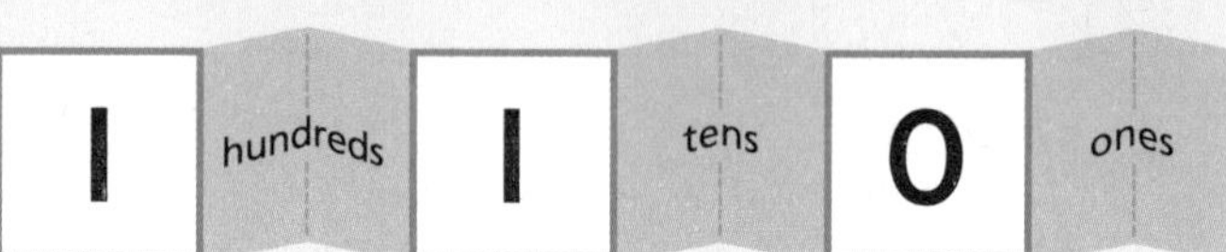

How is this number different from the number on the first expander above?

Step Up 1. Look at the blocks. Write the number on the expanders to match.

a.

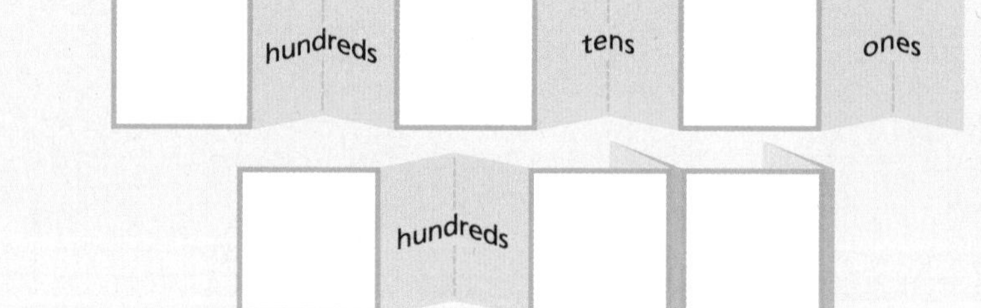

b.

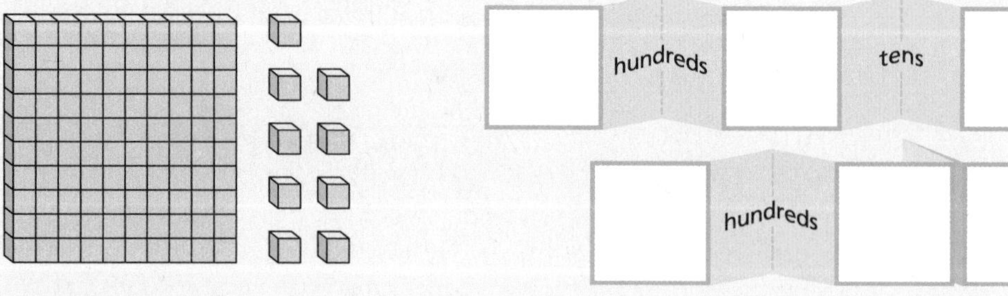

c.

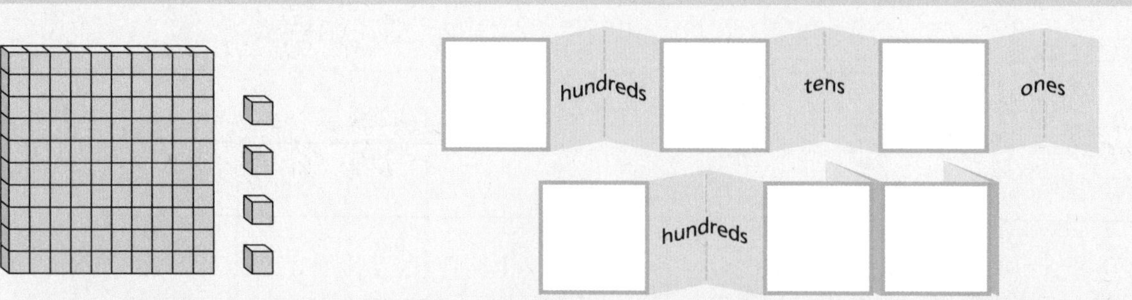

2. Color the blocks to match the number shown on each expander.

a.

1
hundreds
0
5

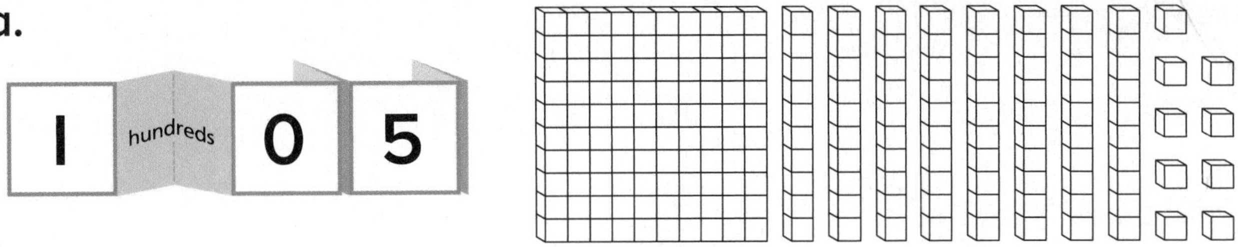

b.

1
hundreds
0
2

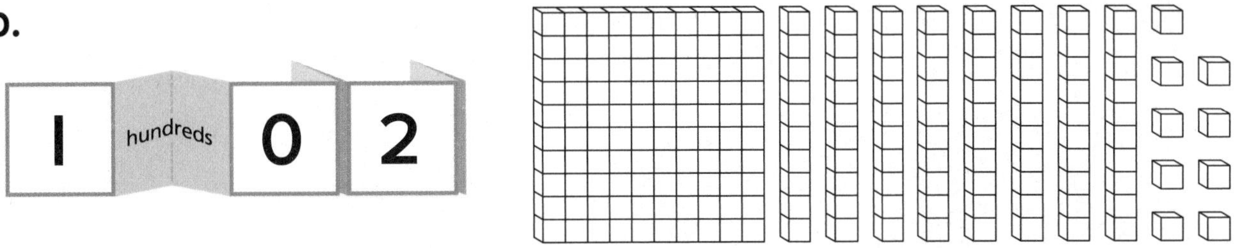

c.

1
hundreds
0
8

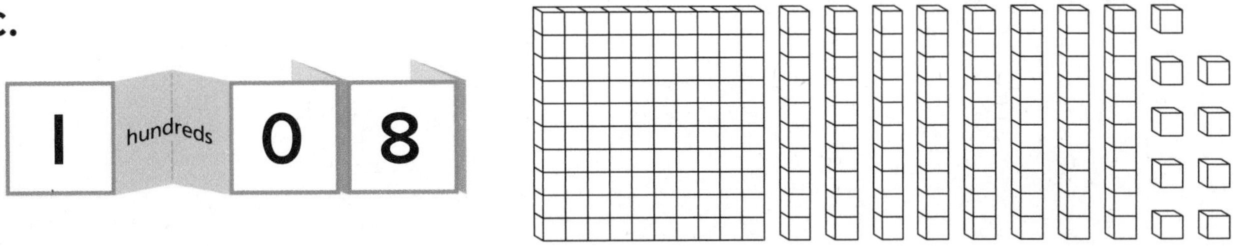

d.

1
hundreds
1
0

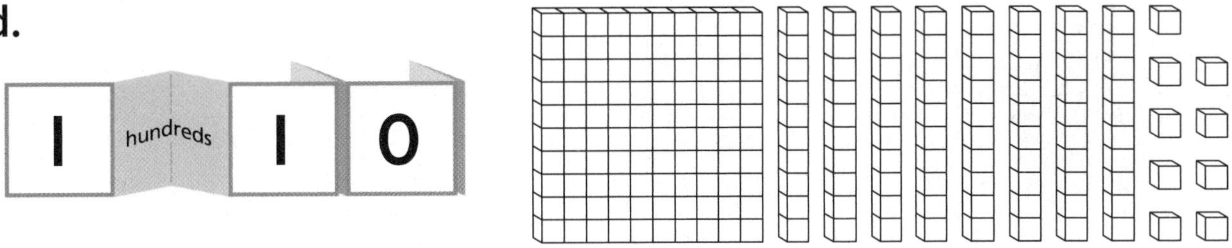

Step Ahead Draw more blocks to match the number on the expander.

1
hundreds
0
9

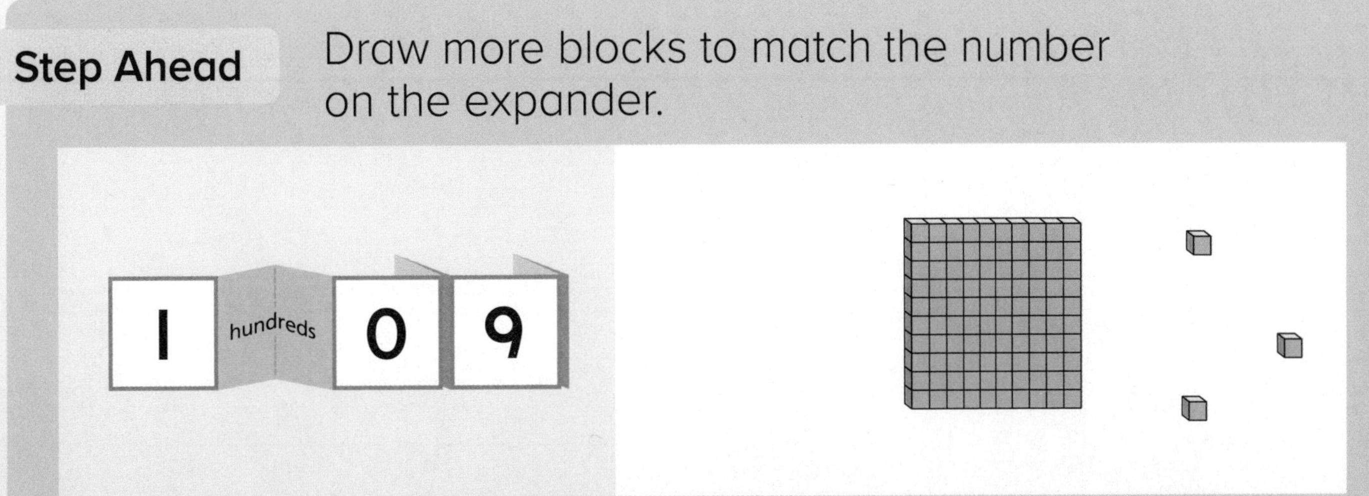

Maintaining concepts and skills

Computation Practice

★ Complete the equations as fast as you can.

start

$8 + 8 =$ ____ $5 + 3 =$ ____ $2 + 6 =$ ____

$2 + 8 =$ ____ $5 - 2 =$ ____ $4 + 4 =$ ____

$3 + 3 =$ ____ $6 + 1 =$ ____ $4 - 3 =$ ____

$7 + 7 =$ ____ $8 + 1 =$ ____ $2 + 3 =$ ____

$5 + 6 =$ ____ $3 + 4 =$ ____ $5 - 4 =$ ____

$5 + 5 =$ ____ $1 + 4 =$ ____ $4 - 2 =$ ____

$8 + 7 =$ ____ $6 + 6 =$ ____

finish

Ongoing Practice 1. Write the number in each part and the total.

FROM 1.6.1

One part is ____.

The other part is ____.

The total is ____.

2. a. Write **100** on each expander.

FROM 1.7.1

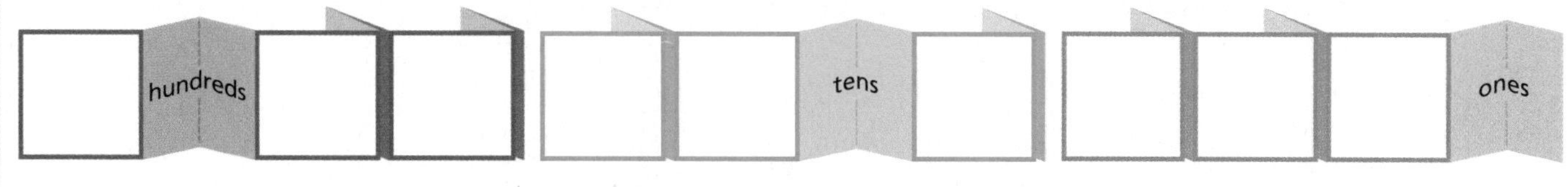

b. How many ones equal 100? 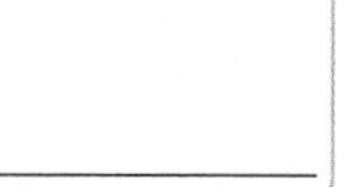 ____

c. How many tens equal 100? ____

d. How many hundreds equal 100? ____

Preparing for Module 8 Draw more dots to make 10. Then complete the matching equation.

a.

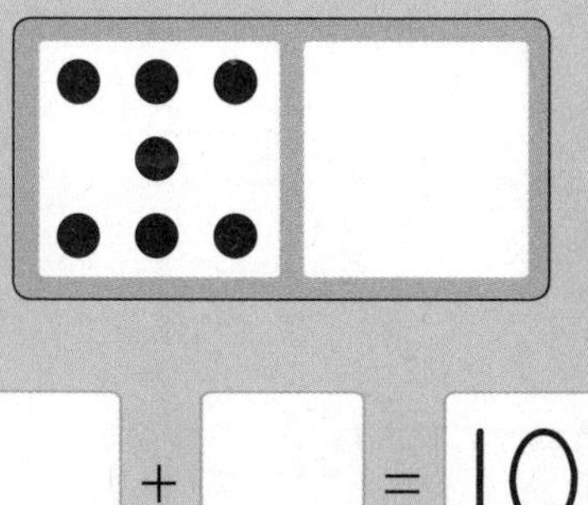

____ + ____ = 10

b.

____ + ____ = 10

7.3 Number: Writing numbers and number names to 120 (without teens)

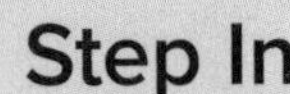

Step In

How would you read and say the number on this expander?

Do you have to say the number of tens?

How would you write the number in words?

How would you read and say these numbers?

What does the zero in each number tell you?

Step Up

1. Look at the blocks. Write the number on the expanders. Then write the matching number name.

a.

hundreds tens ones

hundreds

__________ hundred ____________________

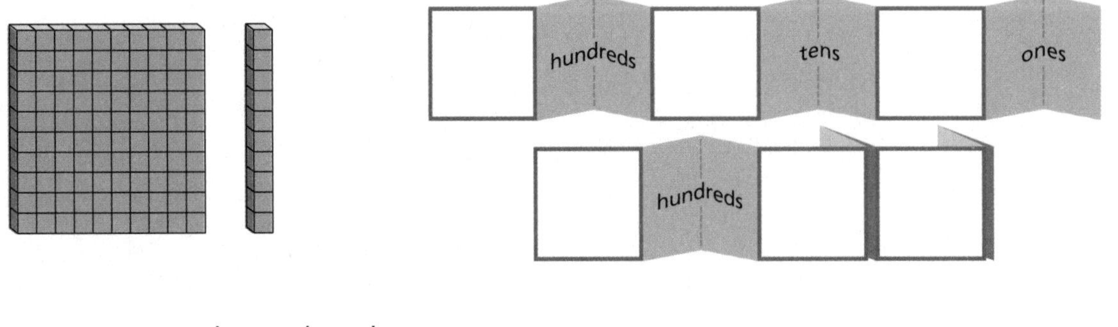

b.

__________ hundred ____________________

2. Read the number name. Write the matching number on the expander.

a. one hundred six

hundreds

b. one hundred eight

hundreds

c. one hundred two

hundreds

d. one hundred one

hundreds

e. one hundred nine

hundreds

f. one hundred twenty

hundreds

g. one hundred ten

hundreds

h. one hundred seven

hundreds

Step Ahead

a. Write a different three-digit number on this expander.

hundreds

b. Color blocks to show your number.

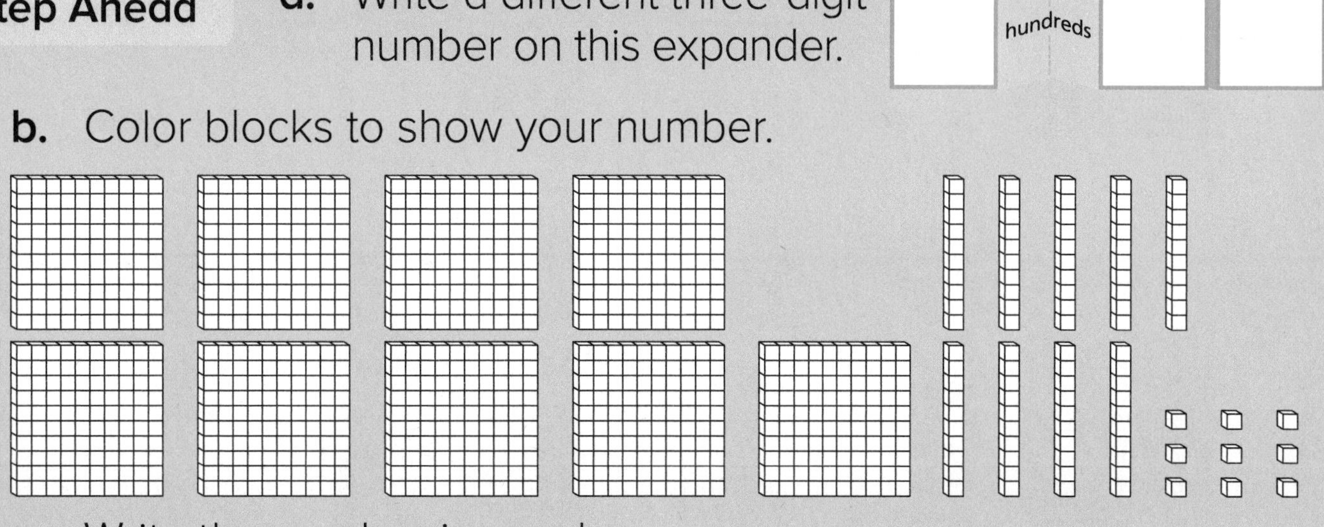

c. Write the number in words.

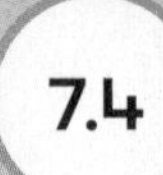

Number: Writing numbers and number names to 120 (with teens)

Step In

How would you read and say the number on this expander?

1 hundreds 1 6

How would you write the number in words?

How would you read and say these two numbers?

What is the same about these numbers?
What is different?

Step Up

1. Look at the blocks. Write the number on the expanders. Then write the matching number name.

a.

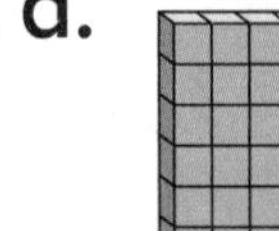

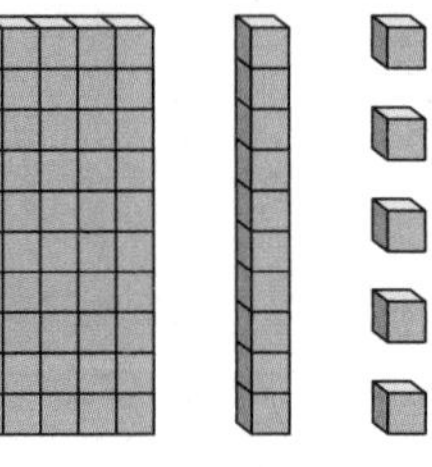

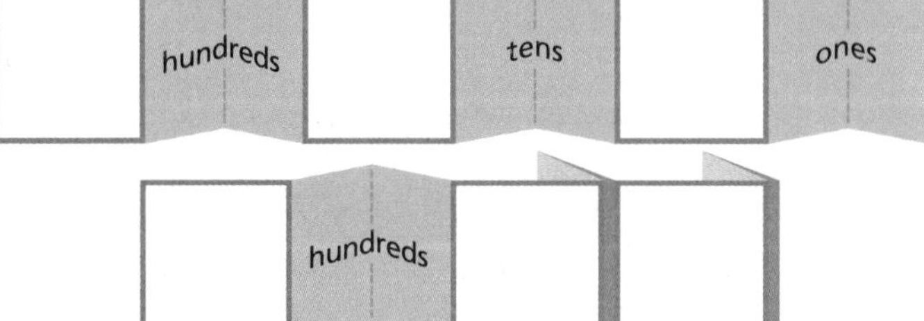

_____________ hundred _____________________________________

b.

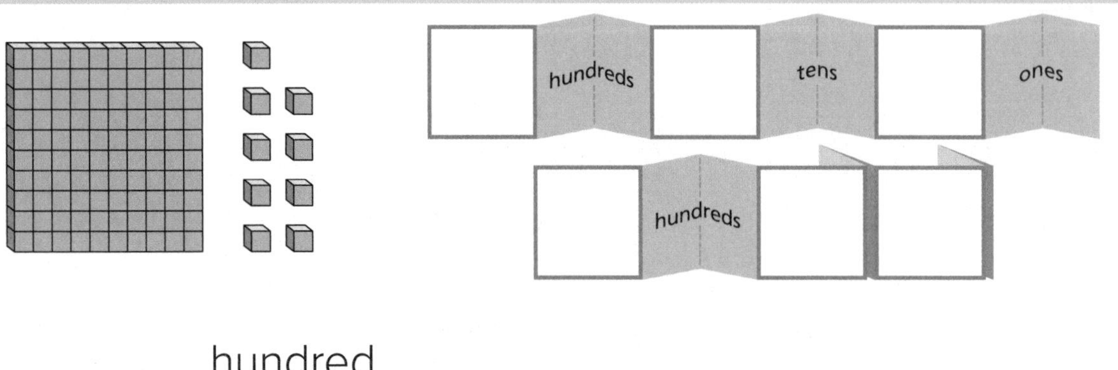

_____________ hundred _____________________________________

2. Read the number name. Write the matching number on the expander.

a. one hundred thirteen

hundreds

b. one hundred eight

hundreds

c. one hundred eleven

hundreds

d. one hundred eighteen

hundreds

e. one hundred seventeen

hundreds

f. one hundred seven

hundreds

g. one hundred twenty

hundreds

h. one hundred twelve

hundreds

Step Ahead Read this number.

1 hundreds 0 2

a. Color blocks to show a number that is **10 greater**.

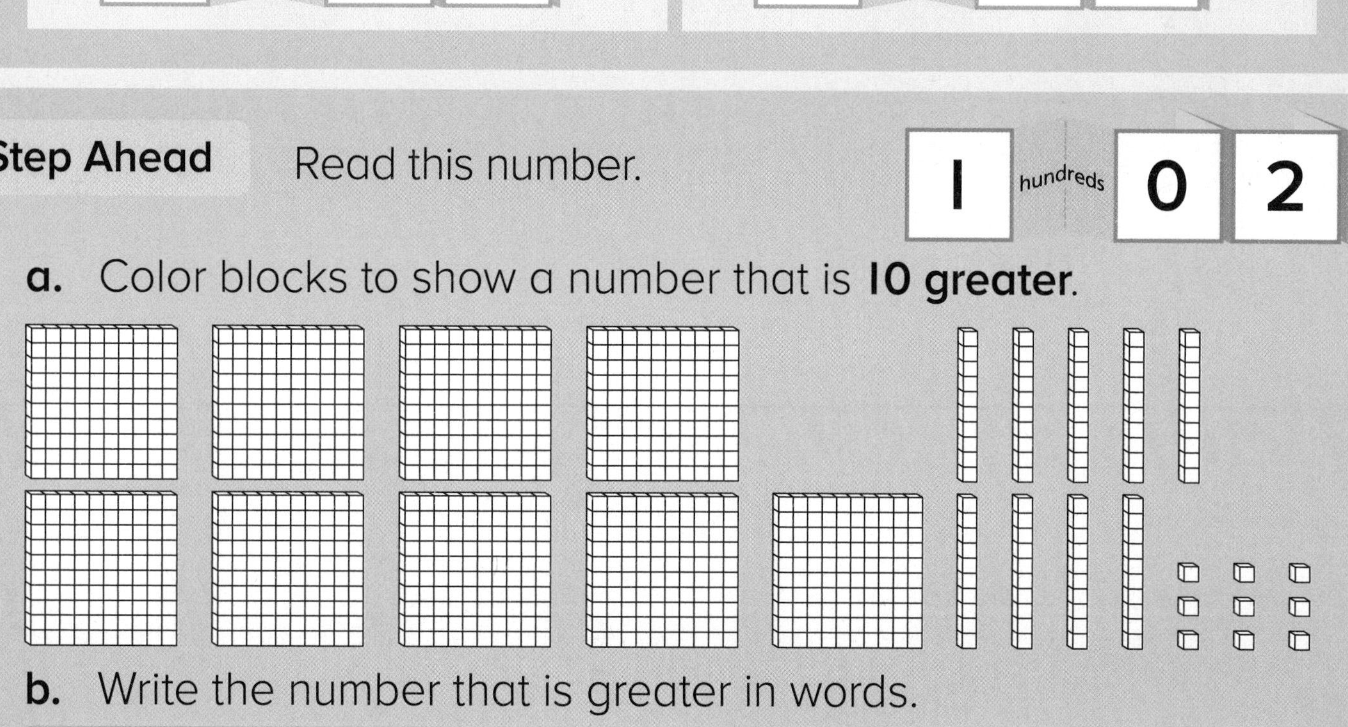

b. Write the number that is greater in words.

Maintaining concepts and skills

Think and Solve

The same shapes are the same number. Write the missing number inside each square to complete the equation.

☐ + ☐ = 9 − ☐

Words at Work

a. Write about where you have seen 100.

b. Draw a picture to show what you saw.

Ongoing Practice

1. Complete the addition fact to figure out the number of carrots that were taken. Then complete the subtraction fact to match.

FROM 1.6.4

a.

6 + ___ = 7

7 − 6 = ___

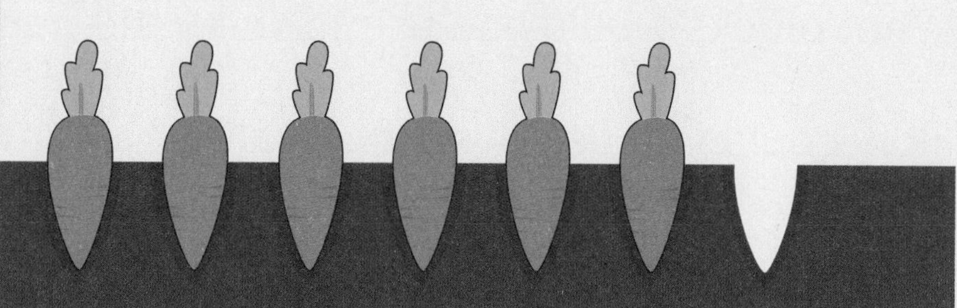

b.

5 + ___ = 8

8 − 5 = ___

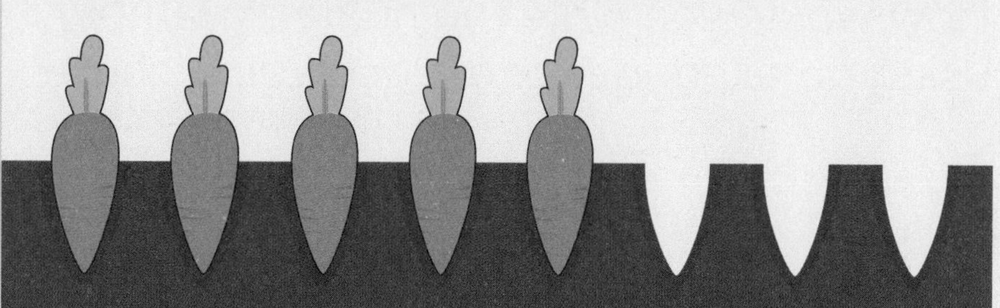

2. Look at the blocks. Write the matching number on the expanders.

FROM 1.7.2

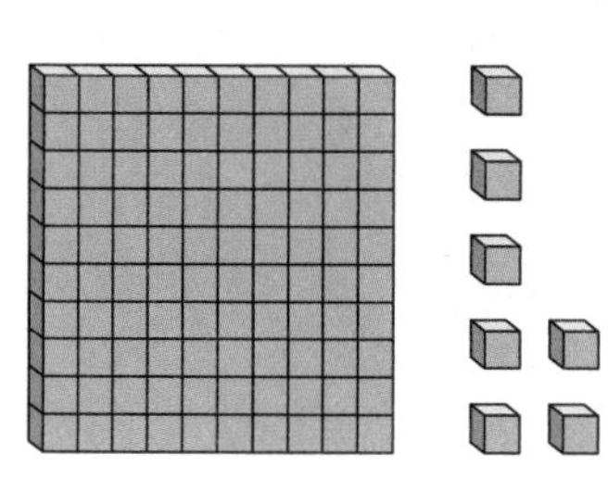

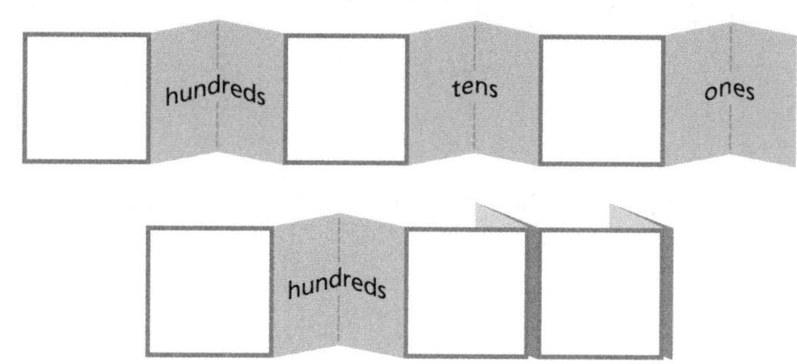

Preparing for Module 8

Draw more dots to make 10.
Then complete the matching equation.

a.

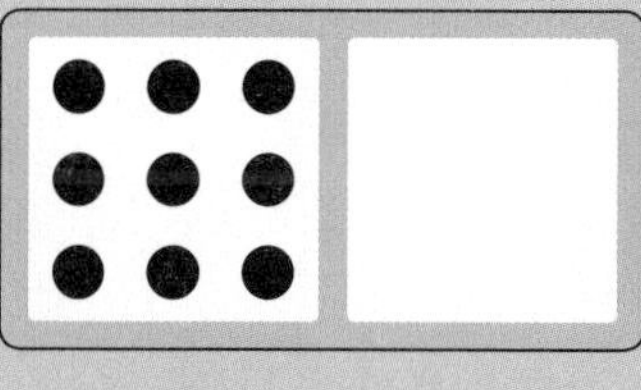

___ + ___ = 10

b.

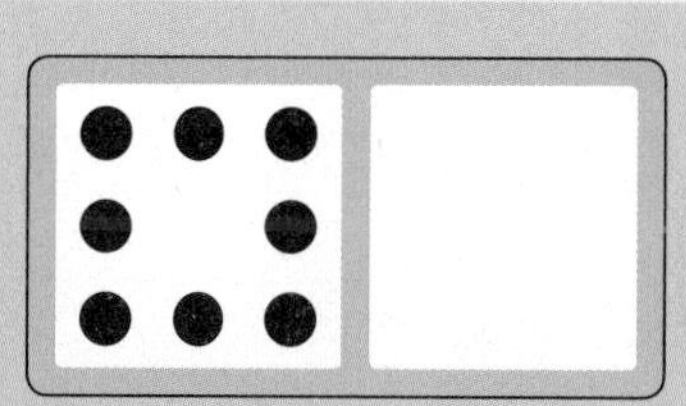

___ + ___ = 10

Number: Writing three-digit numbers to 120

Step In

How do you read and say the number on this expander?

1	hundreds	0	tens	7	ones

What blocks would you use to show the number?

How could you use this place-value chart to show the number?

Hundreds	Tens	Ones

How would you write the numeral without using an expander or a place-value chart?

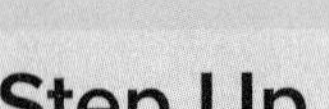

Step Up

1. Look at each picture of blocks. Write the number of hundreds, tens, and ones.

a.

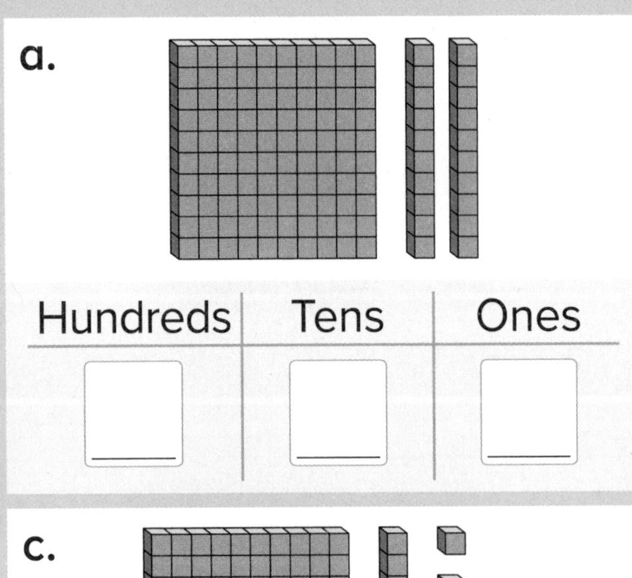

Hundreds	Tens	Ones

b.

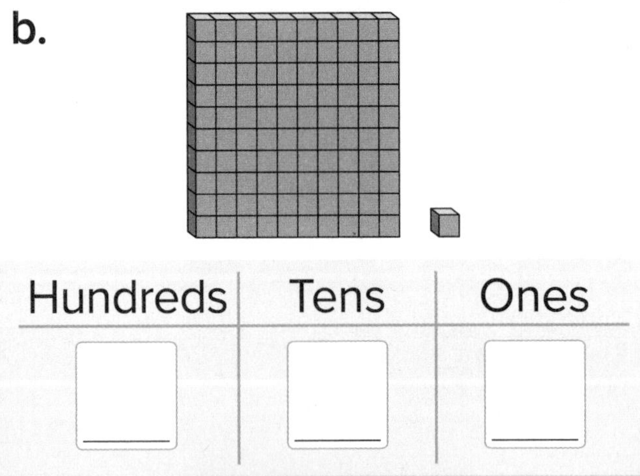

Hundreds	Tens	Ones

c.

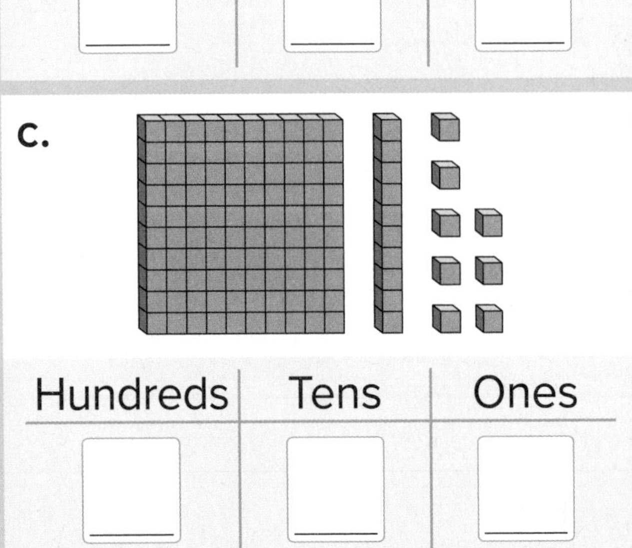

Hundreds	Tens	Ones

d.

Hundreds	Tens	Ones

2. Look at each picture of blocks. Write the matching number in the place-value chart. Then write the numeral without the chart.

a.

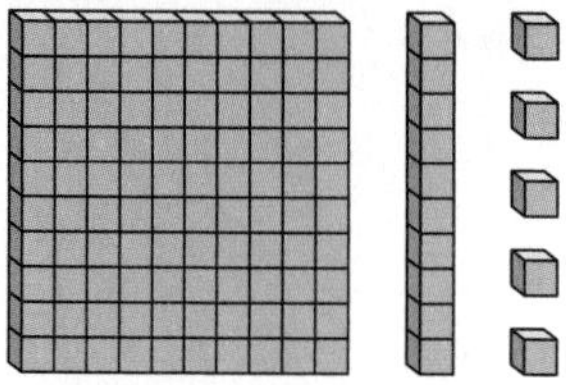

Hundreds	Tens	Ones

b.

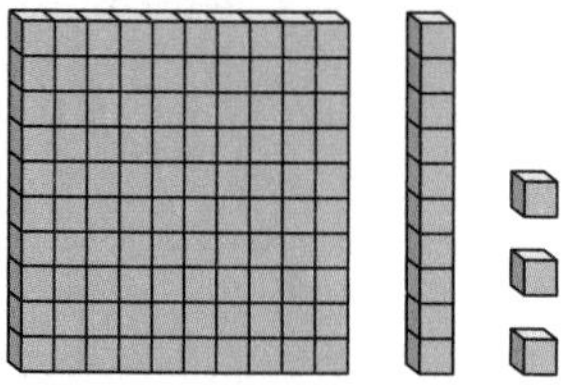

Hundreds	Tens	Ones

c.

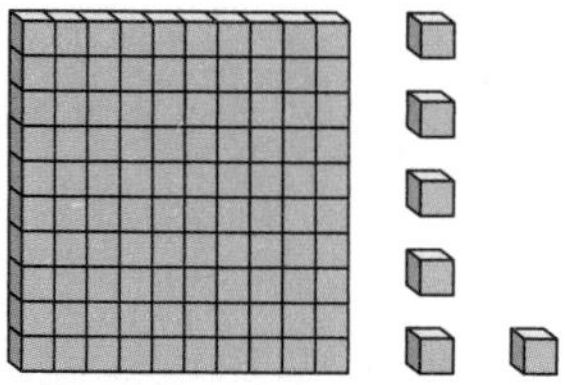

Hundreds	Tens	Ones

d.

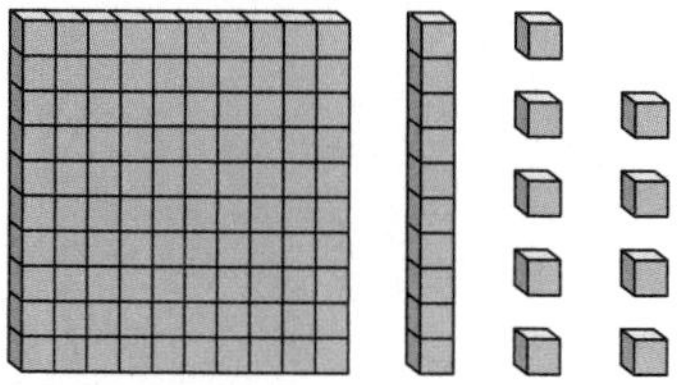

Hundreds	Tens	Ones

e.

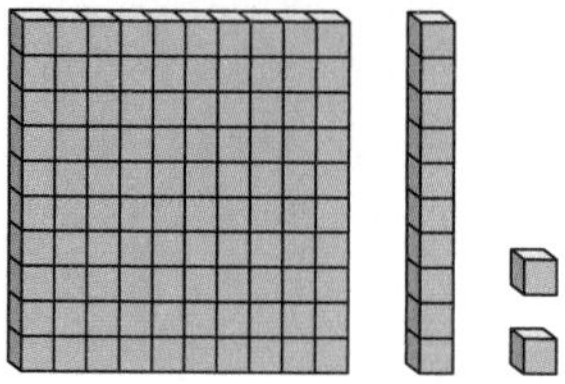

Hundreds	Tens	Ones

Step Ahead Draw **another tens block and a ones block** in each picture. Write the numeral to match the new picture.

a.

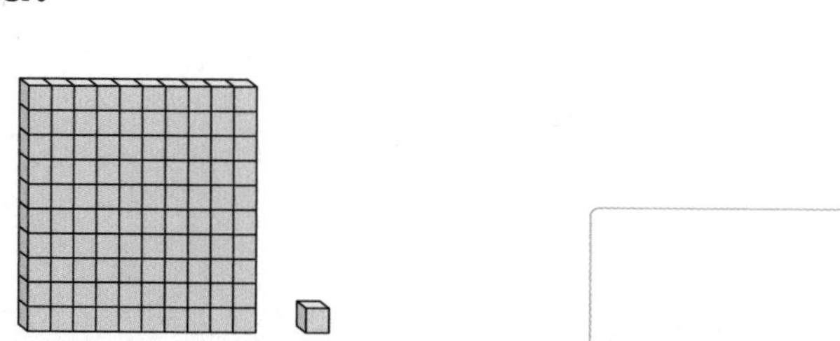

b.

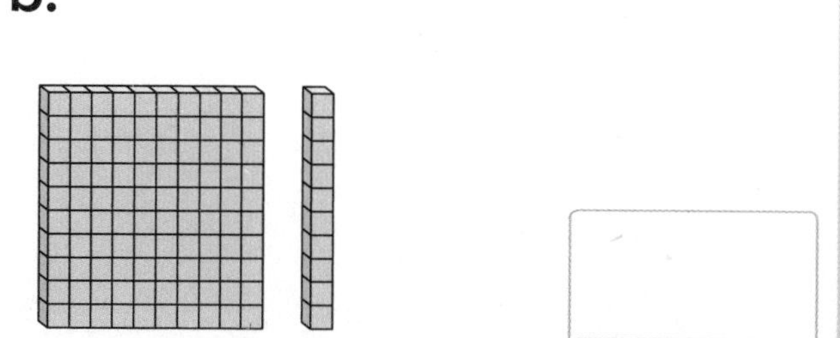

Step In Color blocks to match the numeral. Then write the number name.

112

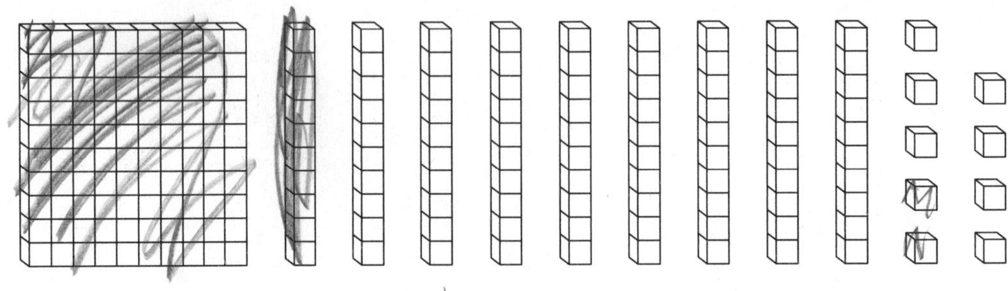

One hundred twelve

How would you write the numeral to show the number of blocks that you did not color?

How would you write the number in words?

Eighty-seventy

Step Up I. Look at each picture of blocks. Write the matching number in the place-value chart. Then write the numeral without the chart.

		Hundreds	Tens	Ones	
a.	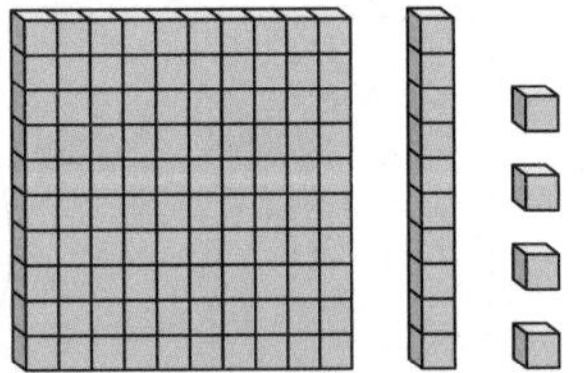	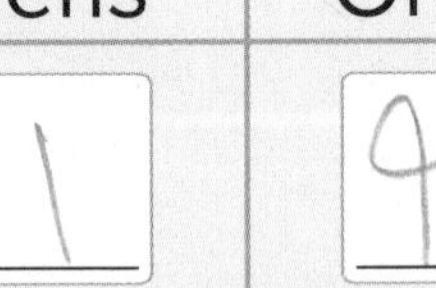			
b.	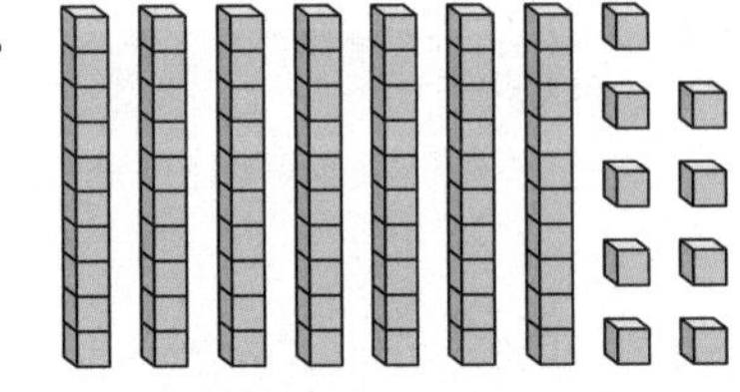				
c.	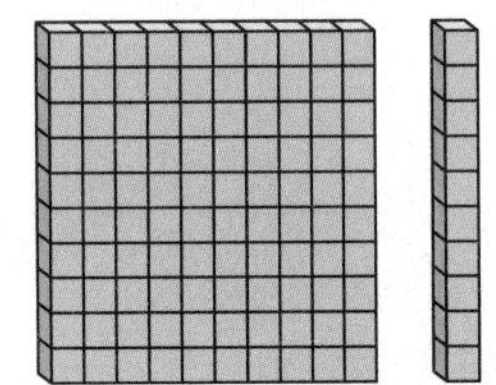		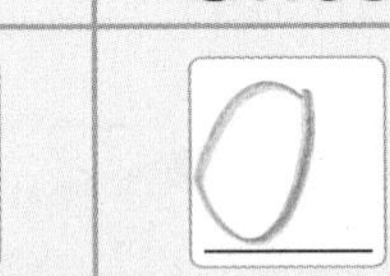		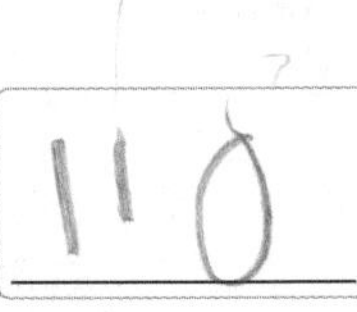

2. Write the numeral and number name to match the blocks.

a. 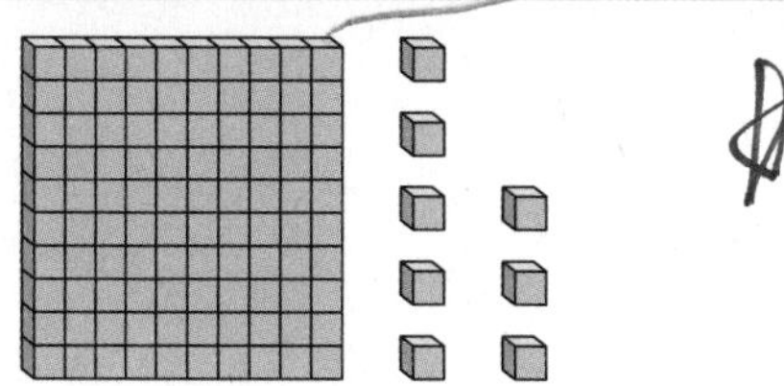

108

One hundred Eight

b. 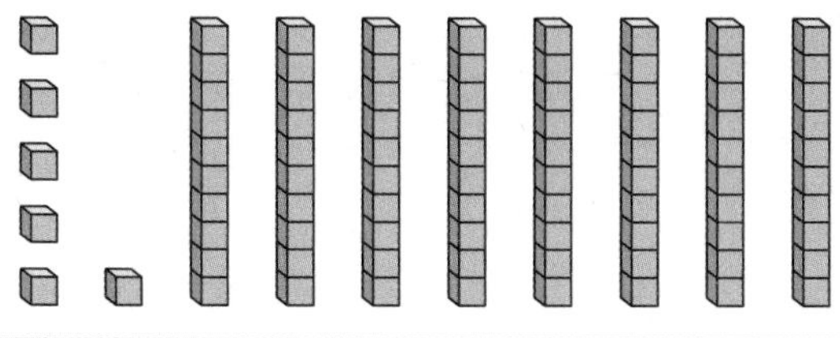

Eighty-six

c. 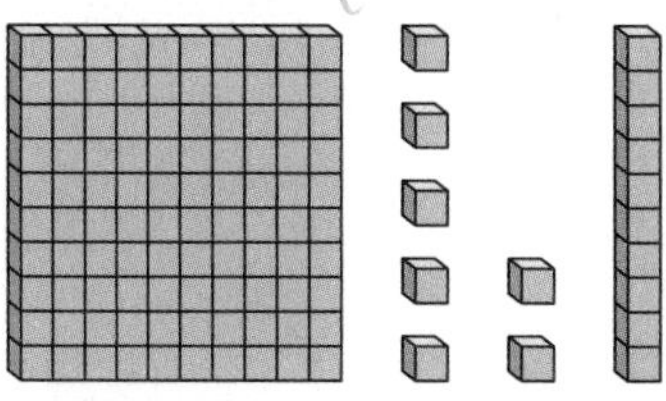

One hundred seventeen

3. Write the numeral to match each number name.

a. one hundred fifteen	b. thirty	c. one hundred one

Step Ahead Write the numeral to match this picture of blocks.

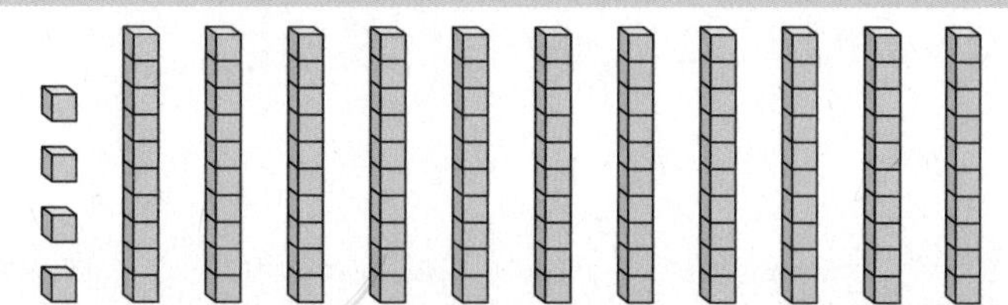

7.6 Maintaining concepts and skills

Computation Practice

Why did the teacher wear dark glasses?

★ Complete the equations.

★ Write each letter above its matching total at the bottom of the page. Some letters are used more than once.

____ = 7 + 5	u	____ = 2 + 8	r
____ = 8 + 9	c	____ = 3 + 4	d
____ = 4 + 1	g	____ = 6 + 7	e
____ = 2 + 2	a	____ = 9 + 9	h
____ = 9 + 7	b	____ = 7 + 2	t
____ = 2 + 6	i	____ = 8 + 6	s

Ongoing Practice

1. Figure out the number of dots that are covered. Then complete the facts.

FROM 1.6.6

a. 8 – 4 = ___

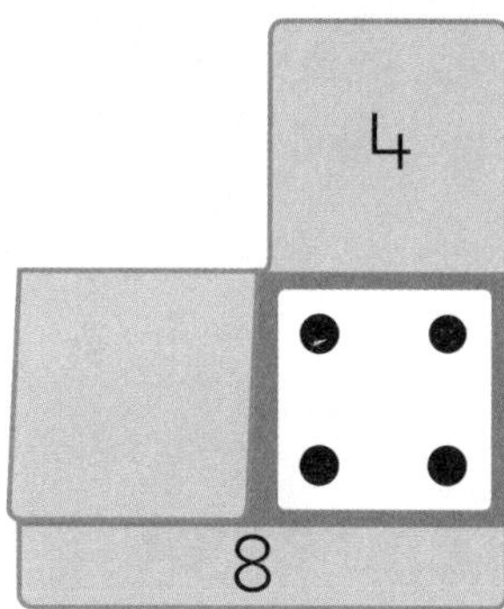

4 + ___ = 8

b. 12 – 6 = ___

6 + ___ = 12

c. 16 – 8 = ___

8 + ___ = 16

2. Read the number name. Write the matching number on the expander.

FROM 1.7.5

a. one hundred three

hundreds

b. one hundred eighteen

Preparing for Module 8

Write two equations to match each domino.

a. ___ + ___ = ___

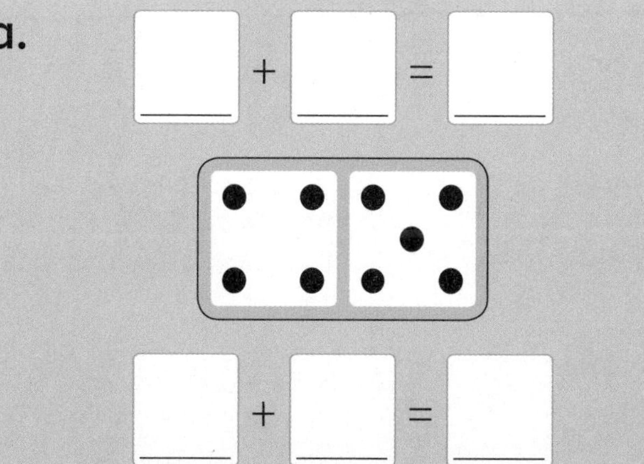

___ + ___ = ___

b. ___ + ___ = ___

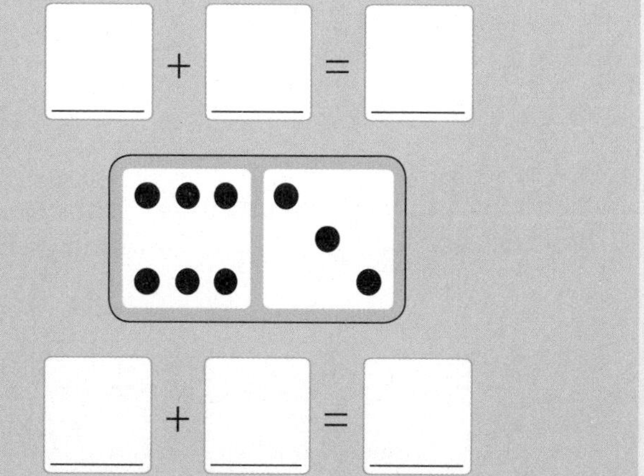

___ + ___ = ___

7.7 Subtraction: Introducing the think-addition strategy (near-doubles facts)

Step In **This train has seven cars. Some of the cars are already in the tunnel.**

How many cars are in the tunnel? How do you know?

I can think addition to figure out the answer. That is 3 + ___ = 7.

Which doubles fact could you use to help figure out the answer?

Write the missing numbers.

3	+	3	=	6
___	+	___	=	7
4	+	4	=	8

Step Up **1.** Write the missing number and draw the matching dots on each card. Then complete the addition facts.

a.

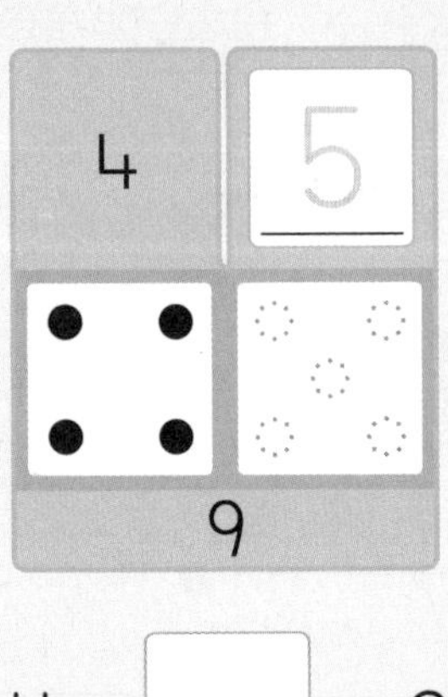

4 + ___ = 9

b.

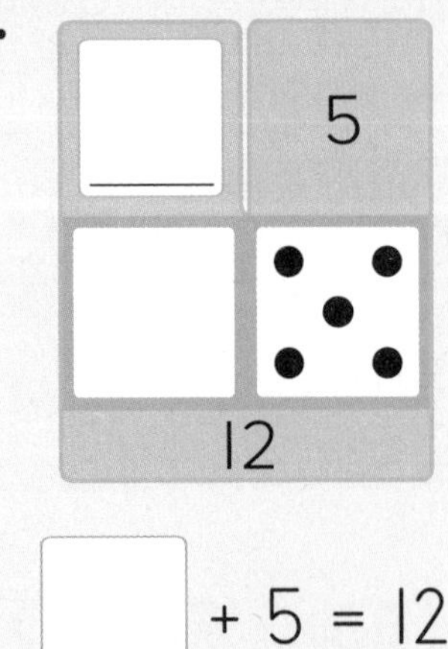

___ + 5 = 12

c.

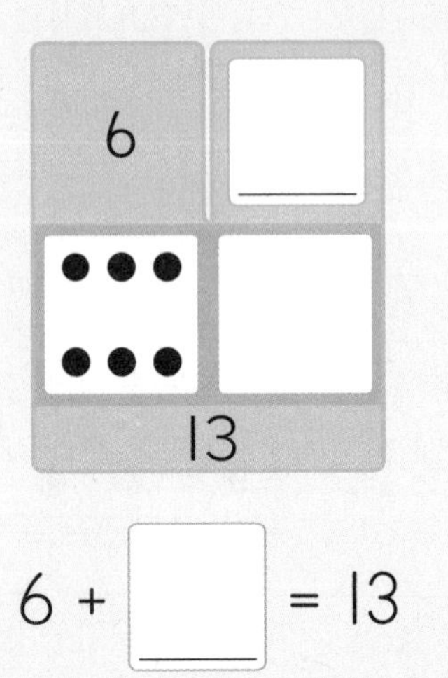

6 + ___ = 13

2. Figure out the number of dots that are covered. Then complete the facts.

a. 10 - 4 = ____

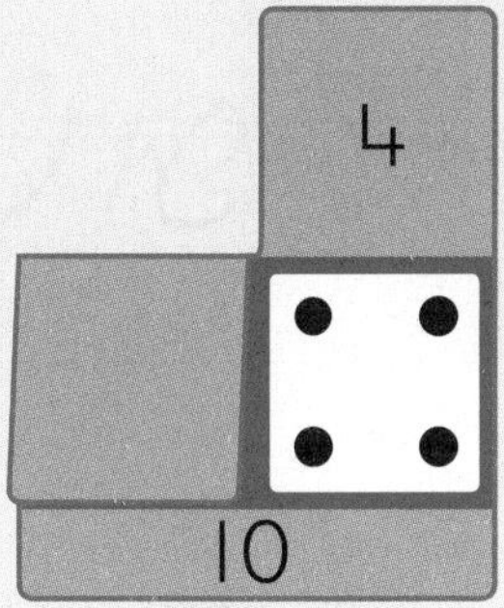

4 + ____ = 10

b. 11 - 5 = ____

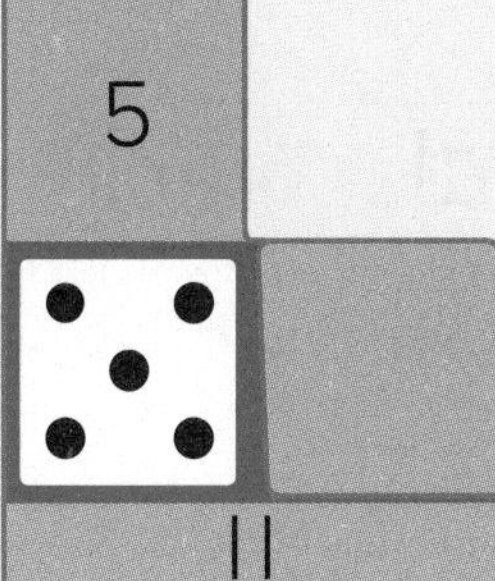

5 + ____ = 11

c. 8 - 3 = ____

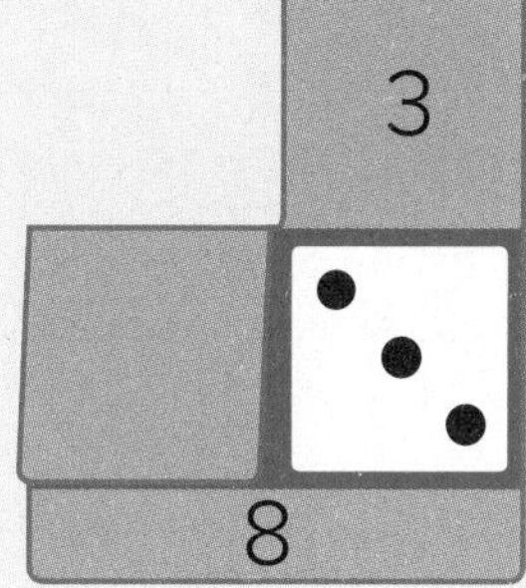

3 + ____ = 8

d. 15 - 7 = ____

7 + ____ = 15

e. 16 - 9 = ____

9 + ____ = 16

f. 14 - 6 = ____

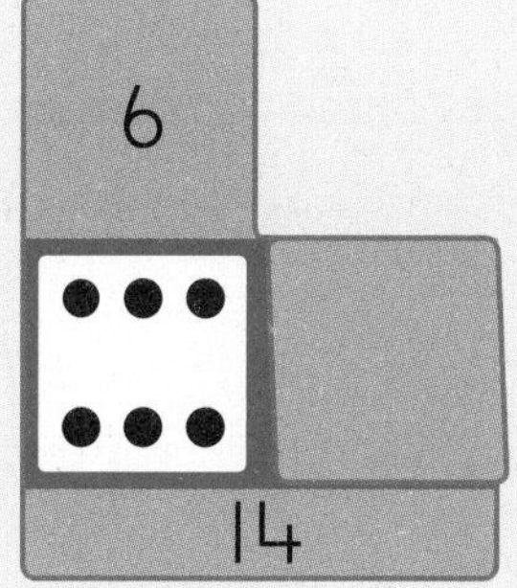

6 + ____ = 14

Step Ahead

Write a doubles fact that you could use to solve the problem. Then write the answer.

Kimie bakes 13 muffins. She gives 6 muffins away and stores the rest in a container.

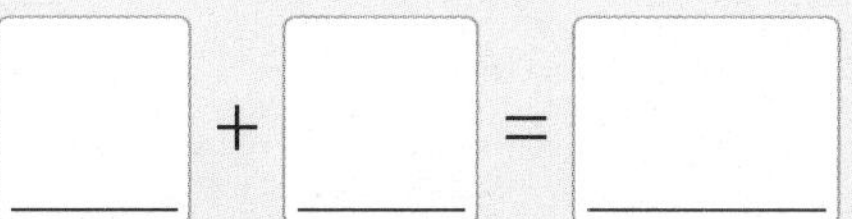

How many muffins are in the container? ____ muffins

Subtraction: Reinforcing the think-addition strategy (near-doubles facts)

12 – 7 = 5

Step In

There are 12 eggs in a carton. Then some eggs are cooked for breakfast. There are now 5 eggs left.

How many eggs were cooked at breakfast?

What doubles fact could you use to help figure out the answer?

I will think addition. That is 5 + 7 = 12.
I know double 5 is 10 and 2 more is 12.
So 5 add 7 is 12.

How can you use the same thinking to figure out 11 – 6?

What doubles fact could you use?

This time I will double 6 and then take one away.

Step Up

1. Draw dots to figure out the missing part. Then complete the addition and subtraction facts to match.

a. 13 dots in total

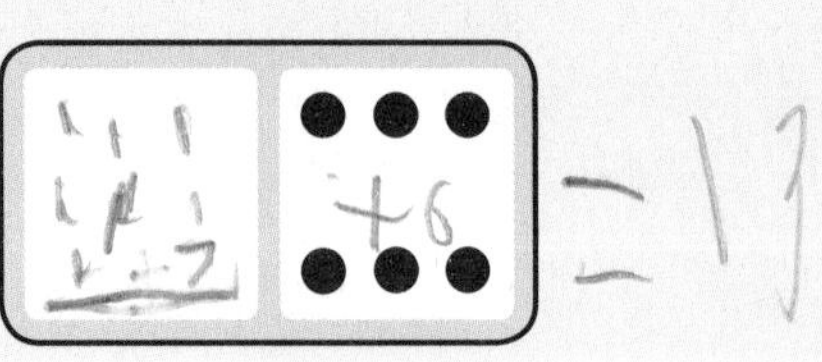

13 – 6 = 7

think

6 + 7 = 13

b. 9 dots in total

9 – 4 = 5

think

4 + 5 = 9

2. Figure out the number of dots that are covered. Then complete the facts.

a. 8 dots in total

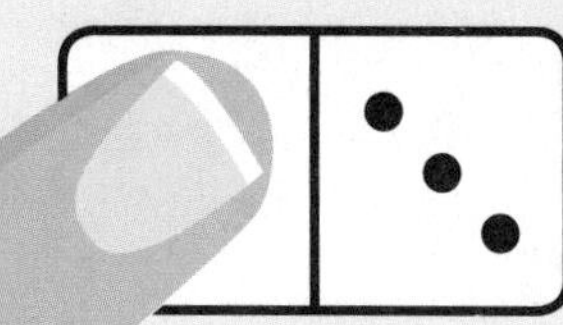

8 - 3 = 5

3 + 5 = 8

b. 15 dots in total

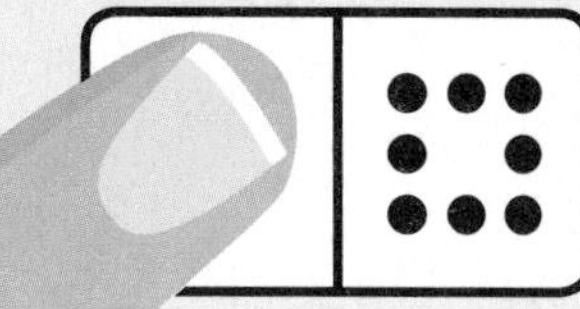

15 - 8 = 7

8 + 7 = 15

c. 14 dots in total

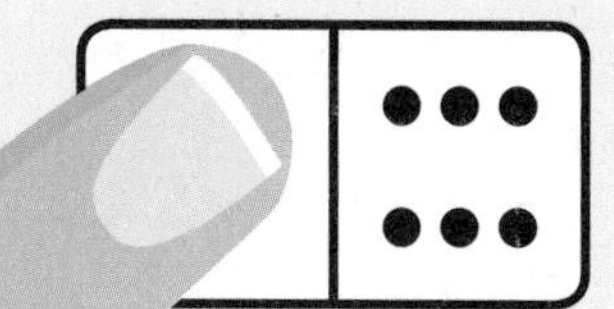

14 - 6 = 8

6 + 8 = 14

d. 16 dots in total

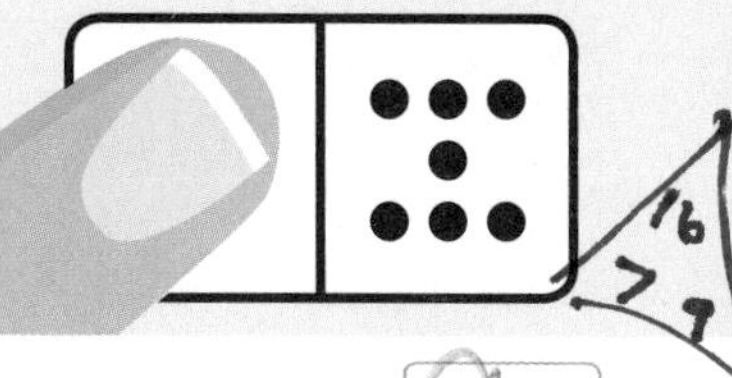

16 - 7 = 9

7 + 9 = 16

e. 7 dots in total

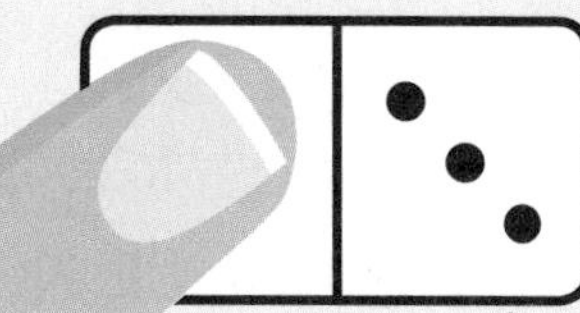

7 - 3 = 4

3 + 4 = 7

f. 17 dots in total

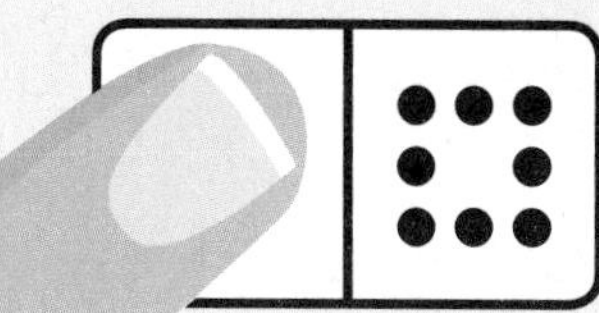

17 - 8 = 9

8 + 9 = 17

3. Write each answer.

a. 5 - 2 = 3

b. 11 - 5 = 7

c. 10 - 4 = 6

Step Ahead Write the addition fact you would use to figure out each answer. Then complete the subtraction facts.

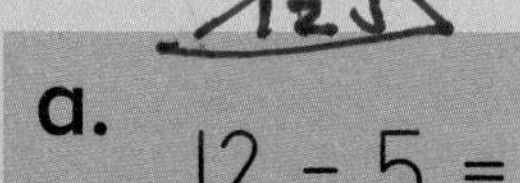

a. 12 - 5 = 7

5 + 7 = 12

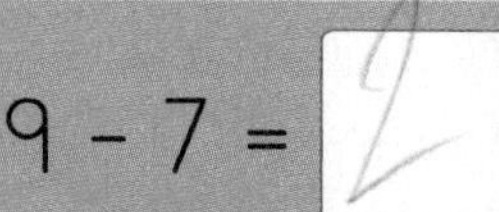

b. 9 - 7 = 2

2 + 7 = 9

c. 8 - 6 = 2

2 + 6 = 8

Maintaining concepts and skills

Think and Solve

Susan is 8 years old.

Jerome is 3 years older than Susan.

Jerome and Amy are the same age.

a. How old is Jerome? 

b. How old is Amy? 

Words at Work

Choose and write a word from the list to complete each sentence. Some words from the list are not used.

thirteen
eighty
ones
place value
expander
tens
hundred

a. ______ is the same value as 8 tens.

b. One less than one ______ is 99.

c. An ______ is used to show the number of hundreds, tens, and ones in a number.

d. The number name for 113 is one hundred ______.

e. 102 has one hundred, zero ______, and two ______.

Ongoing Practice

1. Color **one** part of each picture red. Then circle each picture that shows **one-half** in red.

FROM 1.6.9

a. 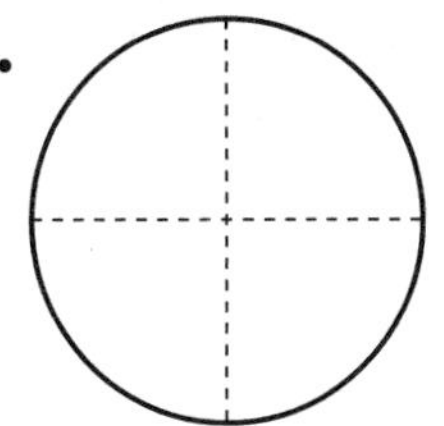

b. 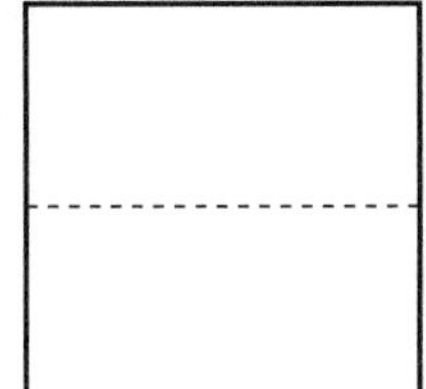

c. 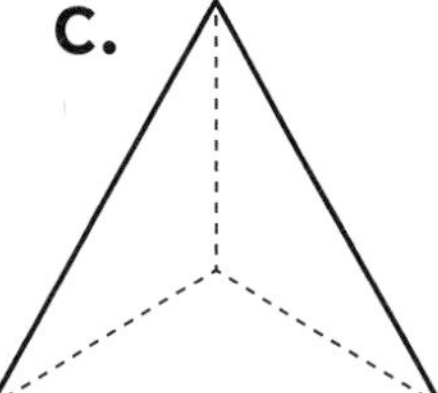

d. 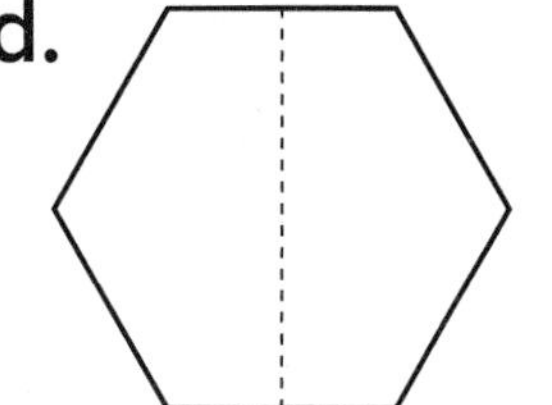

2. Figure out the number of dots that are covered. Then complete the facts.

FROM 1.7.7

a. 9 - 4 = ____

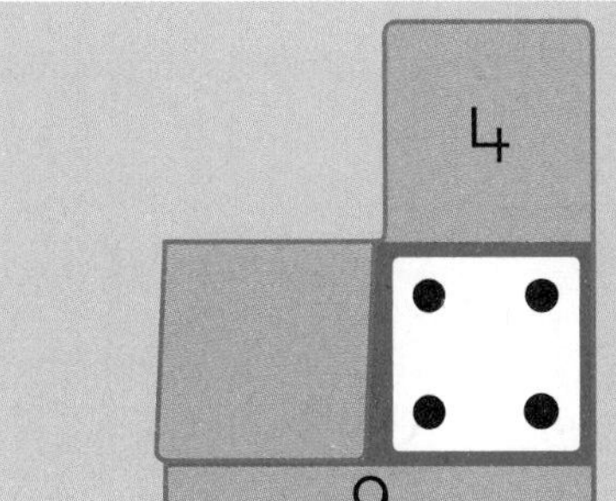

4 + ____ = 9

b. 11 - 6 = ____

6 + ____ = 11

c. 8 - 5 = ____

5
8

5 + ____ = 8

Preparing for Module 8

Draw ◯ in each empty box to make each balance picture true. Then complete the equation to match.

a. 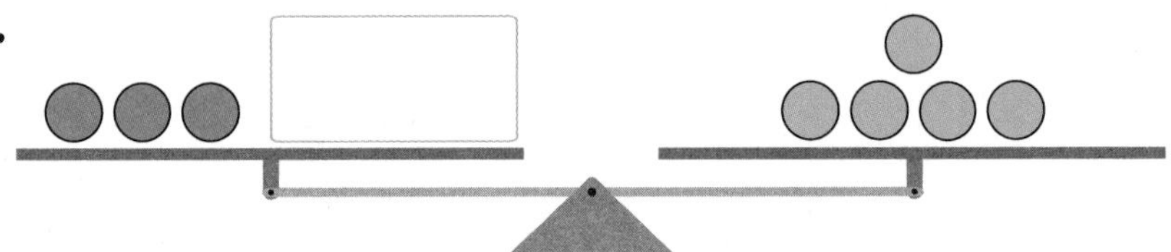

____ and ____ = ____

b. 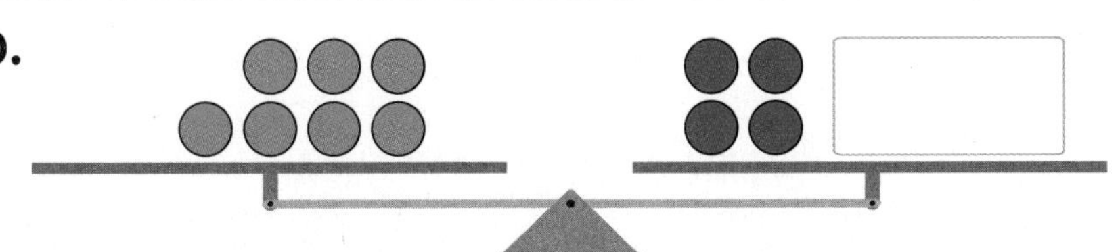

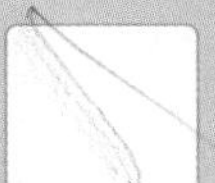 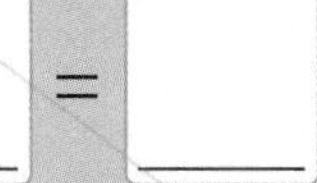

____ = ____ and ____

Subtraction: Reinforcing all strategies

Step In **Solve each problem.**

9 toys are on a shelf. Then 2 toys are sold. How many toys are left?	11 apples are in a bowl. Then some of the apples are eaten. There are 5 apples left. How many apples were eaten?
7 friends are playing at the pool. 5 friends are in the water. The other friends are out of the water. How many friends are out of the water?	15 passengers are on a bus. 8 passengers get off the bus. How many passengers are left on the bus?

Think about the strategy you used to solve each problem.

Write **C** on the problem if you used count-back.
Write **A** on the problem if you used think-addition.
Write **D** on the problem if you used use-doubles.

Which problems could you solve by thinking about addition and using a double?

Step Up

1. Write the answers. Then write **A** beside the equations that you solved by thinking about addition.

a. 8 - 1 = 7	b. 5 - 3 = ☐	c. 7 - 6 = ☐
d. 10 - 2 = ☐	e. 12 - 6 = ☐	f. 9 - 4 = ☐

2. Solve each problem. Show your thinking.

a. There are 15 flowers in a vase. 7 flowers are red. The rest are purple. How many flowers are purple?

8 flowers

b. 8 birds are sitting on a fence. 2 birds fly away. How many birds are now on the fence?

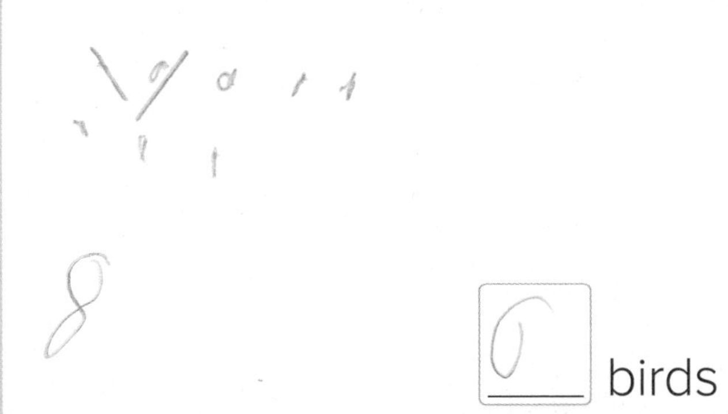

6 birds

c. There are 16 mice in a cage. Some run out. 7 mice are now in the cage. How many ran out?

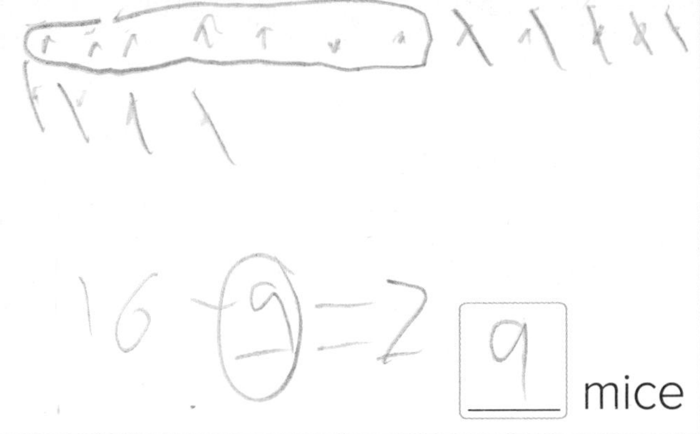

9 mice

d. Cooper runs 5 laps on a track. He wants to run 8 laps. How many more laps does he need to run?

5 + 3 = 8

3 laps

Step Ahead Write numbers to make this word story true.

____ puppies are playing by a fence. ____ puppies run away.

There are now ____ puppies playing by the fence.

7.10 Time: Introducing half-past the hour (analog)

Step In **Look at this analog clock.**

The short hand counts the hours and the long hand counts the minutes.

What time is this clock showing? How do you know?

How long does it take the minute hand to make one full turn around the clock?

Where would the minute hand point if it went halfway around?

When the minute hand is pointing at 6, it is **half-past** an hour.

When the minute hand shows a half-past time, what does the hour hand show?

What time is this clock showing? How do you know?

Step Up 1. Write the time showing on each clock.

a.

half-past

☐ o'clock

b.

half-past

☐ o'clock

c.

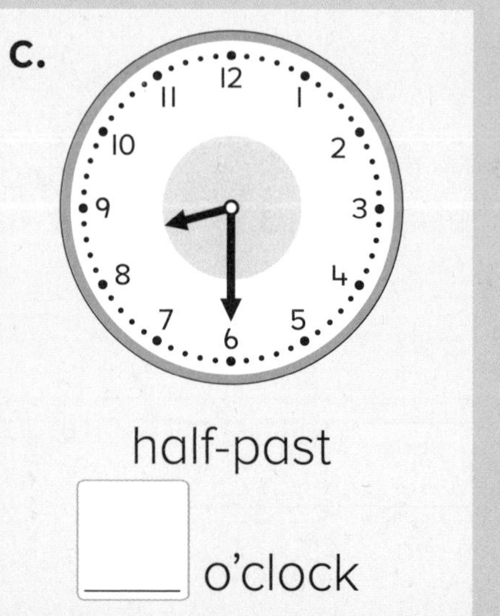

half-past

☐ o'clock

2. Write each time in words.

a.

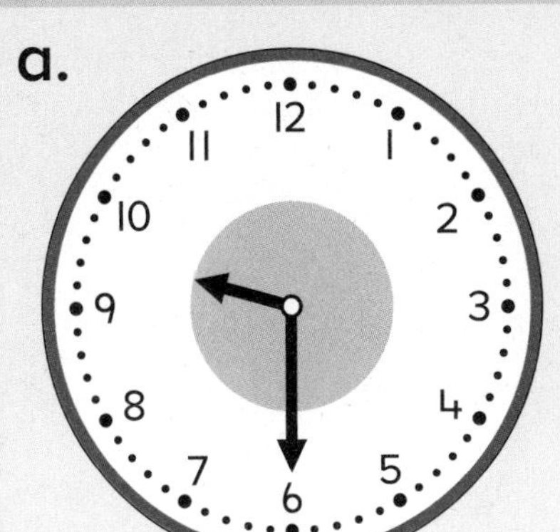

b.

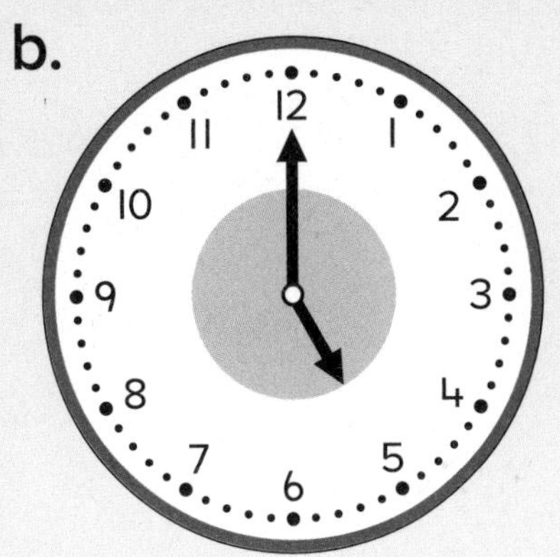

c.

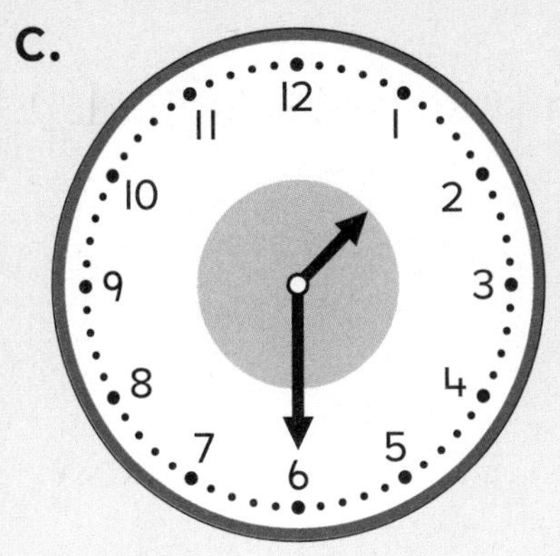

d.

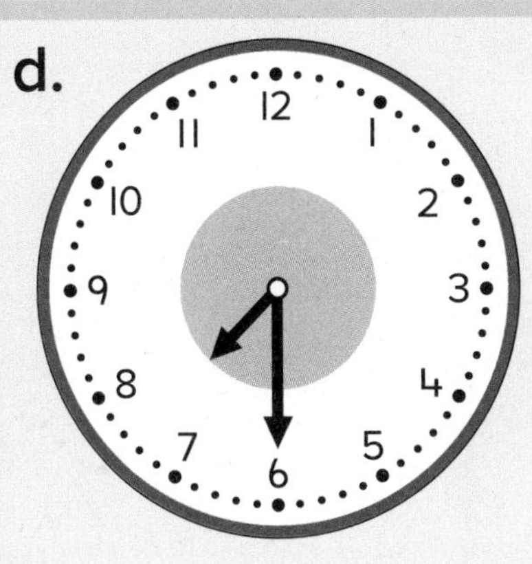

e.

f.

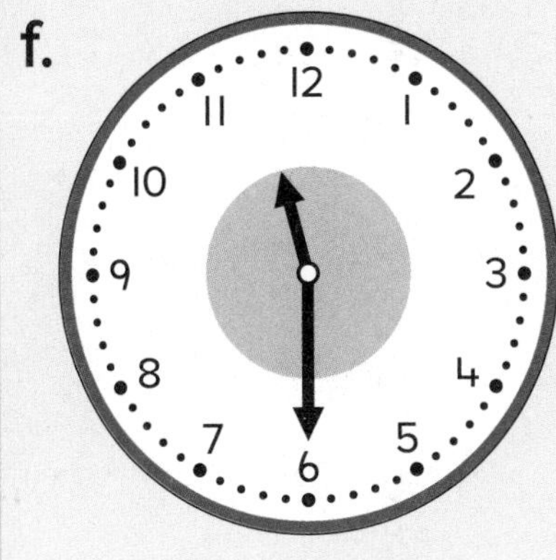

Step Ahead Circle the clocks that show times **between** half-past 7 and 10 o'clock.

Maintaining concepts and skills

Computation Practice

★ Complete the equations.

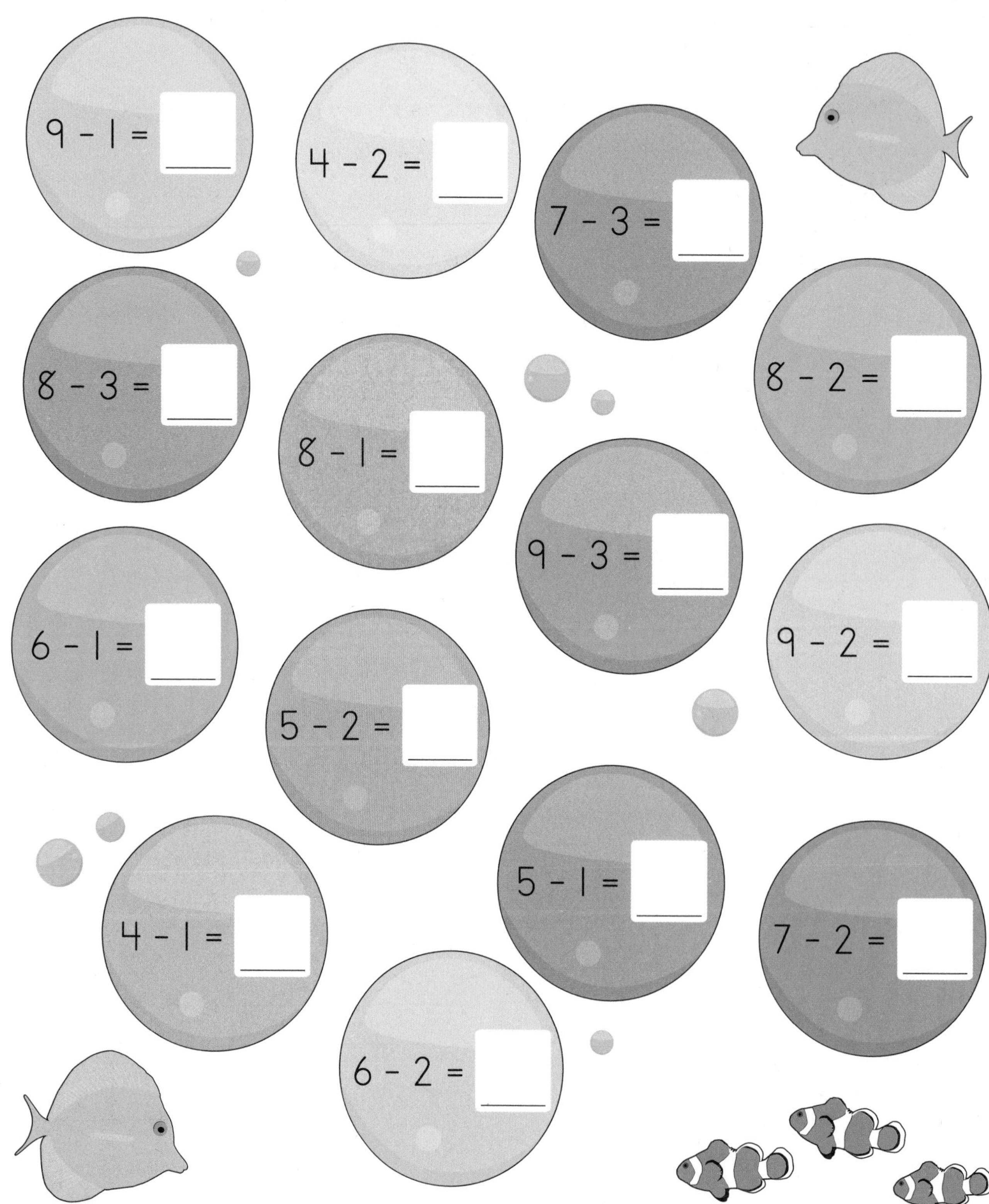

Ongoing Practice

1. Color **one** part of each strip red. Then circle the strip that shows **one-fourth** in red.

FROM 1.6.10

a.

b.

c.

2. Solve each problem. Show your thinking.

FROM 1.7.9

a. There are 11 puppies in a pet store. Then 3 puppies are sold. How many are left in the store?

____ puppies

b. James has 15 pennies. He spends some pennies and has 12 pennies left. How many pennies did he spend?

____ pennies

Preparing for Module 8

Some students voted for their favorite pet.

Draw a ✔ beside each animal to show each vote.

2 students voted for fish.
3 students voted for birds.
6 students voted for dogs.

bird	
fish	
dog	

Time: Reading and writing half-past the hour (digital)

Step In

How many minutes are in one hour?

How many minutes are in half an hour? How do you know?

Look at this digital clock.

How is this clock different from an analog clock?

What do you know about the time on this clock?

The 30 shows me the number of minutes. I know it is a half-past time because 30 minutes is half of one hour.

What time is the clock showing?

Step Up

1. Draw a line from each label to a matching clock. Some clocks do not have a match.

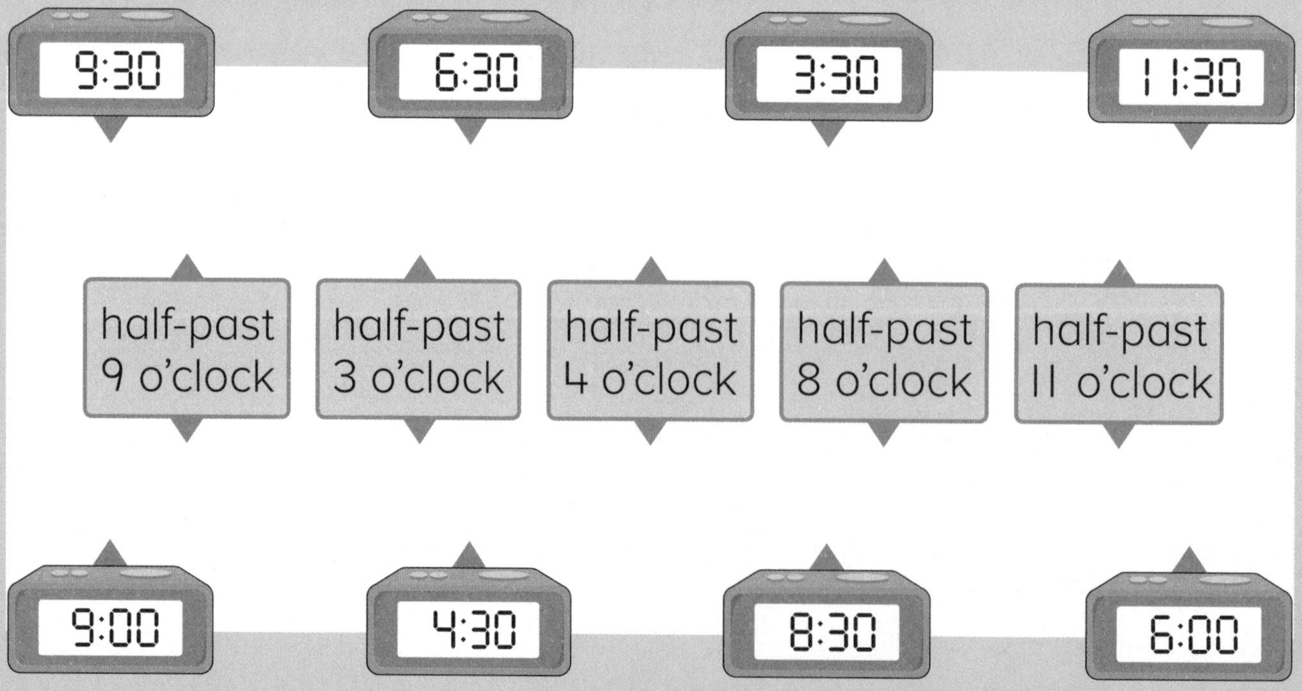

9:30 | 6:30 | 3:30 | 11:30

half-past 9 o'clock | half-past 3 o'clock | half-past 4 o'clock | half-past 8 o'clock | half-past 11 o'clock

9:00 | 4:30 | 8:30 | 6:00

2. Write each time in words.

a.	1:30	______________________
b.	10:30	______________________
c.	3:00	______________________
d.	12:00	______________________
e.	5:30	______________________
f.	8:00	______________________
g.	6:30	______________________

Step Ahead Complete the sentences.

a. 2:30

The time is half-past ____.

One hour **later** will be half-past ____.

b. 12:30

The time is half-past ____.

One hour **later** will be half-past ____.

7.12 Time: Relating analog and digital

Step In What different ways can you say the time shown on these clocks?

Half-past three.

Three thirty.

Step Up 1. Write each time on the digital clock.

a.

b.

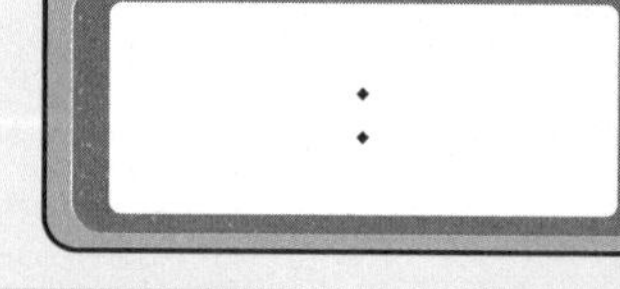

c.

d.

e.

f.

2. Draw lines to connect matching times.

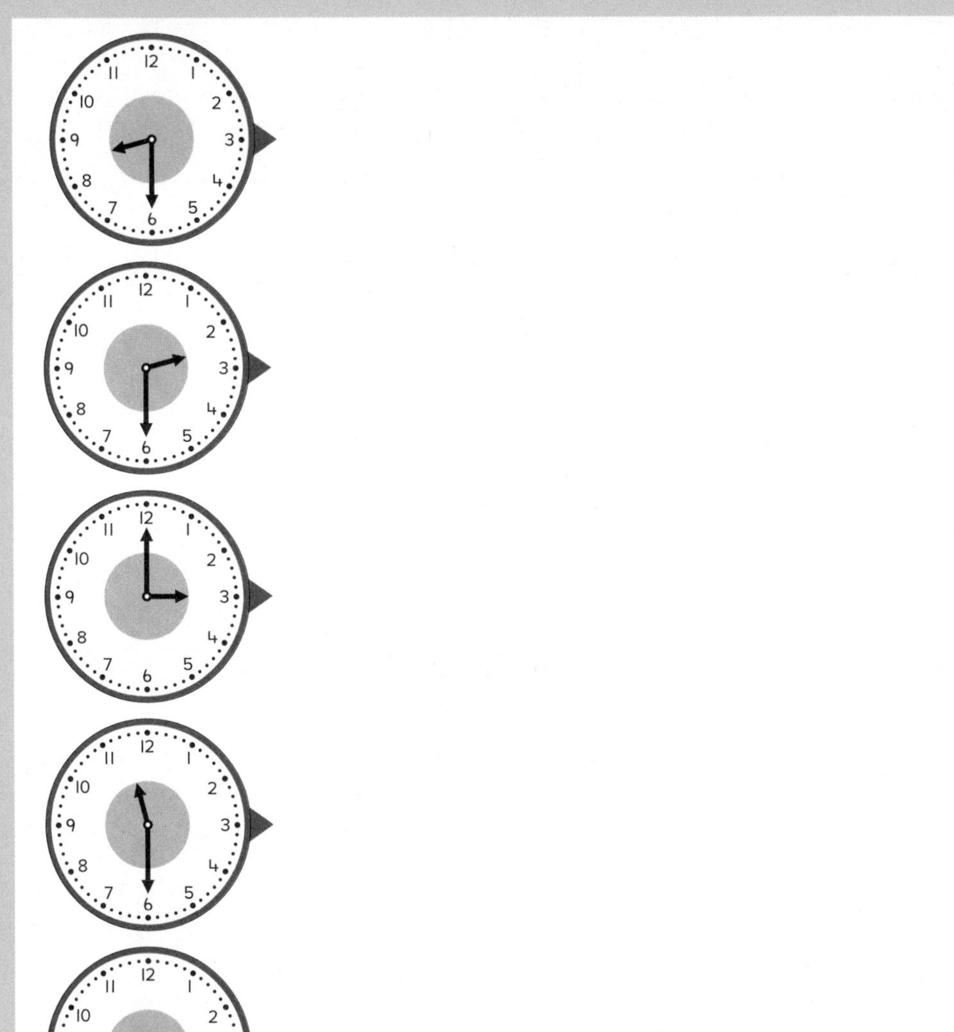

Step Ahead Gemma has breakfast at 7:00 on Monday morning. She has baseball practice at 4:00 in the afternoon.

How many half-past the hour times will there be on the clock between breakfast and the start of baseball practice?

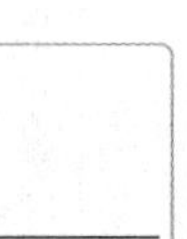

Maintaining concepts and skills

Think and Solve

The same shapes weigh the same.
Write the missing value inside each shape.

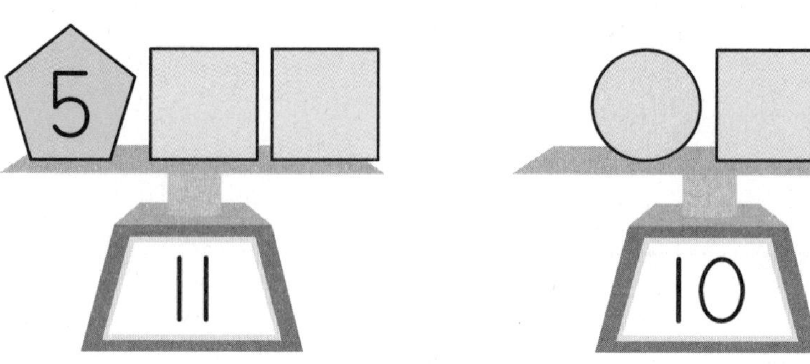

Words at Work

Write about this clock. You can use words from the list to help.

time
counts
minutes
minute hand
hour hand
half-past
hour
analog
digital

Ongoing Practice

1. For each strip, write the fraction that is purple.

FROM 1.6.12

a.

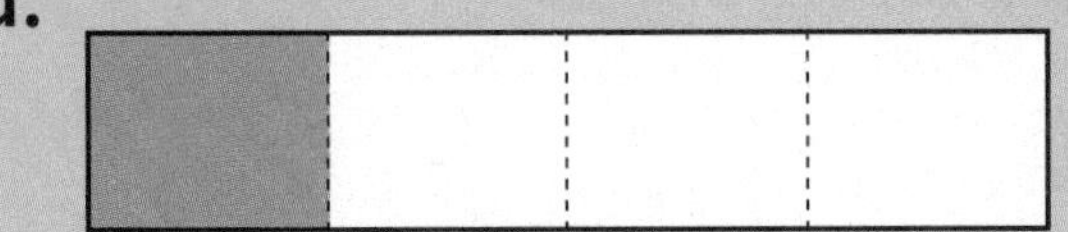

b.

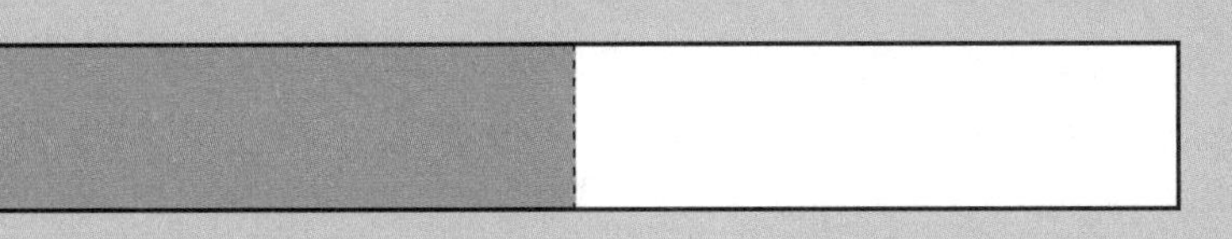

2. Write the time shown on each clock.

FROM 1.7.10

a.

half-past

 o'clock

b.

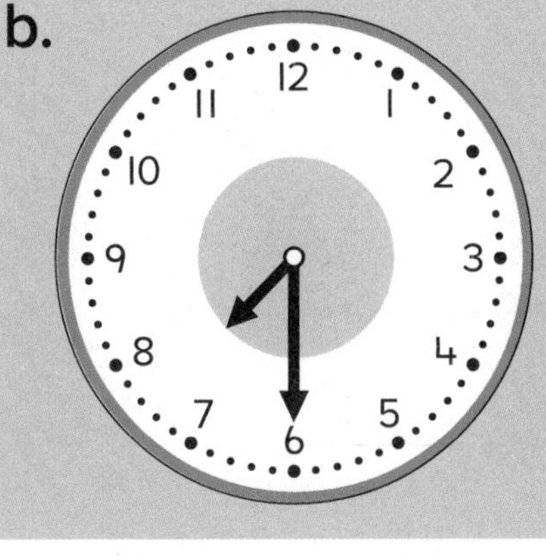

half-past

 o'clock

c.

half-past

____ o'clock

Preparing for Module 8

Draw tally marks on the chart to show the votes.

8 students voted yes.
6 students voted no.

Do you like vegetables?	
Yes	
No	

Working Space

8.1 Addition: Exploring combinations of ten

Step In **Look at these cubes.**

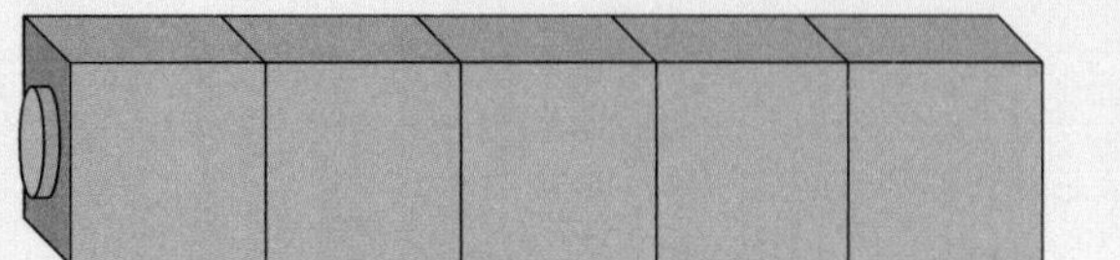

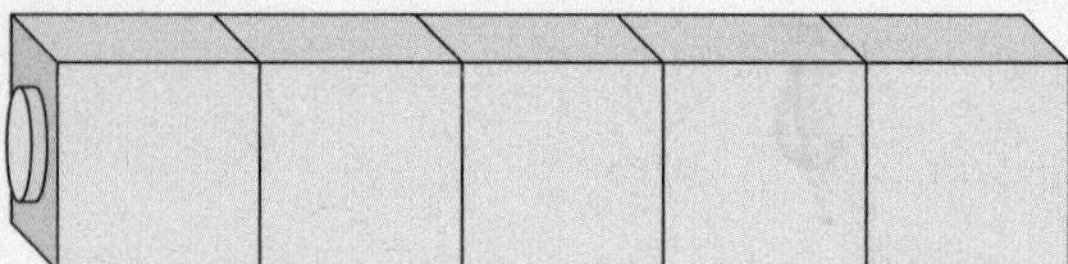

What addition fact matches the picture?

How else could you break up the cubes?

What other addition facts could you write?

Step Up 1. Color some of the cubes.
Then write a matching addition fact.

a. ___ + ___ = ___

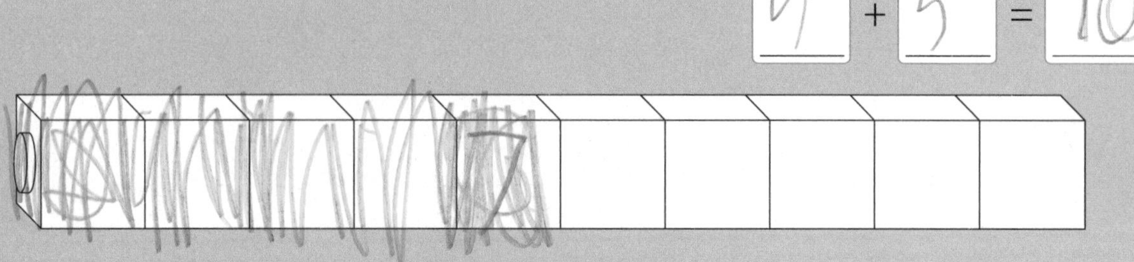

b. ___ + ___ = ___

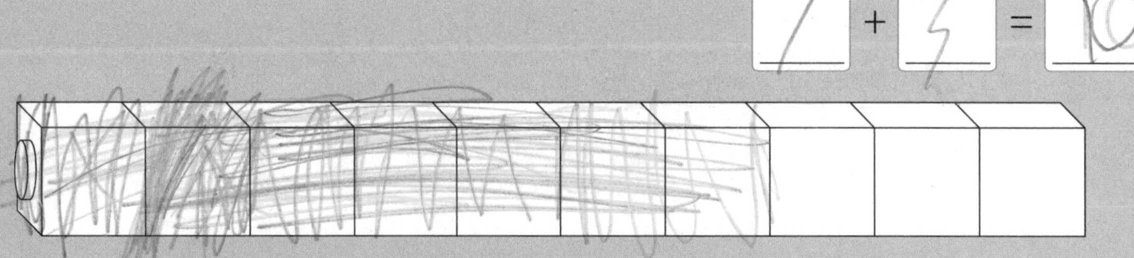

c. ___ + ___ = ___

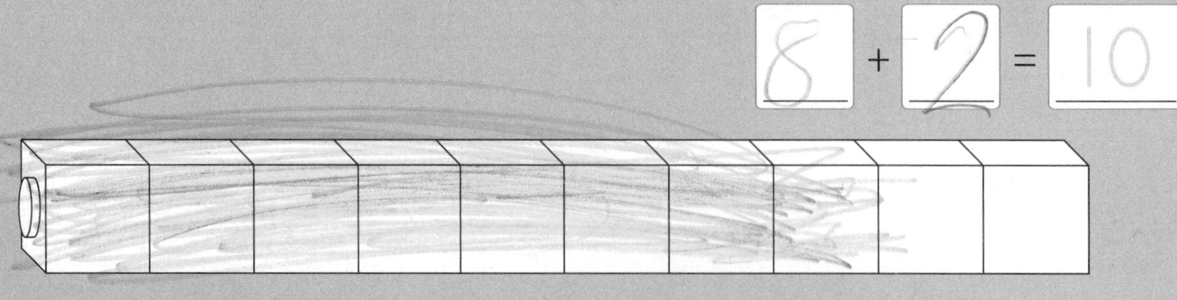

2. Use different colors to show three parts.
Then write a matching equation.

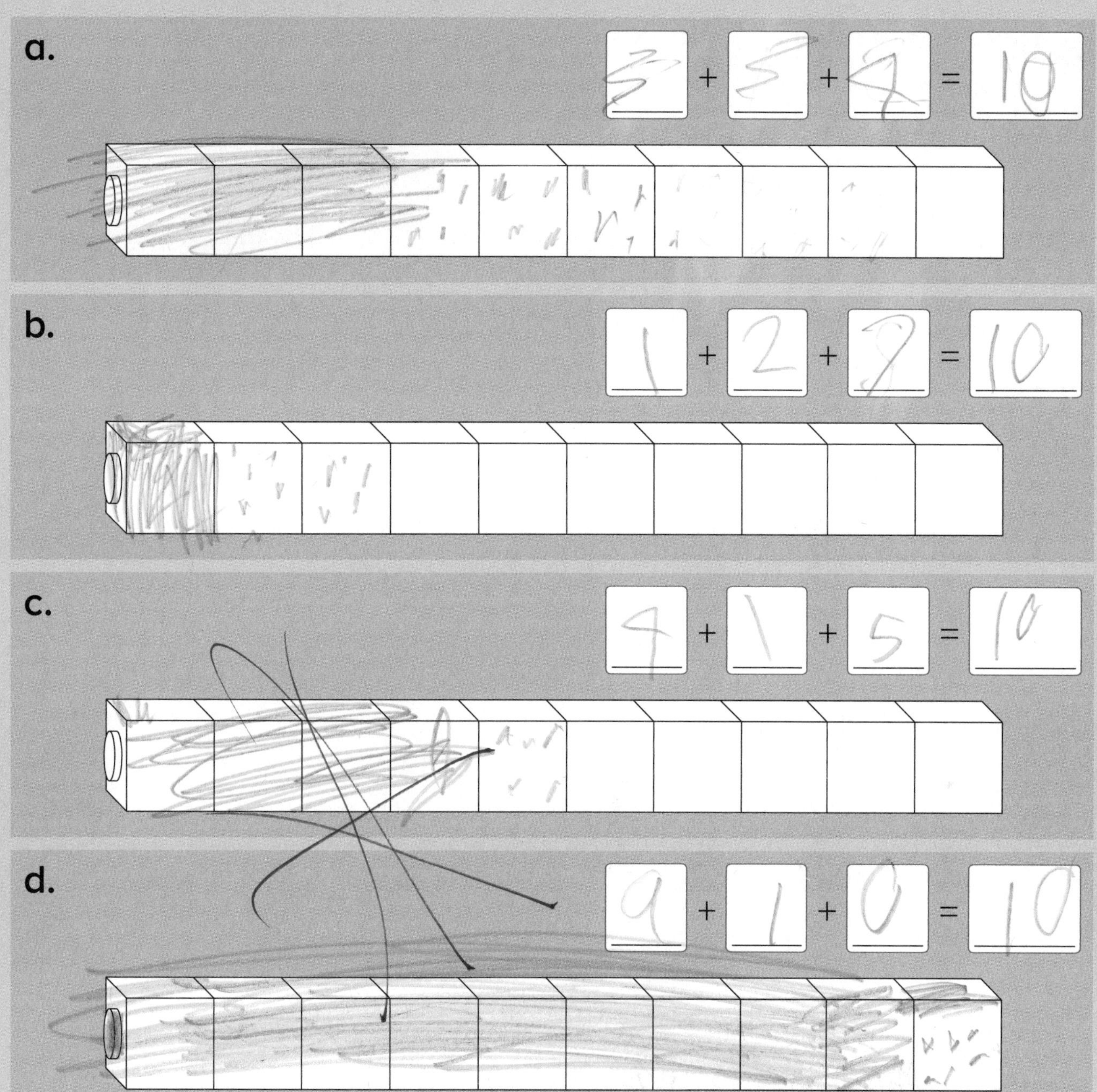

Step Ahead Think of some different ways to break up **11** cubes. Then complete these equations to match.

___ + ___ = ___ ___ = ___ + ___

___ + ___ + ___ = ___ ___ = ___ + ___ + ___

8.2 Addition: Using the associative property

Step In How many bugs are on each leaf?

How would you figure out the total number of bugs?

In what order did you decide to add the number of bugs on each leaf?

I looked for two numbers that make 10. I then added the last number.

Write an equation to show the order that you decided to add.

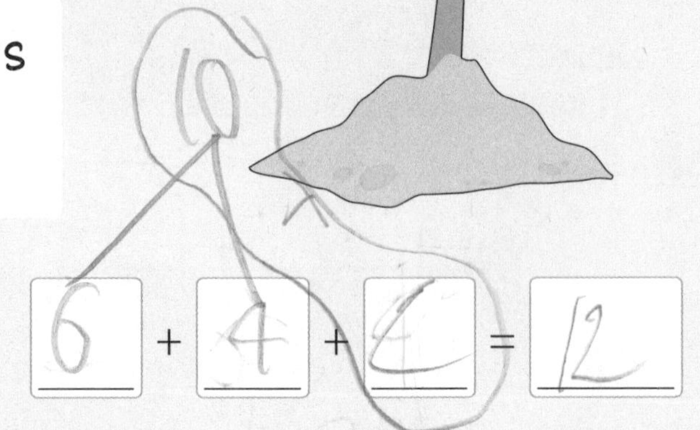

Does the total change if you add them in a different order?

Step Up 1. Draw ↶↷ to show two groups that make 10. Write an equation to show how you add to find the total.

a.

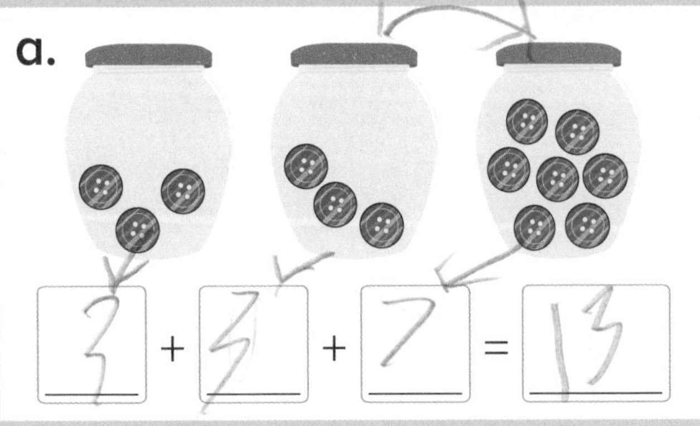

b.

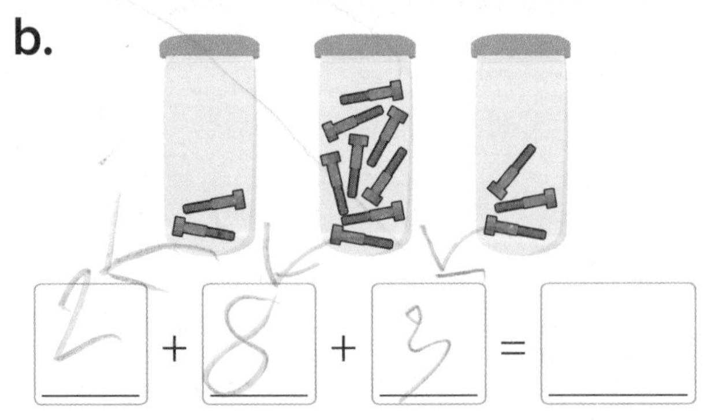

c.

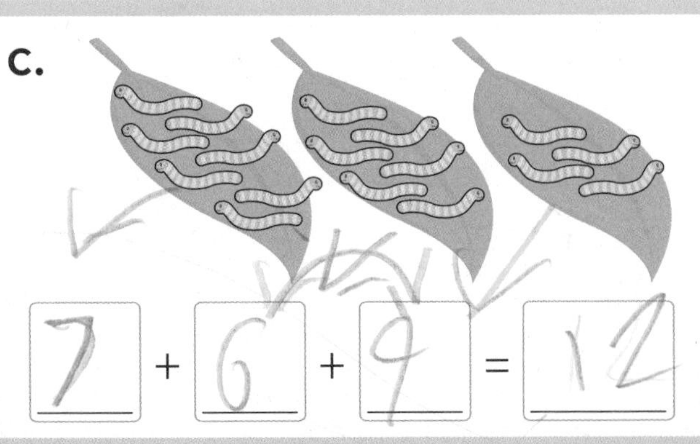

d.

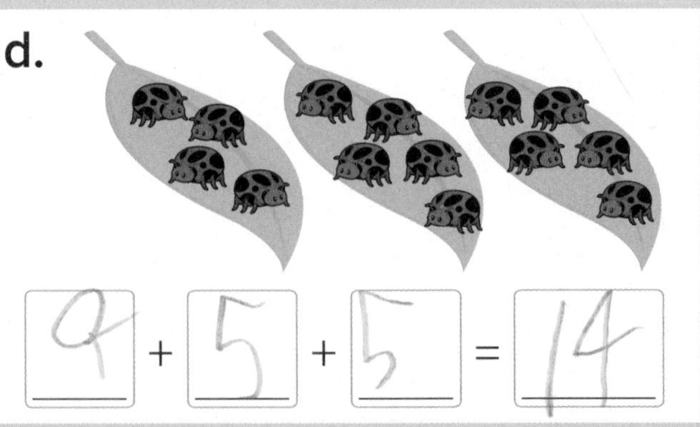

2. Draw ↶↷ to show two numbers that make 10. Then write an equation to show how you add to find the total.

a.

b.

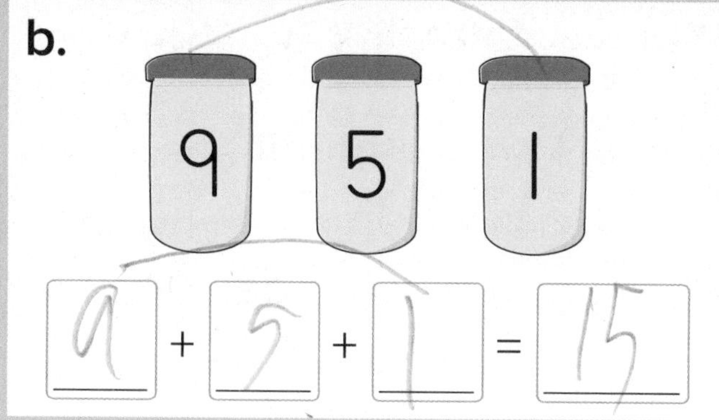

c.

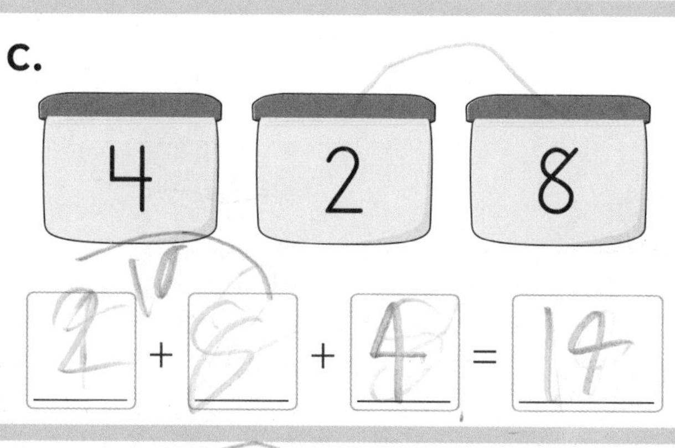

d.

e.

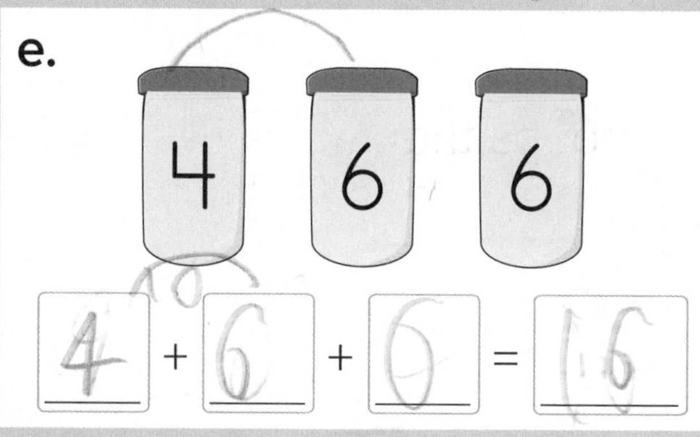

f.

3 8 2

___ + ___ + ___ = ___

Step Ahead Write three different equations to match this picture.

___ + ___ + ___ = ___

___ + ___ + ___ = ___

___ + ___ + ___ = ___

Computation Practice

★ Complete the equations.

★ Draw a line to join each light and switch that have matching totals.

8 + 6 = ____

9 + 3 = ____

7 + 6 = ____

6 + 5 = ____

12 + 3 = ____

7 + 7

3 + 8

7 + 8

11 + 2

5 + 7

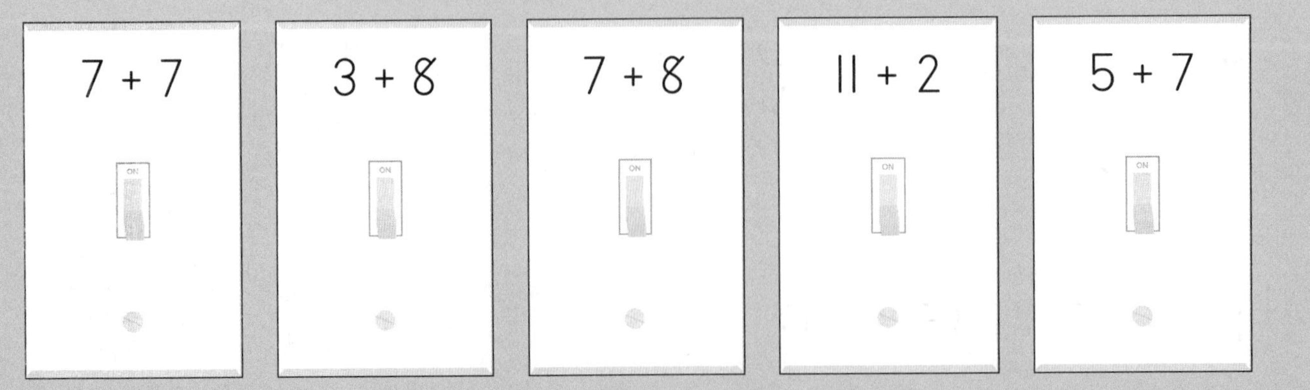

Ongoing Practice

1. Color blocks to show the number of ones. Then write the number of ones left over.

FROM 1.7.1

a. 30 ones

______

b. 90 ones

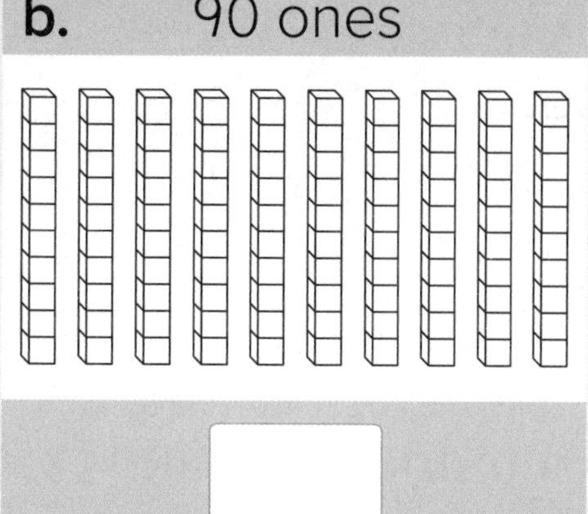

______

c. 50 ones

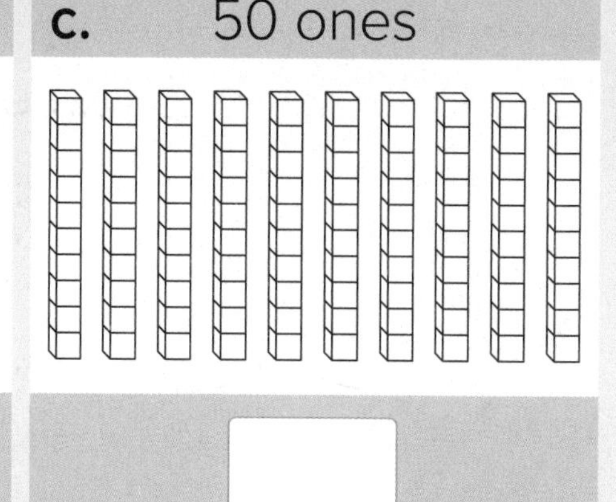

______

2. Use different colors to show two or three parts. Then write the matching equation.

FROM 1.8.1

a. ______ + ______ = 10

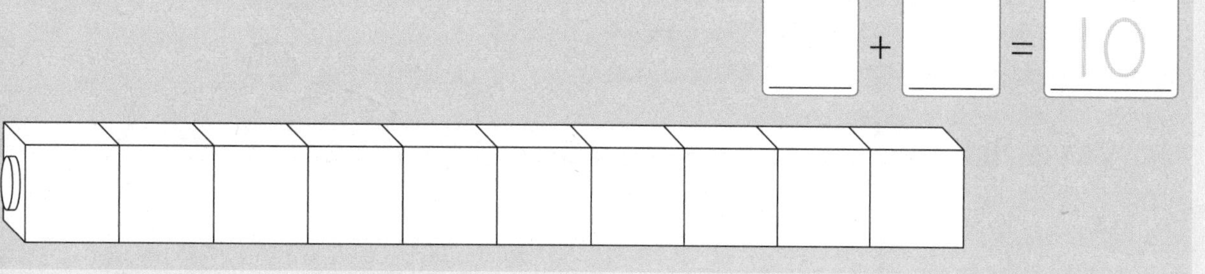

b. ______ + ______ + ______ = ______

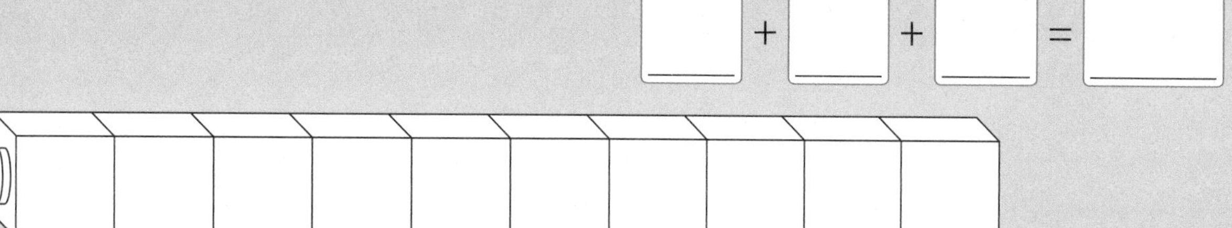

Preparing for Module 9

Draw jumps to help you count on. Write two addition facts to match.

Count on **2**.

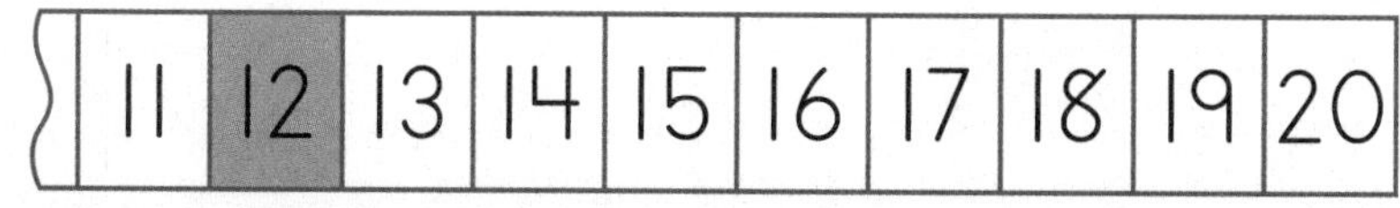

______ + ______ = ______

______ + ______ = ______

Addition: Introducing the make-ten strategy

Step In **Look at this picture of counters.**

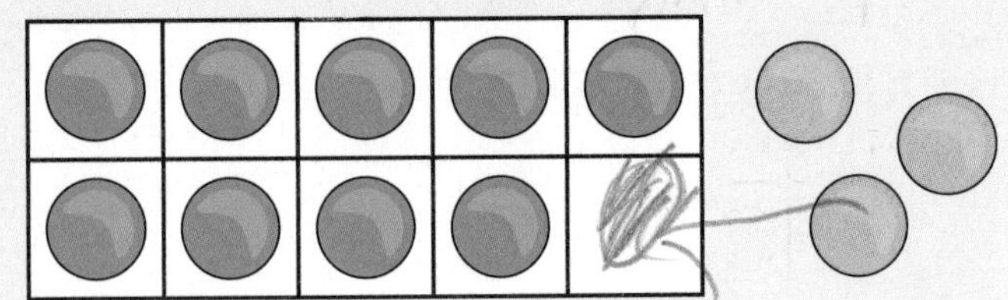

How can you figure out the total?

I moved one counter to make a group of 10. This made it easier to add.

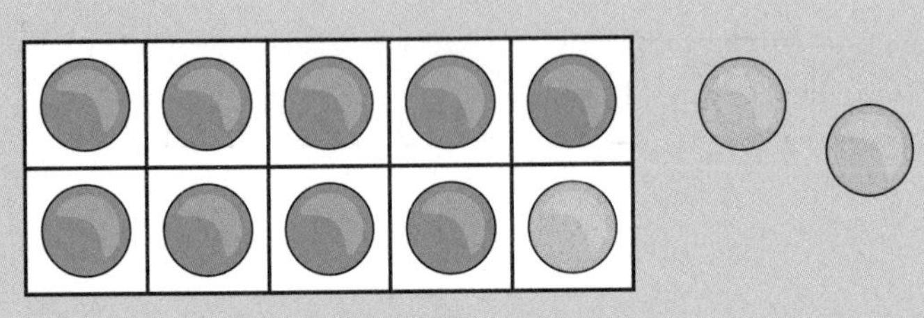

9 + 3
is the same value as 10 + 2.
10 + 2 is 12.

How would you use this strategy to figure out 9 + 6?

Step Up 1. Draw more counters. Then write the numbers to match.

a. Draw 5 more.

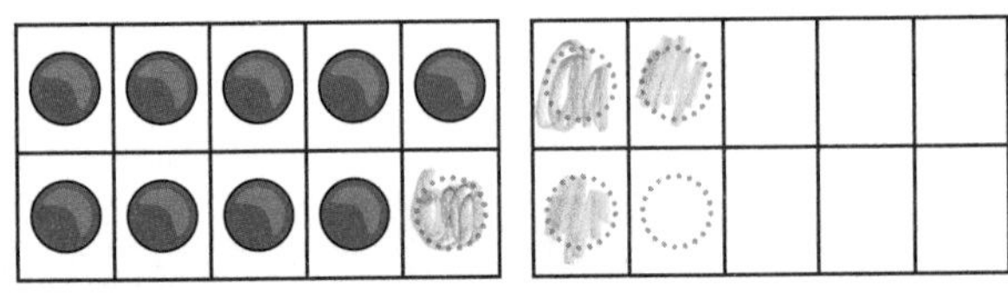

b. Draw 3 more.

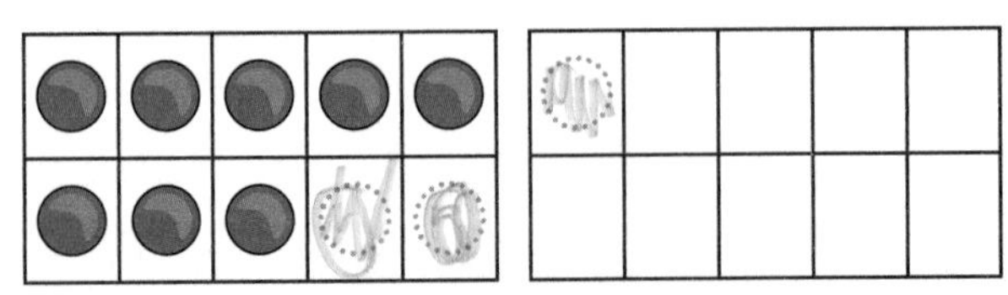

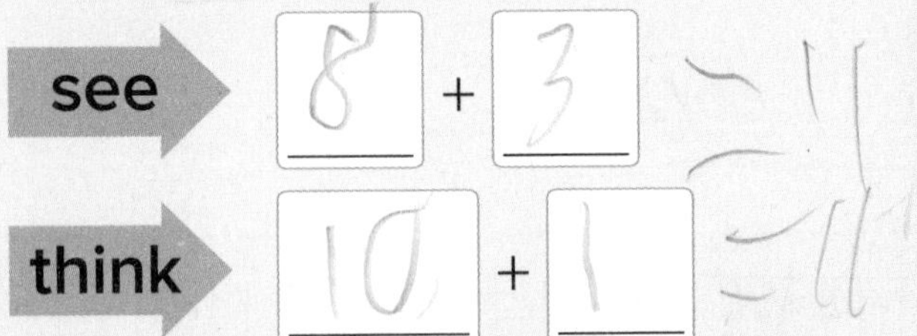

2. Draw more counters. Then write the numbers to match.

a. Draw 6 more.

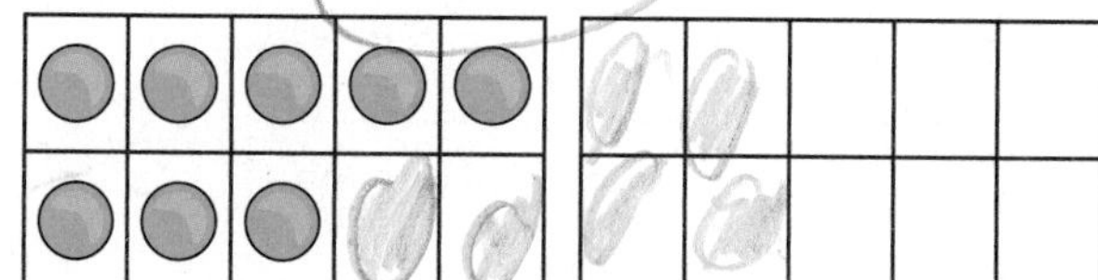

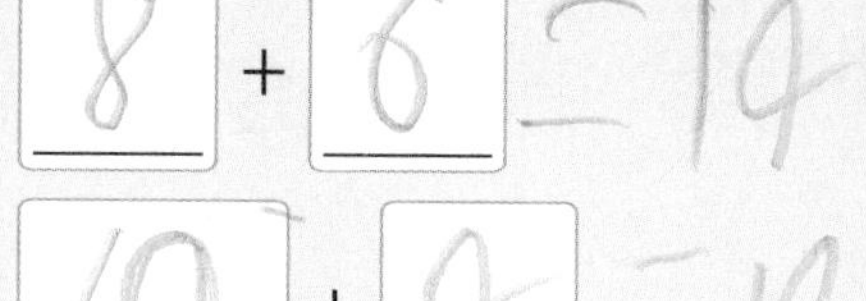

see ___ + ___

think ___ + ___

b. Draw 7 more.

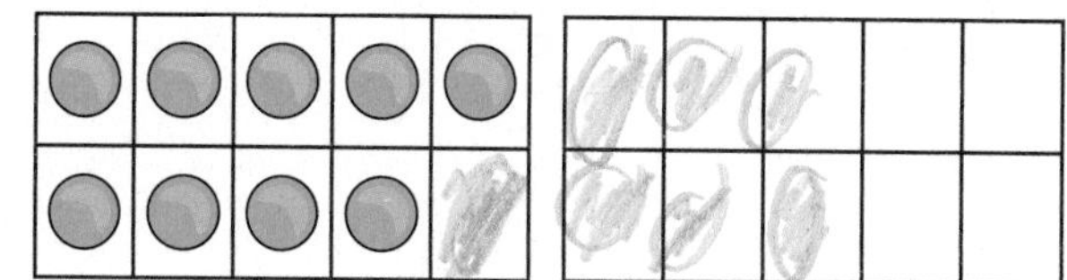

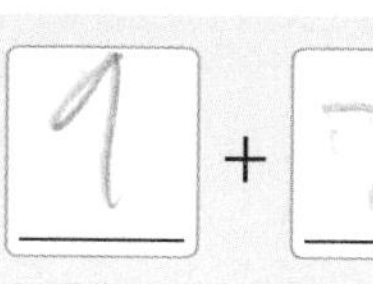

see ___ + ___

think ___ + ___

c. Draw 4 more.

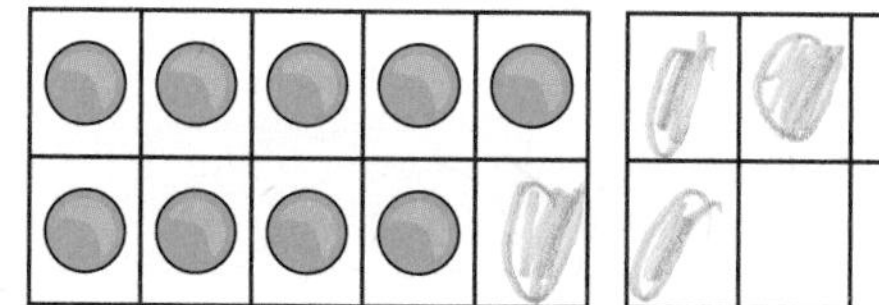

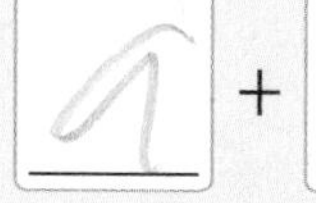

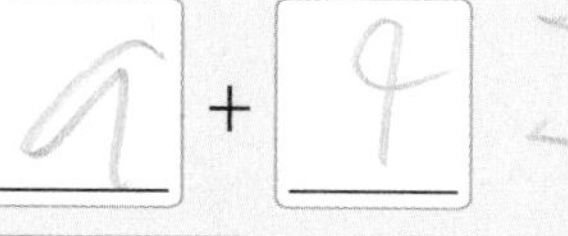

see ___ + ___

think ___ + ___

d. Draw 5 more.

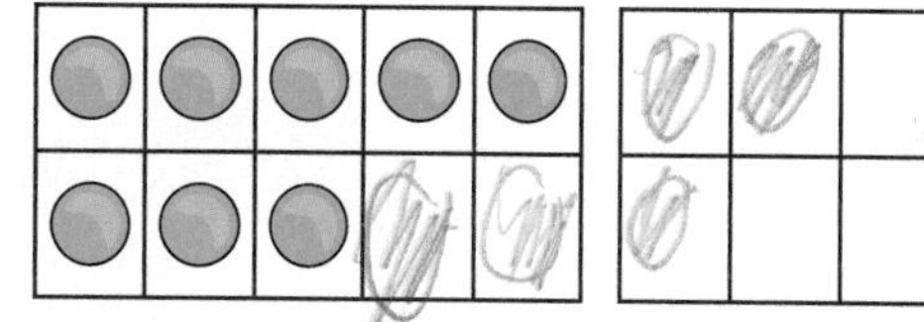

see ___ + ___

think ___ + ___

Step Ahead

Think of **six** different ways this cube train could be broken into two groups. Complete the equations to match.

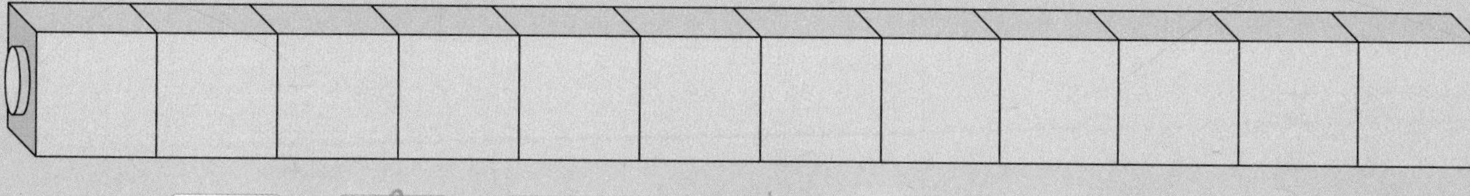

___ + ___ = ___　　___ + ___ = ___

___ + ___ = ___　　___ + ___ = ___

___ + ___ = ___　　___ + ___ = ___

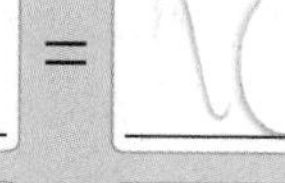

Addition: Reinforcing the make-ten strategy

Step In

Look at this picture of counters.

How many counters are **on** the ten-frame?
How many counters are **off** the ten-frame?

How could you use the ten-frame to figure out the total?

I could move two counters to fill the ten-frame.

Circle the box below that matches the thinking above.

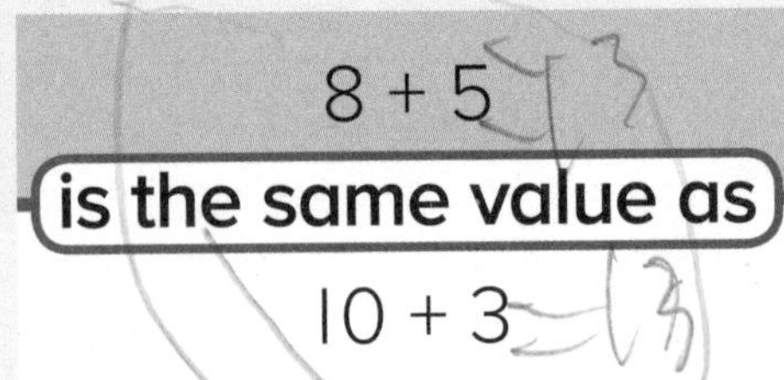

8 + 5	8 + 5	8 + 5
is the same value as	is the same value as	is the same value as
10 + 2	10 + 5	10 + 3

How could you use a ten-frame to figure out 9 + 4?

Step Up

1. Draw more counters to figure out the total. Fill the ten-frame first. Then write the tens fact to match the picture.

a. 9 + 3 = ☐

☐ + ☐ = ☐

b. 9 + 6 = ☐

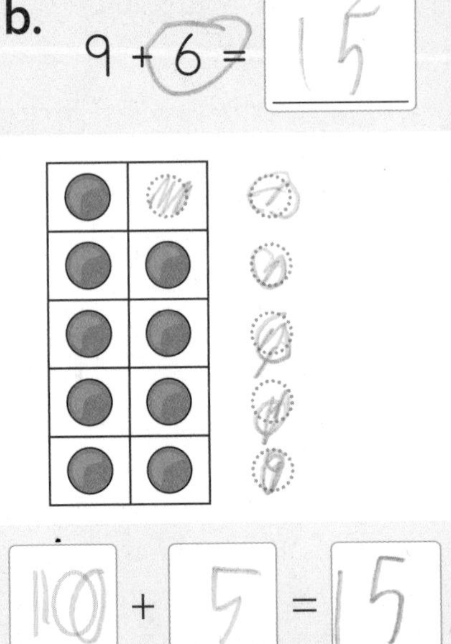

☐ + ☐ = ☐

c. 8 + 4 = ☐

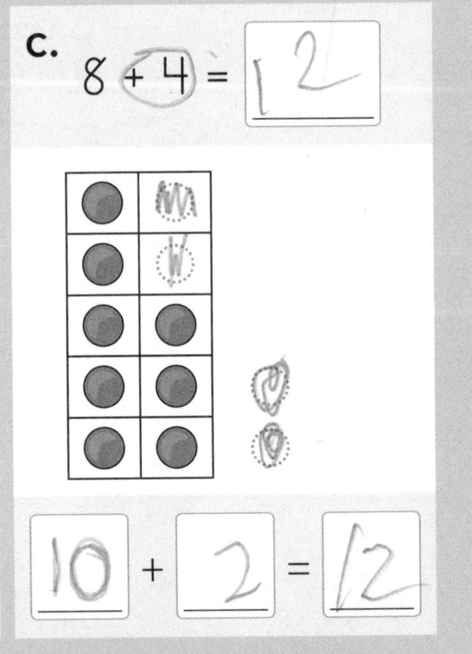

☐ + ☐ = ☐

2. Draw more counters to figure out the total. Fill the ten-frame first. Then write the tens fact to match the picture.

a.

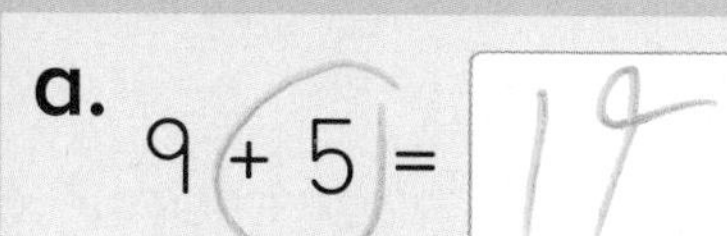

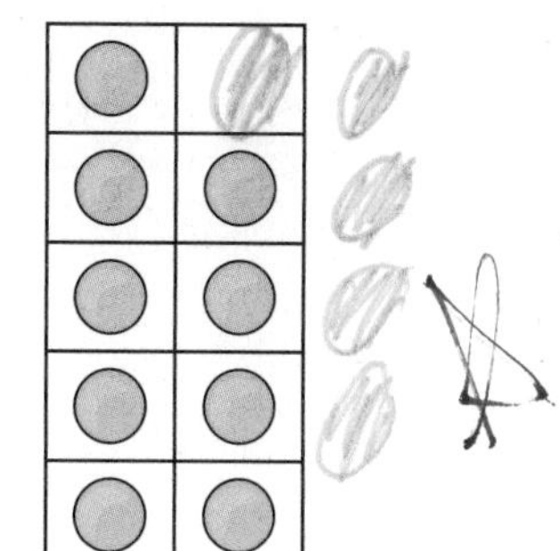

b.

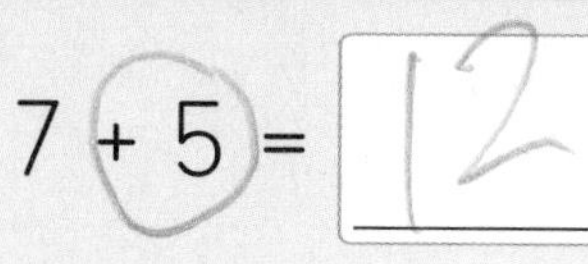

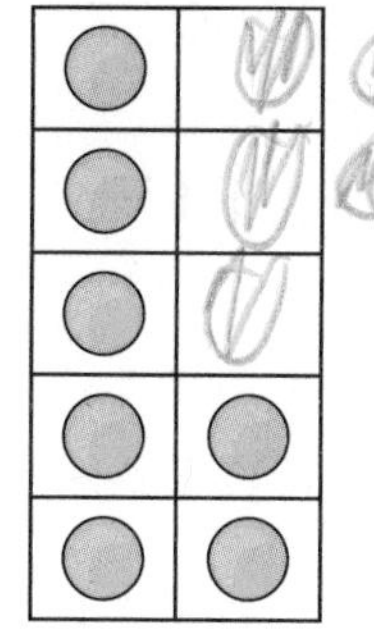

☐ + ☐ = ☐

c. 9 + 7 = ☐

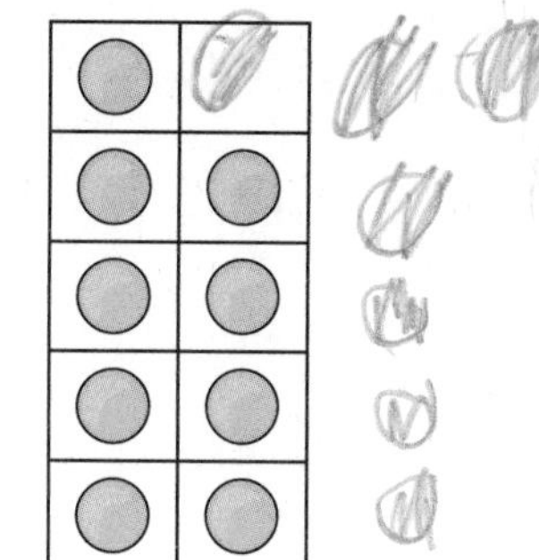

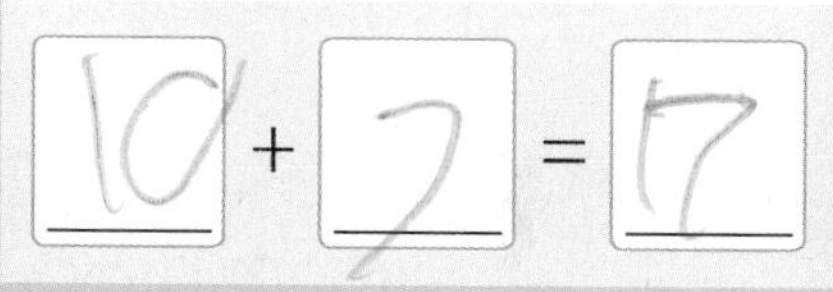

d.

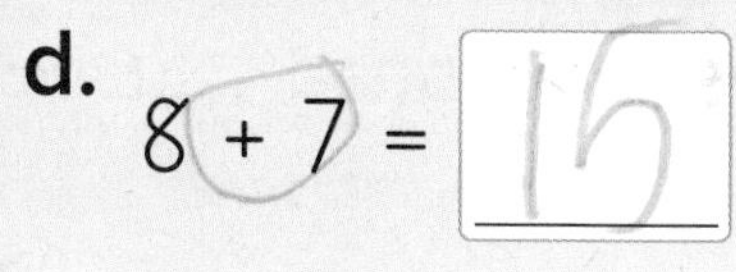

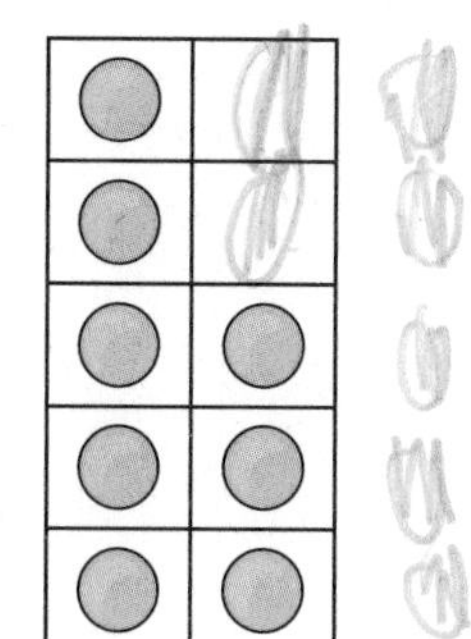

☐ + ☐ = ☐

e.

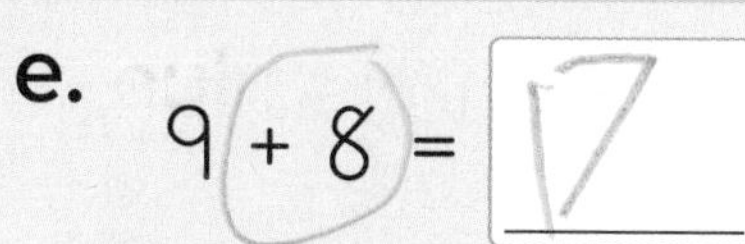

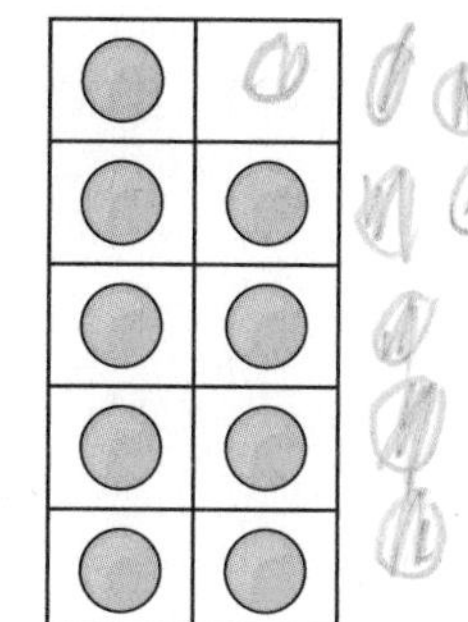

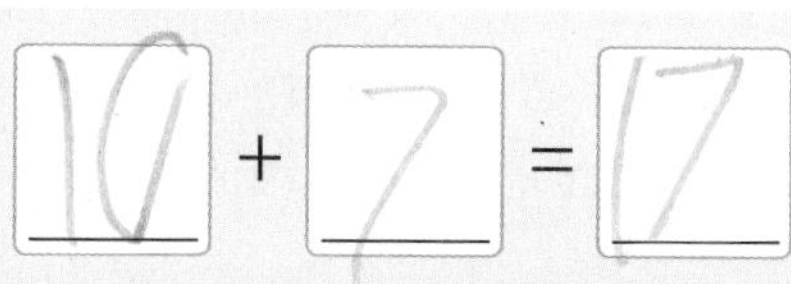

f.

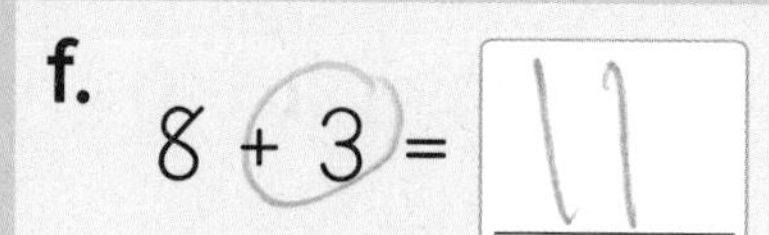

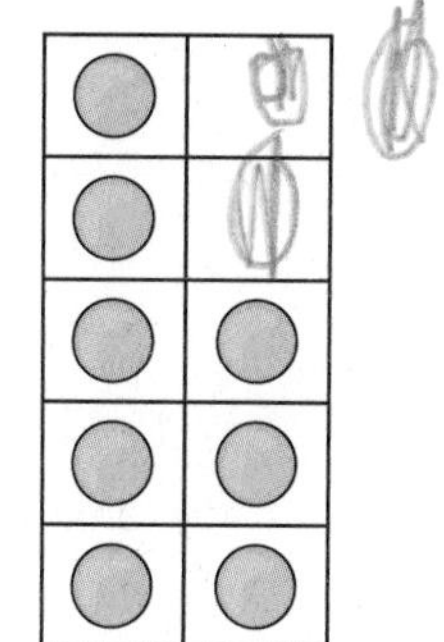

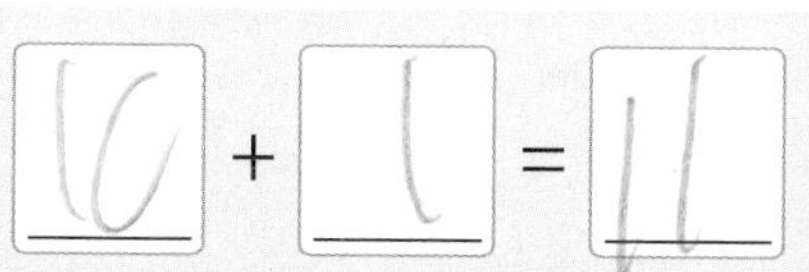

Step Ahead

Circle the facts that have the same total as the counters in this picture.

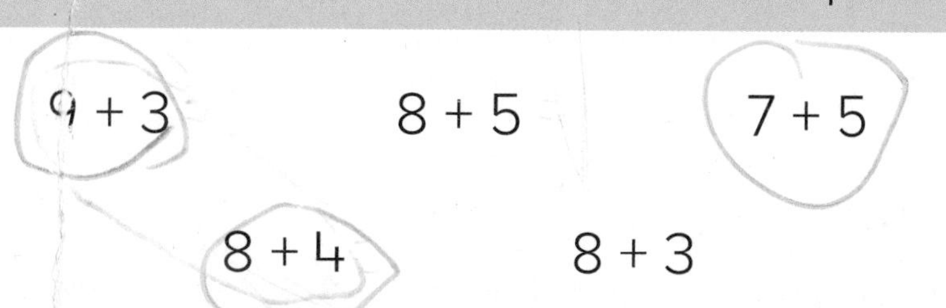

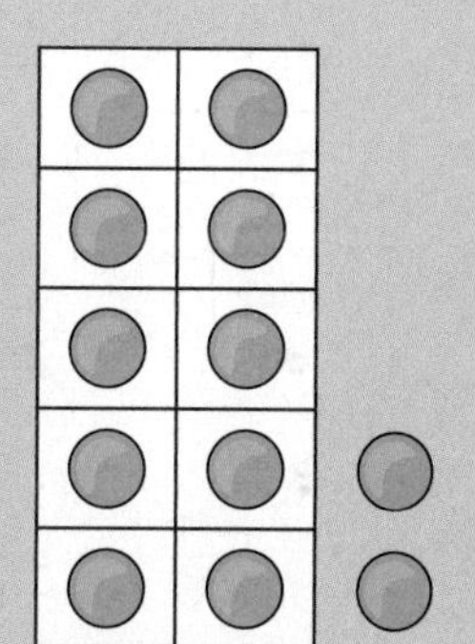

Maintaining concepts and skills

Think and Solve

Imagine you can only move ⟶ or ↑.

•—• is 1 unit.

How many units will be in the **shortest** path from **A** to **B**? ____ units

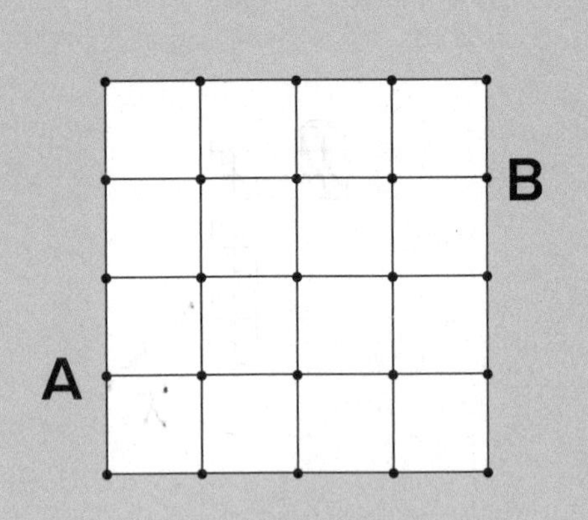

Words at Work

A coach buys some new balls, bats, and gloves for the baseball team. She buys 10 things in total.

a. Draw a picture to show how many balls, bats, and gloves there could be.

b. Write a sentence to describe your picture.

Ongoing Practice

1. Look at the blocks. Write the matching number on the expanders.

FROM 1.7.2

a.

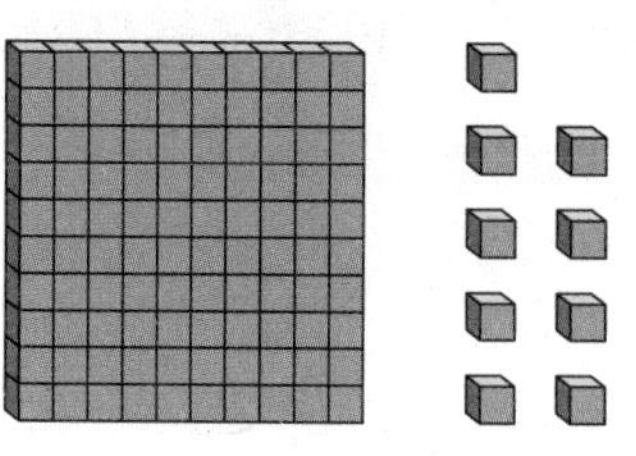

hundreds tens ones

hundreds

b.

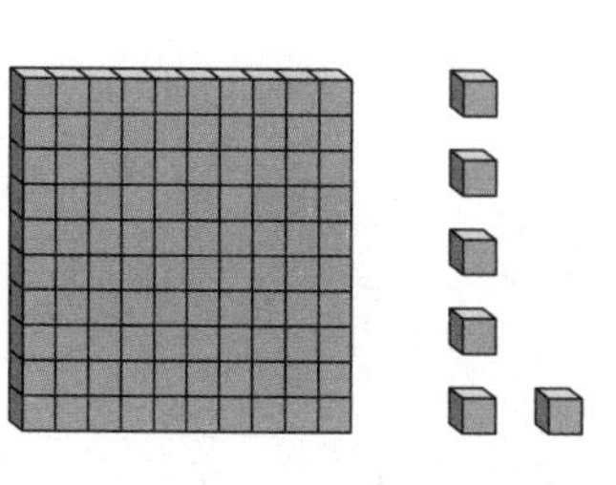

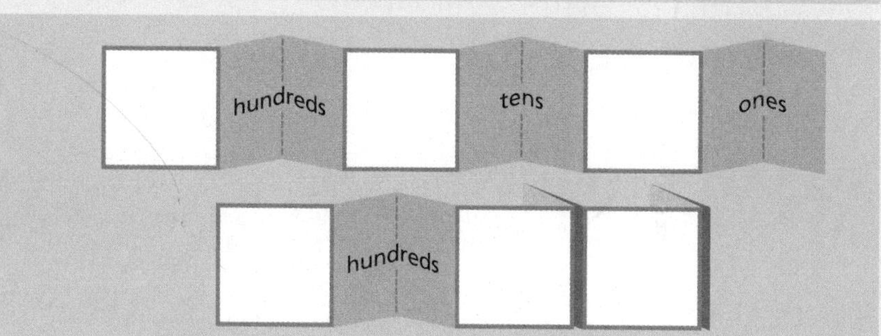

2. Draw ⤺ to show two numbers that make 10.
Write an equation to show how you add to find the total.

FROM 1.8.2

a.

___ + ___ + ___ = ___

b.

___ + ___ + ___ = ___

Preparing for Module 9

Write the missing numbers on these number track pieces.

a.

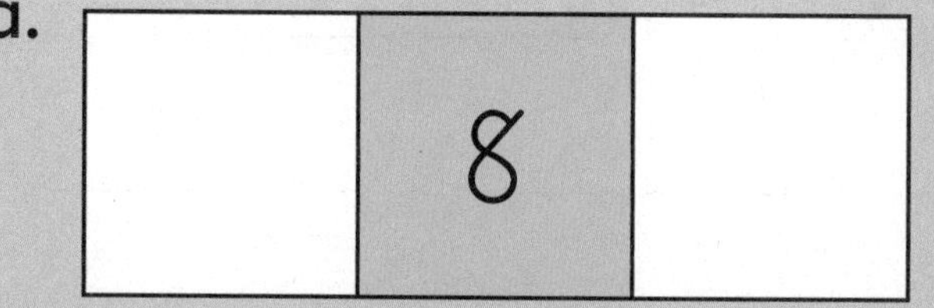

b.

8.5 Addition: Reinforcing the commutative property

Step In What two addition facts match this picture?

Which fact do you think is easier to figure out? Why?

I find it easier to figure out 9 + 4, then write the turnaround.

9 + 4 = 13
4 + 9 = 13

Step Up 1. Write an addition fact to match each picture. Then write the turnaround fact.

a.

9 + 5 = 14

5 + 9 = 14

b.

8 + 3 = 11

3 + 8 = 11

c.

6 + 8 = 14

8 + 6 = 14

d.

9 + 2 = 11

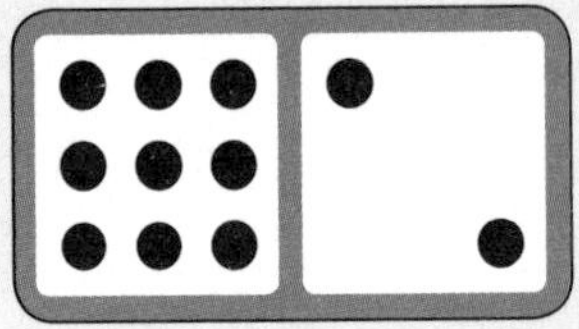

2 + 9 = 11

e.

4 + 7 = 11

7 + 4 = 11

f.

9 + 7 = 16

7 + 9 = 16

2. Write an addition fact to match each picture. Then write the turnaround fact.

a.

___ + ___ = ___

(5 dots) | 8

___ + ___ = ___

b.

___ + ___ = ___

9 | (8 dots)

___ + ___ = ___

c.

___ + ___ = ___

(8 dots) | 6

___ + ___ = ___

d.

___ + ___ = ___

(9 dots) | 3

___ + ___ = ___

e.

___ + ___ = ___

7 | (8 dots)

___ + ___ = ___

f.

___ + ___ = ___

(4 dots) | 9

___ + ___ = ___

Step Ahead

a. Add the numbers in each row. Then add the numbers in each column. Write the totals around the outside.

8	1	6	___
3	5	7	___
4	9	2	___
___	___	___	

b. Write an equation to show three other numbers that will add to make the same total.

___ + ___ + ___ = ___

Addition: Reinforcing all strategies

Step In **Look at these pictures. How could each picture show addition?**

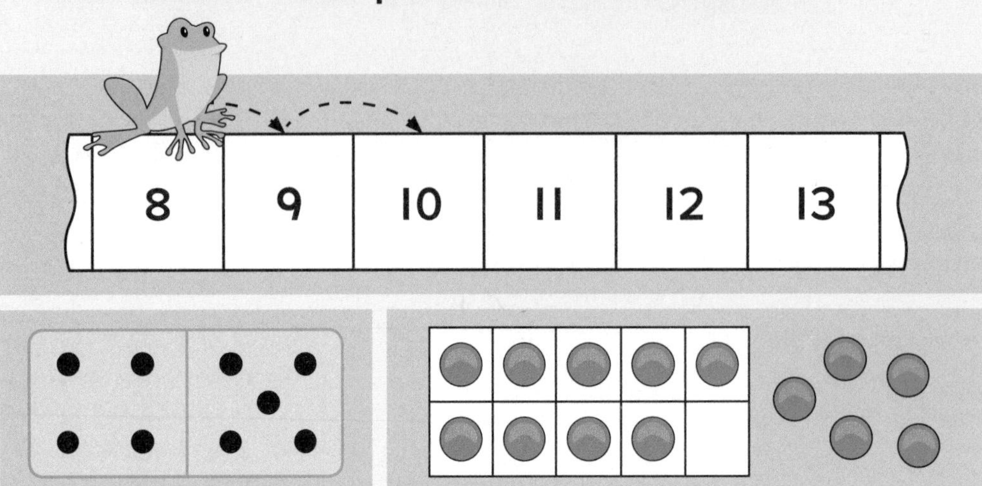

How could you figure out the total in each picture?
Which addition strategy would you use?

Which addition strategy would you use to solve each of these facts?

6 + 7 = ____ 2 + 9 = ____ 5 + 8 = ____

How can different strategies be used to solve the same fact?

Step Up 1. Write the total. Then write **C**, **D**, or **M** in the circle to show the strategy you used to figure out the total.

Addition strategy

Ⓒ count-on

Ⓓ doubles

Ⓜ make-ten

○ 8 + 0 = ____ ○ 9 + 5 = ____

○ 5 + 6 = ____ ○ 3 + 9 = ____ ○ 2 + 5 = ____

○ 8 + 8 = ____ ○ 9 + 2 = ____ ○ 7 + 9 = ____

2. Write the answer. Then draw a line to the strategy you used to figure it out.

2 + 6 = ____		3 + 1 = ____
9 + 3 = ____	count-on	7 + 5 = ____
7 + 8 = ____	doubles	1 + 7 = ____
9 + 9 = ____	make-ten	6 + 8 = ____
9 + 6 = ____		5 + 9 = ____

Step Ahead

You can use more than one strategy to solve the same fact. Complete these to show the different ways these totals can be figured out.

a. Use the make-ten strategy

9 + 8 = ____

is the same value as

10 + ____ = ____

Use the doubles strategy

9 + 8 = ____

is the same value as

double 8 plus ____ = ____

b. Use the make-ten strategy

8 + 6 = ____

is the same value as

10 + ____ = ____

Use the doubles strategy

8 + 6 = ____

is the same value as

double 6 plus ____ = ____

Maintaining concepts and skills

Computation Practice

- ★ Complete the equations.
- ★ Use the same color to show keys and locks with matching answers. One key does not have a match.

Ongoing Practice

1. Figure out the number of dots that are covered. Then complete the facts.

FROM 1.7.8

a. 16 - 7 = ___

7 + ___ = 16

b. 12 - 5 = ___

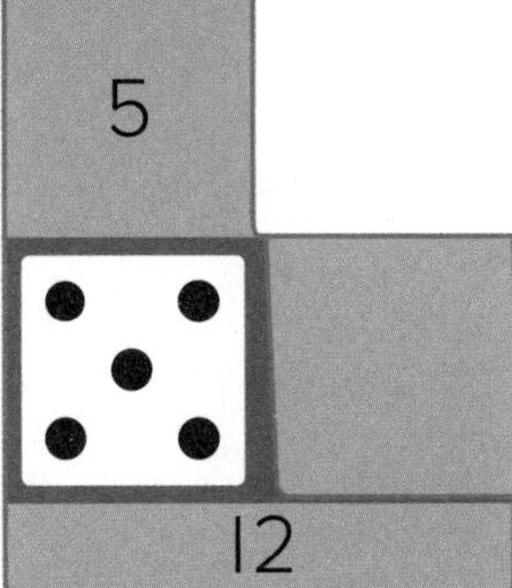

5 + ___ = 12

c. 14 - 6 = ___

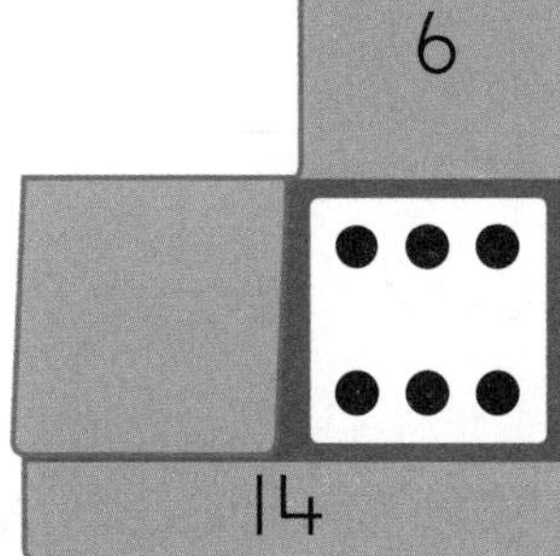

6 + ___ = 14

2. Draw more counters. Then write the numbers to match.

FROM 1.8.3

a. Draw 6 more.

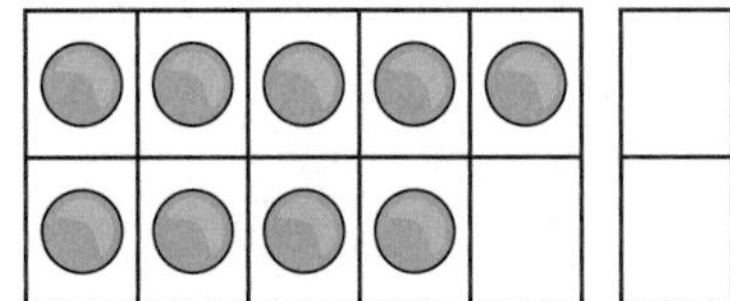

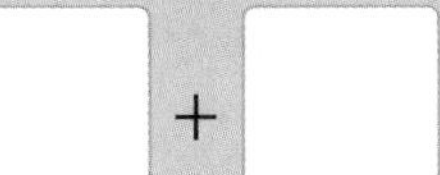

see ___ + ___

think ___ + ___

b. Draw 4 more.

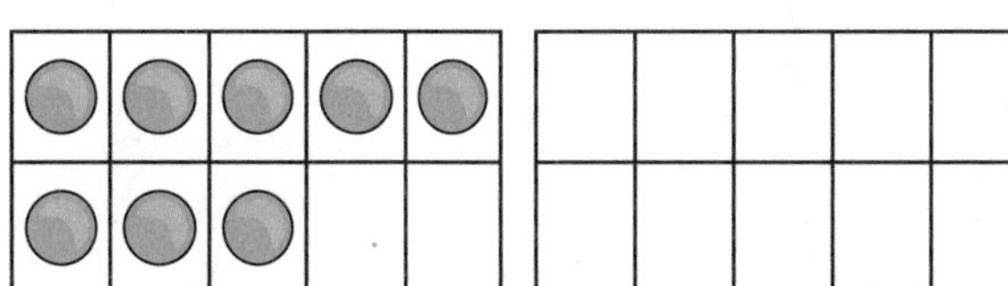

see ___ + ___

think ___ + ___

Preparing for Module 9

Draw jumps to help you count on. Write two addition facts to match.

Count on **2**.

___ + ___ = ___

___ + ___ = ___

8.7 Equality: Reviewing concepts

Step In

What is wrong with this balance picture?

How many more circles do you need to draw to make the balance picture true?

Draw the circles on the picture.

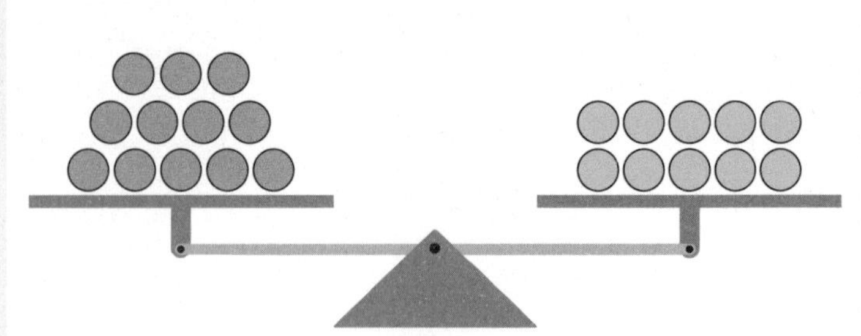

What equation could you write to match the picture?

___ = ___ + ___

Step Up

1. Draw **more circles** on one side of each pan balance to make the balance picture true. Then write the matching equation.

a.

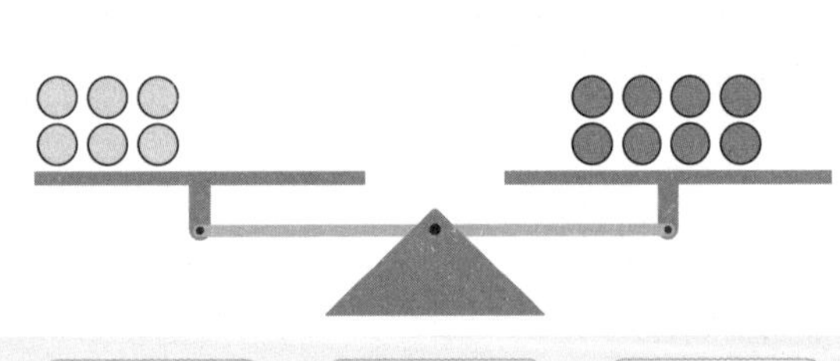

6 + ___ = 8

b.

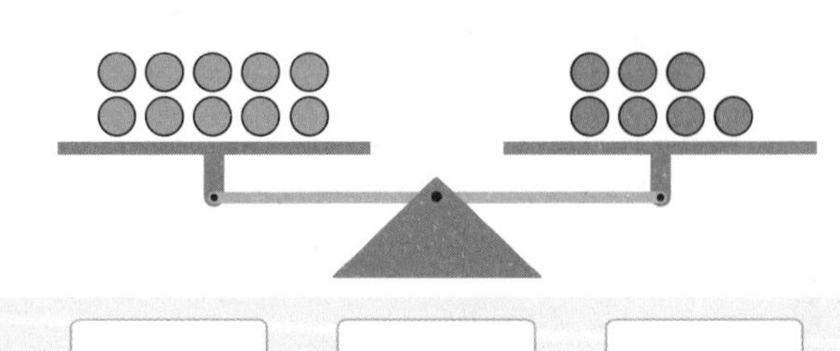

___ = ___ + ___

c.

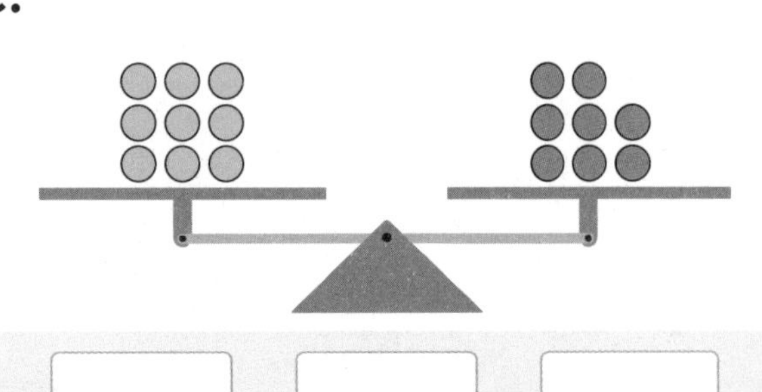

___ = ___ + ___

d.

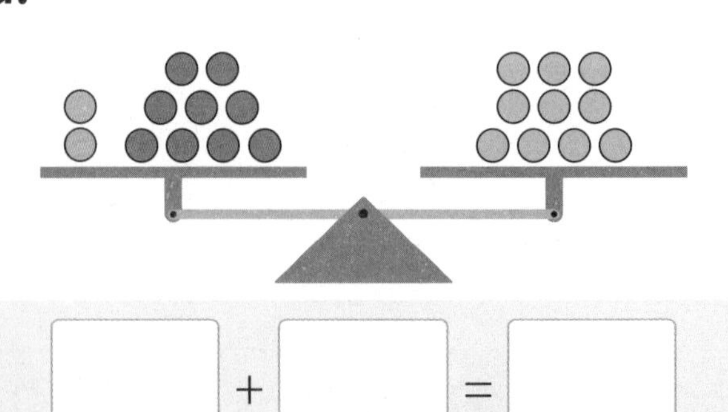

___ + ___ = ___

2. Write the missing numeral to make each balance picture true. Then write the matching equation.

a. 13 2 ___

___ + ___ = ___

b.

___ = ___ + ___

c. 14 1 ___

___ = ___ + ___

d.

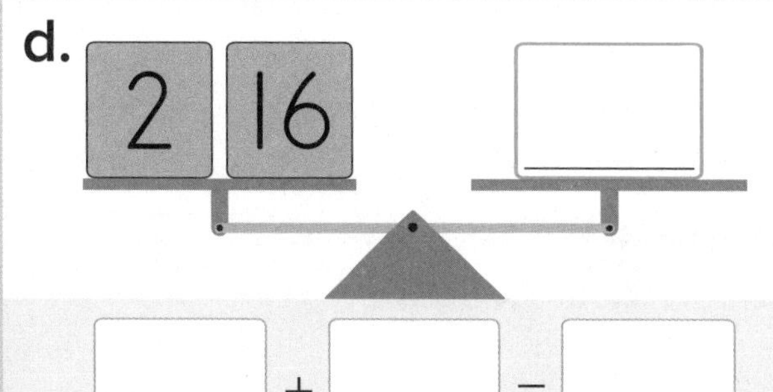

___ + ___ = ___

e.

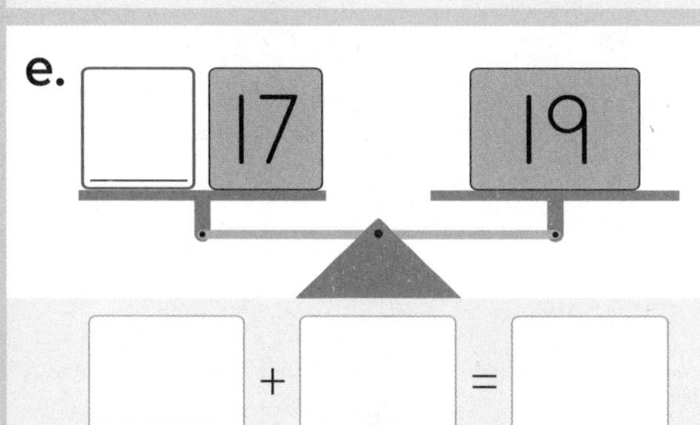

___ + ___ = ___

f.

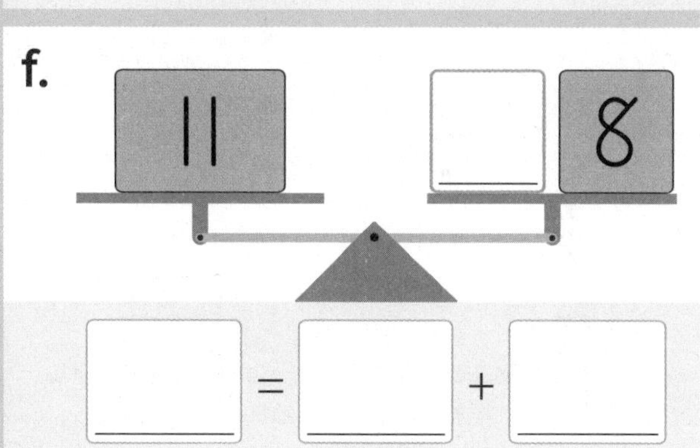

___ = ___ + ___

Step Ahead Write three different equations that would make this balance picture true.

___ + ___ = ___

___ + ___ = ___

___ + ___ = ___

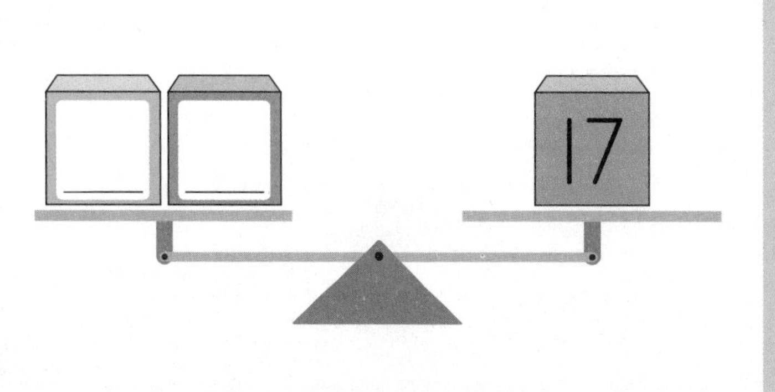

Equality: Working with balance situations

Step In

Look at the circles in this balance picture.

How many more circles do you need to draw to make the balance picture true?

How do you know?

Draw the circles on the picture.

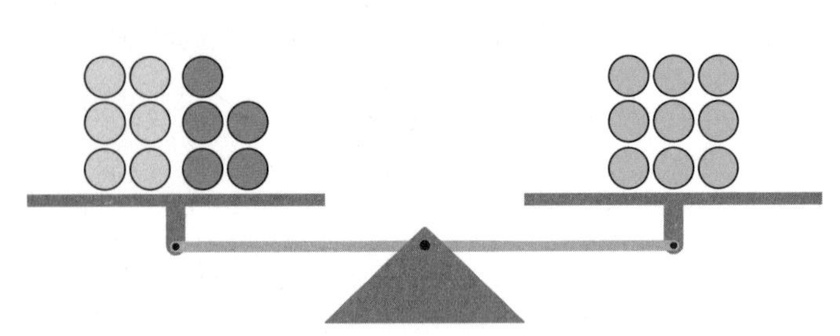

What equation could you write to match the picture?

☐ + ☐ = ☐ + ☐

Step Up

1. Draw **more circles** to make each balance picture true. Then write the matching equation.

a.

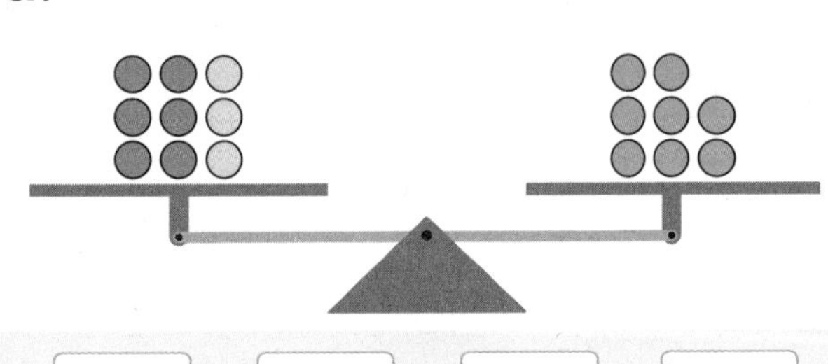

6 + 3 = 8 + ☐

b.

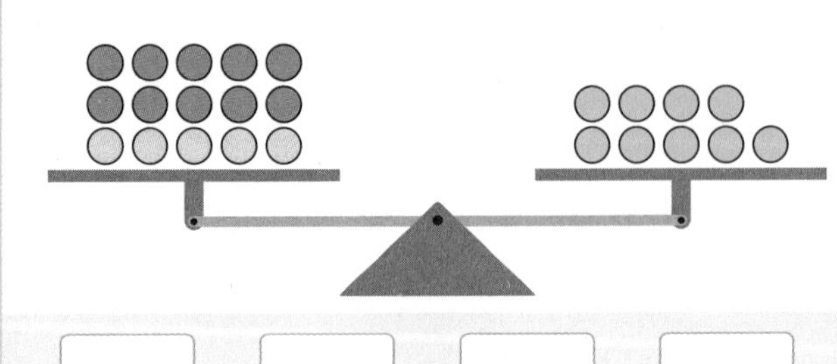

☐ + ☐ = ☐ + ☐

c.

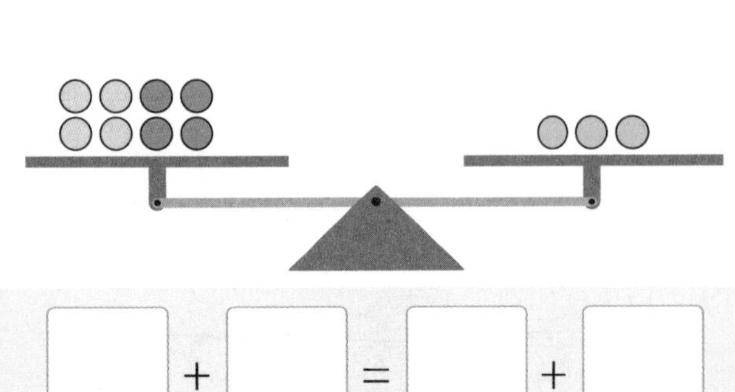

☐ + ☐ = ☐ + ☐

d.

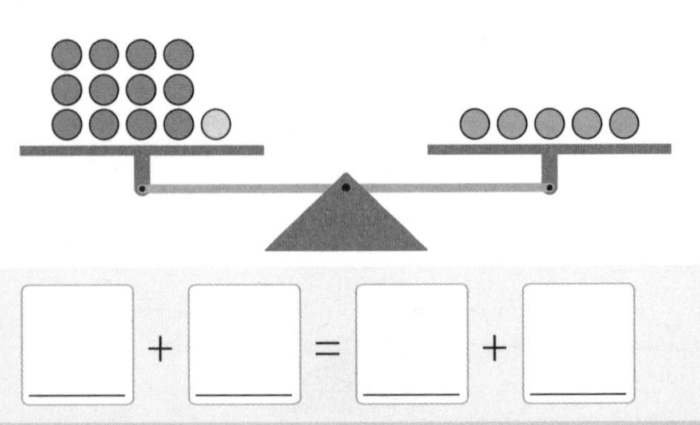

☐ + ☐ = ☐ + ☐

2. Write numerals to make each balance picture true. Then write the matching equation.

a. 5 6 7 ___

5 + 6 = 7 + ___

b.

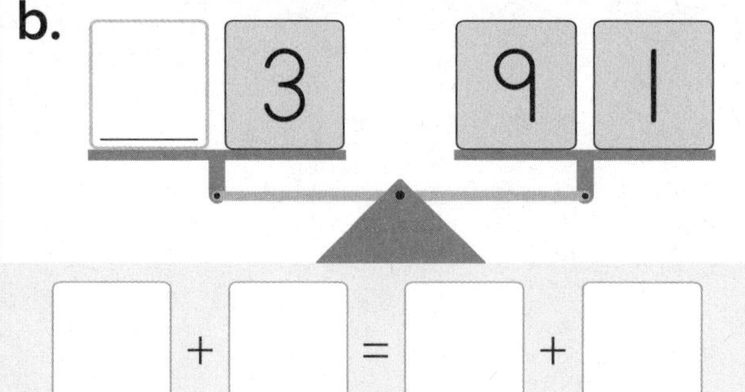

___ + ___ = ___ + ___

c.

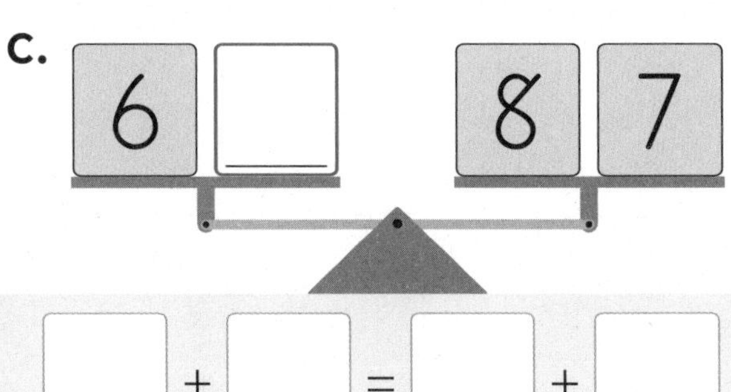

___ + ___ = ___ + ___

d.

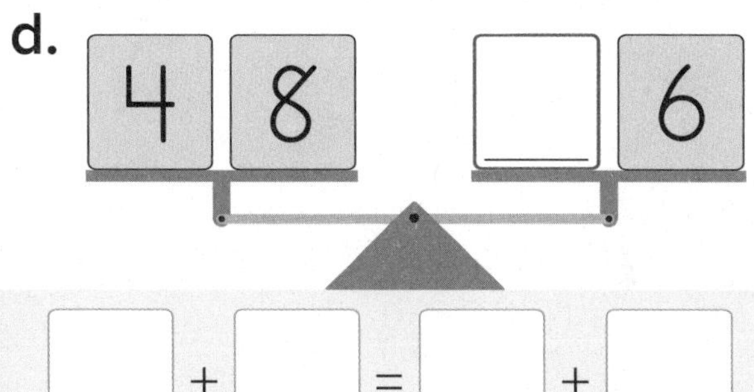

___ + ___ = ___ + ___

e.

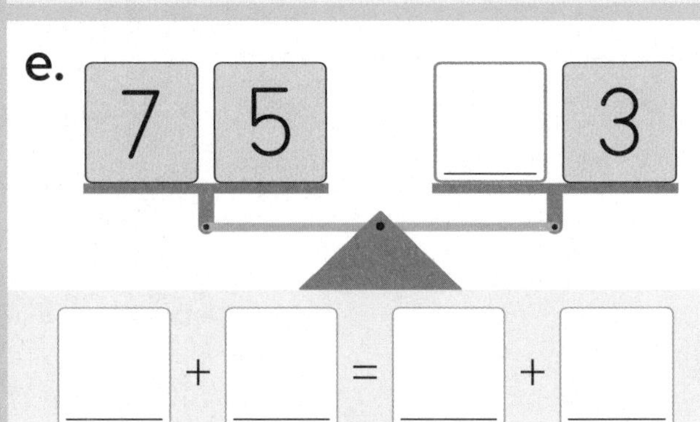

___ + ___ = ___ + ___

f.

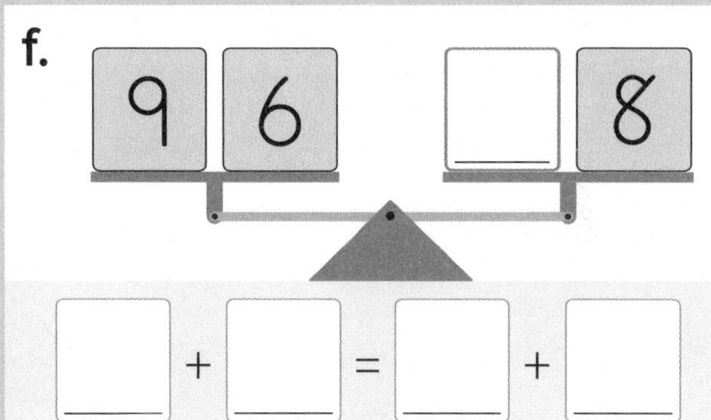

___ + ___ = ___ + ___

Step Ahead

Use these numbers to make each balance picture true. Each number can be used only once.

a. 7 ___ ___ 8

b.

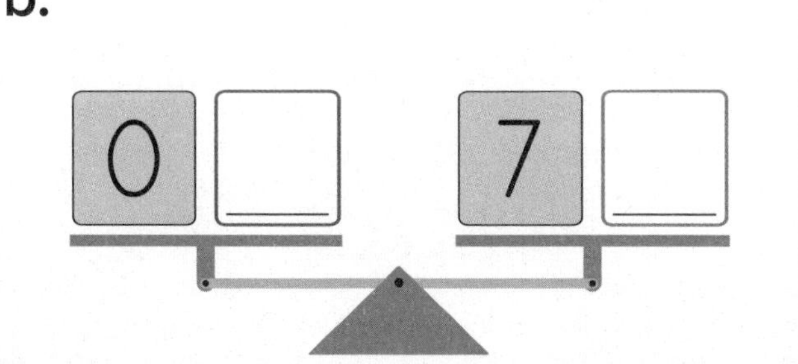

Maintaining concepts and skills

Think and Solve 

Read the clues. Use the letters to answer.

Clues

A is heavier than **C**.

C is heavier than **B**.

A is lighter than **D**.

a. Which is heaviest? 

b. Which is lightest? 

Words at Work

Choose and write words from the list to complete the sentences below. One word is used more than once. Some words are not used.

same
add
between
balances
does not
take away

a. Nine add six ____________ 15.

b. Eight add five equals ten ____________ three.

c. Eleven take two ____________ four add five.

d. Twelve take four ____________ balance ten.

e. In an equation, the total value on each side of the = must be the ____________.

Ongoing Practice

1. Complete the equations. Then write **A** on the equations that you solved by thinking about addition.

FROM 1.7.9

a. 9 - 8 = ___

b. 10 - 4 = ___

c. 7 - 2 = ___

d. 4 - 4 = ___

e. 5 - 1 = ___

f. 6 - 5 = ___

g. 9 - 6 = ___

h. 11 - 8 = ___

2. Write the missing numeral to make each balance picture true. Then write the matching equation.

FROM 1.8.7

a.

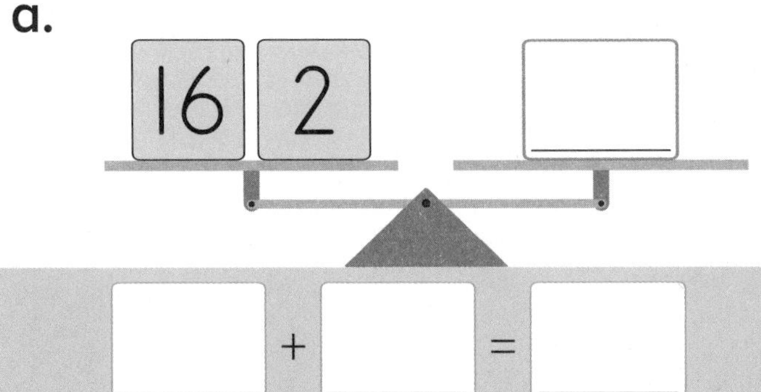

___ + ___ = ___

b.

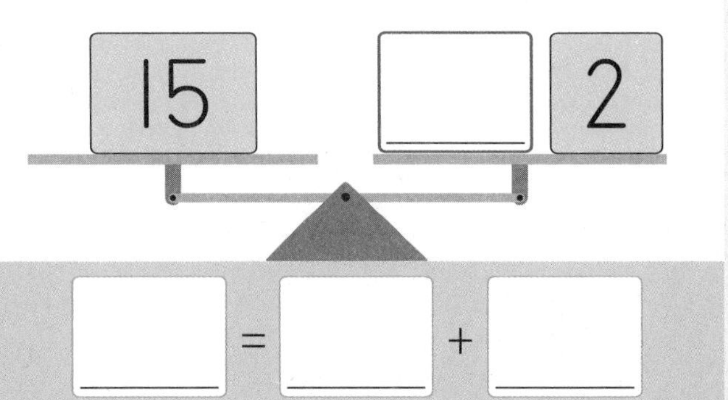

___ = ___ + ___

Preparing for Module 9

Look at each picture of blocks. Write the matching number in the place-value chart. Then write the numeral without the chart.

a.

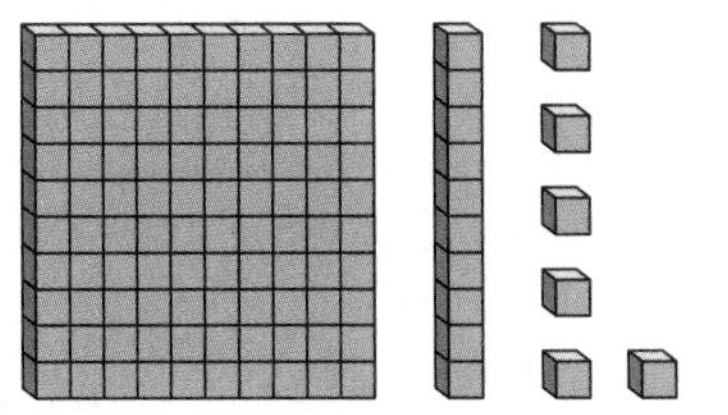

Hundreds	Tens	Ones

b.

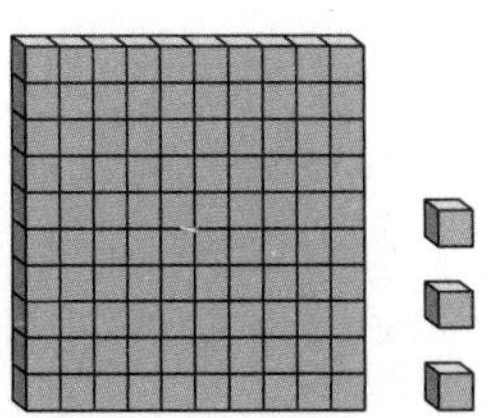

Hundreds	Tens	Ones

___

8.9 Equality: Balancing equations

Step In **Look at this balance picture.**

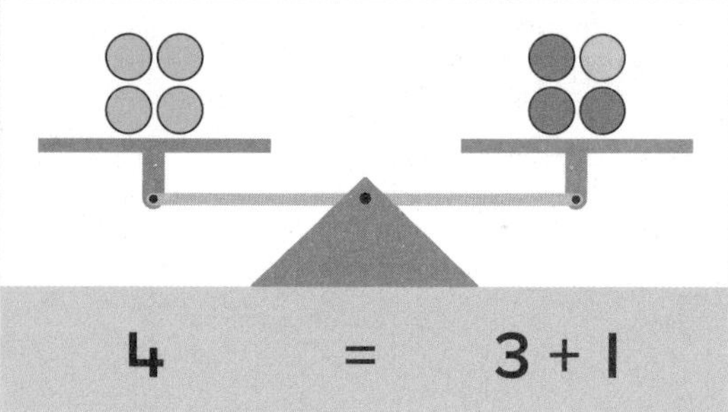

How does the picture match the equation?

Draw ○ on this pan balance to match the equation.

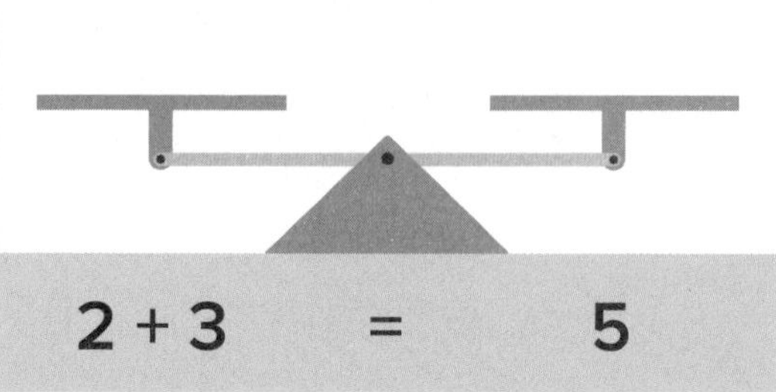

What does = mean?

The value on either side of the = symbol is the same.
4 is equal to 3 add 1.
2 add 3 is equal to 5.

Write the missing numeral to balance each equation.

4 + 2 = ☐ | 9 = 4 + ☐ | ☐ + 3 = 6

Step Up I. Write the numeral that is missing.

a. 2 + 5 = ☐	b. 6 + 1 = ☐	c. 11 - 3 = ☐
d. ☐ = 4 + 4	e. ☐ = 5 - 0	f. ☐ = 8 + 7

2. Write **true** or **false** beside each equation.

a. 4 + 2 = 3 + 3 ______	**b.** 9 = 5 + 4 ______
c. 12 - 3 = 8 ______	**d.** 7 = 9 - 2 ______

3. Complete each equation.

a. 7 + ___ = 9	**b.** ___ + 4 = 12	**c.** 15 - 8 = ___
d. 5 = ___ - 5	**e.** 11 = ___ + 9	**f.** 7 = 0 + ___

4. Write the missing number to make each equation true.

a. 3 + ___ = 4 + 1	**b.** 6 + 3 = 5 + ___	**c.** ___ - 2 = 1 + 8
d. 2 + ___ = 5 + 6	**e.** ___ + 1 = 0 + 7	**f.** 3 + 5 = 14 - ___

Step Ahead Use these numbers to balance each equation. Each number can be used only once.

a. 3 + ___ = 7 + ___

b. ___ + 11 = 8 + ___

0 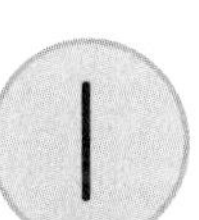

3 5

8.10 Data: Recording in a tally chart

Step In These buttons are sorted into groups.

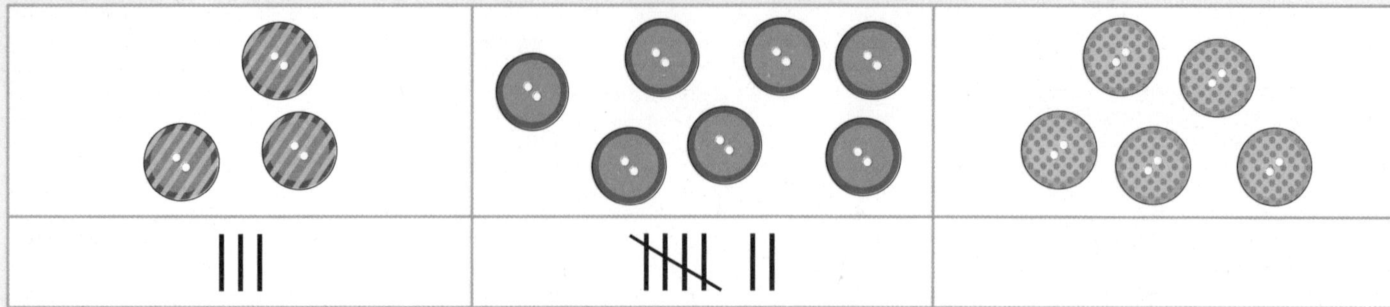

How have the buttons been sorted?

What do the marks below each group tell you?

Draw tally marks to show the number of spotted buttons.

> **Tally marks** can be organized into groups of five.

How many buttons are there in total?

How many more buttons are plain than spotted? Write an equation you could use to figure it out.

____ – ____ = ____

Step Up 1. Sort these buttons by **shape**. Draw tally marks in the chart at the top of page 309 to show the number of buttons in each group.

Shape	Tally	Total
Square button		
Triangle button		
Circle button		

2. Write the total number of tally marks beside each group.

3. Use the results in the table to answer each question.

a. What button shape is the most common? ______

b. How many buttons are shaped like a **square** or **triangle**? ______

c. How many buttons are shaped like a **triangle** or **circle**? ______

d. How many **more** buttons are shaped like a **circle** than a **square**? ______

e. What is the total number of buttons? ______

Step Ahead Complete the missing information in this table.

Shape	Tally	Total
Hexagon button	𝍸 𝍸 IIII	
Square button		12

8.10 Maintaining concepts and skills

Computation Practice

- ★ Complete the equations.
- ★ Find each total in the puzzle and color that part brown.
- ★ Color all the other numbered parts green.
  Two parts have no numbers. Leave them white.

4 + 5 = ___ = 5 + 4	8 + 7 = ___ = 7 + 8	2 + 4 = ___ = 4 + 2
3 + 1 = ___ = 1 + 3	6 + 7 = ___ = 7 + 6	5 + 3 = ___ = 3 + 5
8 + 6 = ___ = 6 + 8	7 + 5 = ___ = 5 + 7	7 + 9 = ___ = 9 + 7
9 + 8 = ___ = 8 + 9	6 + 4 = ___ = 4 + 6	3 + 4 = ___ = 4 + 3

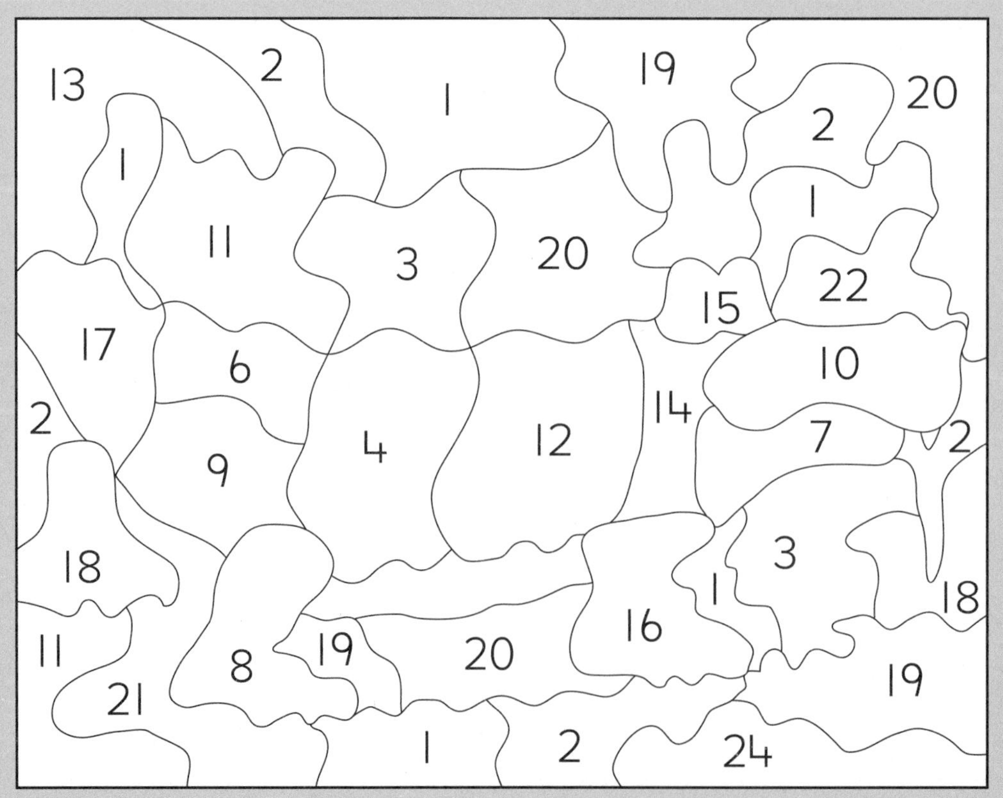

Ongoing Practice 1. Write each time in words.

a. 

b. 

c. 

FROM 1.7.10

2. Write the missing numeral to make each balance picture true. Then write the matching equation.

a. 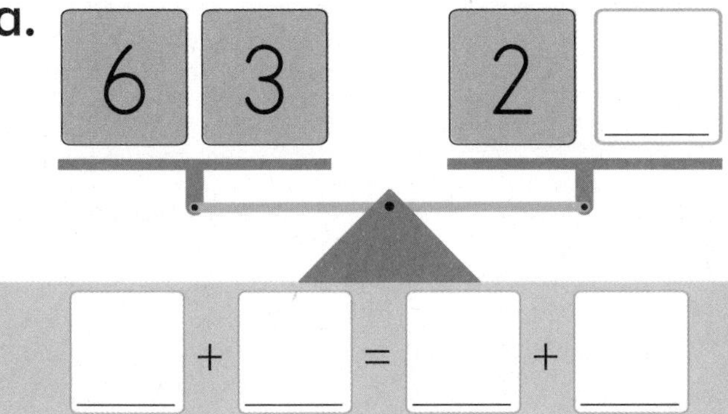

☐ + ☐ = ☐ + ☐

b. 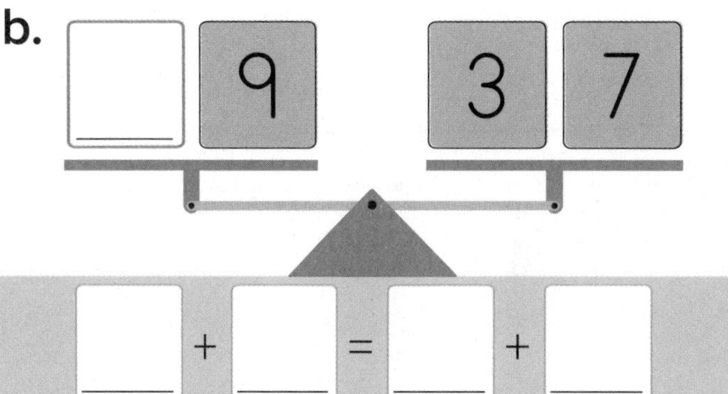

☐ + ☐ = ☐ + ☐

FROM 1.8.8

Preparing for Module 9 Draw more counters to figure out the total. Then write the tens fact to match.

a. 9 + 5 = ☐

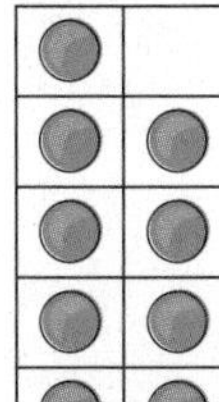

☐ + ☐ = ☐

b. 8 + 5 = ☐

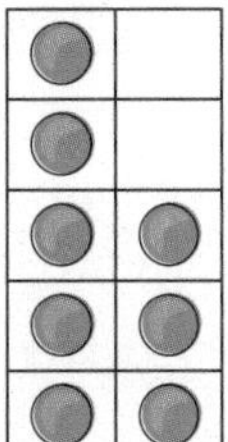

☐ + ☐ = ☐

c. 9 + 7 = ☐

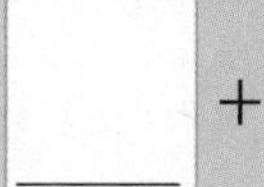

☐ + ☐ = ☐

Data: Collecting in a tally chart

Step In What does this table show?

Where We Go for Lunch Recess

Place	Tally	Total
Gym	卌 卌 卌 II	
Playground	卌 卌	
Library	卌 II	

What do the marks in the **Tally** column mean?

How could you figure out what numbers to write in the **Total** column?

I added groups of five and some ones.
The total for the gym is 5 + 5 + 5 and 2 more.

Where is the most popular place to go for lunch recess?
Where is the least popular place to go?

How many more students go to the playground than the library?
How do you know?

I compared the groups of tallies.
The playground has 3 more tallies,
so there were 3 more students there.

How many students go inside for their lunch recess?

How many students were asked where they go for lunch recess?

How did you figure out this total?

Step Up

a. Write three places where your friends like to go for lunch recess.

b. Write the place names you wrote above on this chart.

Place	Tally	Total

c. Ask other students which of these places they like to go to for lunch recess. Draw tallies on the chart to show their answers.

d. Write the totals in the chart.

e. What was the most popular place? ____________

f. How many students voted in total? ____

g. How many more students voted for the most popular place than the least popular place? ____

Step Ahead

Look at this tally chart.
Find and correct the two mistakes that were made.

Where We Go for Lunch Recess

Place	Tally	Total
Gym	𝍸 𝍸 𝍸 𝍸 |||	23
Playground	𝍸 𝍸 |||	13
Library	𝍸	6

8.12 Data: Interpreting a tally chart

Step In Three students recorded the number of vehicles in the parking lot at a weekend baseball game.

Vehicles in the Parking Lot

Vehicle	Tally	Total
Car	𝍸 𝍸 𝍸 𝍸 II	22
Truck	𝍸 𝍸	10
Motorcycle	𝍸	5

Ricardo said, “There were more trucks than cars in the parking lot.”

Jessica said, “There were more cars in the parking lot than trucks and motorcycles together.”

Caleb said, “There were more than 30 vehicles in the parking lot.”

Look at the tally chart and decide which statements are true.

What other information does the data in the tally chart tell you?

Step Up

1. Look at this tally chart. Color the ⬭ beside the statements that are true.

Vehicles in the Parking Lot

Vehicle	Tally	Total
Truck	𝍸 III	8
Car	𝍸	5
Motorcycle	II	2

⬭ More than 10 vehicles were in the parking lot.

⬭ There were more motorcycles than trucks in the parking lot.

⬭ There were more cars than motorcycles in the parking lot.

2. Read each clue. Then write **Car**, **Truck**, and **Motorcycle** to complete each tally chart.

Clue 1

Fewer than 10 trucks were in the parking lot.

Clue 2

More cars than motorcycles were in the parking lot.

a. **Vehicles in the Parking Lot**

Vehicle	Tally	Total
	𝍸 𝍸 𝍸 I	16
	𝍸 𝍸 𝍸 𝍸 𝍸 IIII	29
	𝍸 I	6

Clue 1

There were 25 cars in the parking lot.

Clue 2

Fewer trucks than motorcycles were in the parking lot.

b. **Vehicles in the Parking Lot**

Vehicle	Tally	Total
	𝍸 I	6
	𝍸 𝍸 𝍸 𝍸 𝍸	25
	𝍸 𝍸 III	13

Step Ahead Draw tally marks to show that 10 more trucks were in the parking lot than motorcycles.

Vehicle	Tally	Total
Truck		
Motorcycle	𝍸 II	7

Maintaining concepts and skills

Think and Solve  a. Color pairs of numbers that **add to 10**.

5	6	2	8	0	4	5	7	10

b. Circle the leftover number.

c. Use the number you circled to complete this equation. ☐ + ☐ = 10

d. Write a pair of numbers that are **not** shown above to complete this equation. ☐ + ☐ = 10

Words at Work Look at this tally chart. Write two sentences about the data it shows. You can use words from the list to help you.

Flowers We Like		
Flower	**Tally**	**Total**
Daisy	卌 III	8
Rose	卌	5
Lily	卌 卌	10

most popular
least popular
more
fewer
how many
votes

Ongoing Practice **1.** Write these times on the digital clocks.

FROM 1.7.12

a.

b.

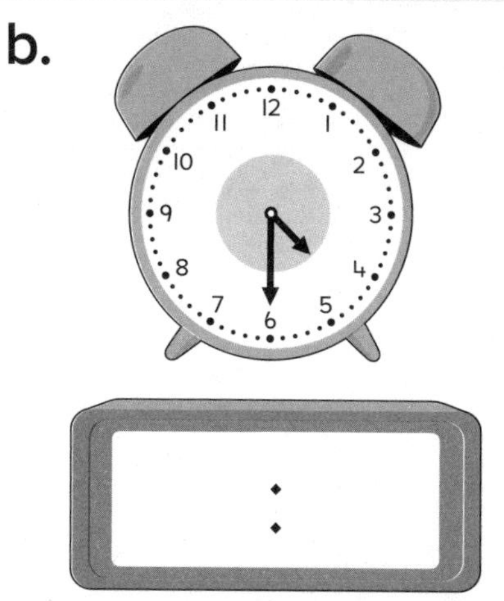

c.

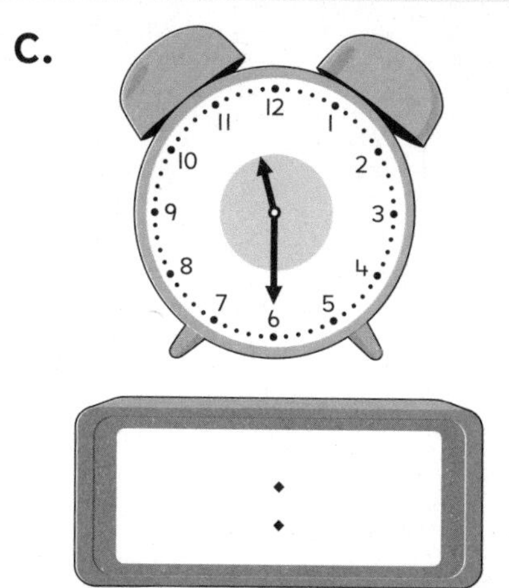

2. Use the tally chart to answer the questions.

FROM 1.8.10

Our Favorite Fruit

Orange	𝍸 𝍸 𝍸 𝍸 |
Banana	𝍸 𝍸 𝍸 |||
Apple	𝍸 𝍸 ||||

a. Which fruit is the most popular? ____________

b. Which fruit is the least popular? ____________

Preparing for Module 9 Write an addition fact to match each picture.

a.

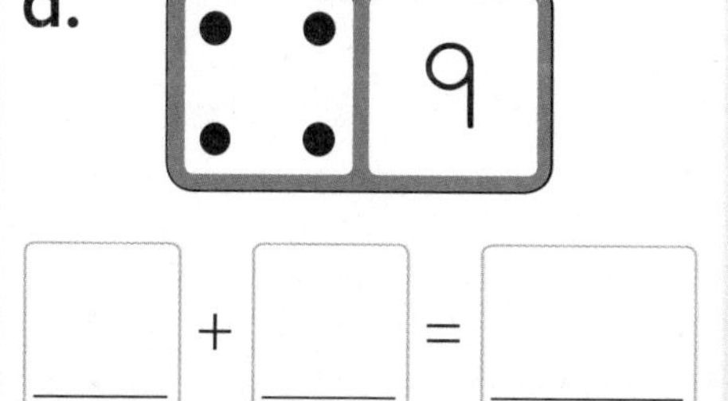

___ + ___ = ___

b.

___ + ___ = ___

c.

___ + ___ = ___

Working Space

9.1 Addition: Extending the count-on strategy

Step In

Look at this part of a number track.

50	51	52	53	54	55	56	57	58	59	60	61	62

Imagine you were standing on 53 and made one jump to 55.
How can you show your jump on the number track?

You could draw an arrow like this.

50	51	52	53	54	55	56	57	58	59	60	61	62

What equation could you write to show what you did?

53 + 2 = 55

What other jumps could you make on this number track?
What equations could you write to show what you did?

Step Up

1. Write the totals.

a. 24 + 1 = 25

b. 27 + 1 = 28

c. 31 + 1 = 32

2. Write the totals. Draw jumps on the number track to help you.

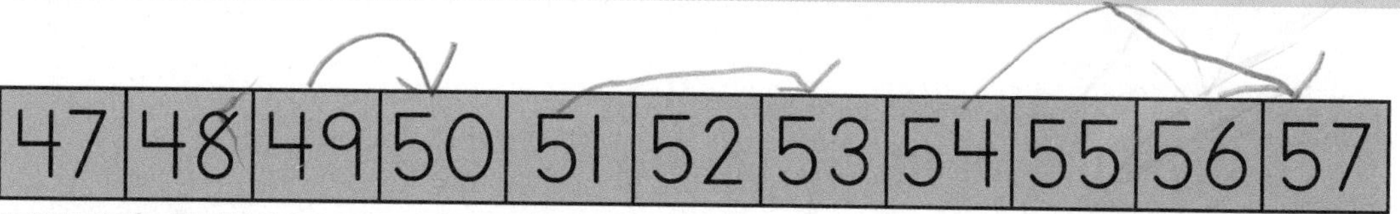

47	48	49	50	51	52	53	54	55	56	57

a. 49 + 1 = 50

b. 51 + 2 = 53

c. 54 + 3 = 57

65	66	67	68	69	70	71	72	73	74	75

d. 66 + 1 = 67

e. 69 + 2 = 71

f. 72 + 3 = 75

3. Use this number track to complete different equations.

84	85	86	87	88	89	90	91	92	93	94

a. 89 + 2 = 91

b. 92 + 1 = 93

c. 90 + 3 = 93

d. 90 + 2 = 92

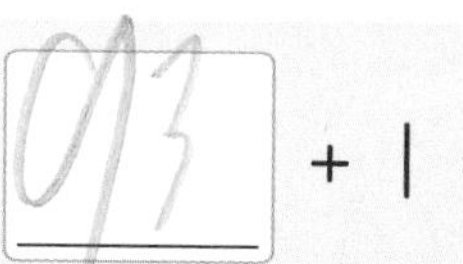

e. 93 + 1 = 94

f. 84 + 3 = 87

Step Ahead Use the number track in Question 3 to help you figure out the answer.

Valentina has 87 cents.
Noah has 2 cents more than Valentina.
Mary has 3 cents more than Noah.
Ryan has 2 cents more than Mary.

How much money does Ryan have?

2 cents

Addition: Identifying one or ten greater or less (hundred chart)

Step In Two friends play a game.
They take turns to roll the cubes.
They then move their counter to match what they roll.

1	2	3	4	5	6	7	8	9	10
11	12	13	14	15	16	17	18	19	20
21	22	23	24	25	26	27	28	29	30
31	32	33	34	35	36	37	38	39	40
41	42	43	44	45	46	47	48	49	50

Adianna has the yellow counter. She rolls **10 less.**

What number should she move her counter to?

Max has the purple counter. He rolls **1 greater**.

What number should he move his counter to?

Janice joins the game.
She starts on 17, rolls **10 greater**, and then rolls **1 less**.
What number does she finish on?

Step Up 1. These are parts of a hundred chart.
Write the missing numbers.

a. | | 37 | |

b. (top) | |
| | 75 | |

c. (top) | |
| 49 | |
(bottom) | |

d. | |
| 22 |
| |

2. Write numbers that are **1 greater** and **1 less**.

3. Write numbers that are **10 greater** and **10 less**.

4. Solve each problem.

a. 2 friends are reading the same book. Layla has read 10 more pages than Cody. Cody has read 42 pages. How many pages has Layla read?

 pages

b. Victor has sold 83 tickets for a charity. He has sold one more ticket than Nancy. How many tickets has Nancy sold?

 tickets

Step Ahead

Look at this part of a hundred chart. Use the list to write the missing numbers. Cross out the numbers not shown.

45	55	36	37
34	38	65	33

Maintaining concepts and skills

Computation Practice

What has four legs but does not walk?

- Complete the equations.
- Use a ruler to draw a straight line to join matching totals. Each line will pass through a letter.
- Write the letter above its matching total at the bottom of the page.

$3 + 9 =$ ____

$8 + 7 =$ ____

$5 + 8 =$ ____

$9 + 2 =$ ____

$8 + 6 =$ ____

$7 + 9 =$ ____

l

t

a

b

a

e

____ $= 9 + 6$

____ $= 8 + 3$

____ $= 9 + 5$

____ $= 5 + 7$

____ $= 4 + 9$

____ $= 8 + 8$

11	12	13	14	15	16
____	____	____	____	____	____

Ongoing Practice

1. Draw **more** counters to figure out the total. Fill the ten-frame first. Then write the tens fact to match the picture.

FROM 1.8.4

a. 9 + 4 = ___

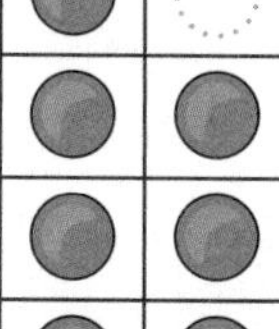

___ + ___ = ___

b. 9 + 7 = ___

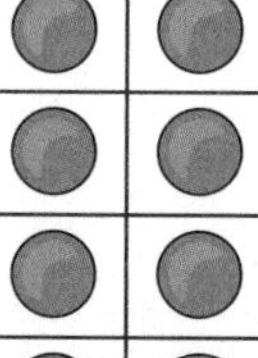

___ + ___ = ___

c. 8 + 5 = ___

___ + ___ = ___

2. Write the totals. Draw jumps on the number track to help you.

FROM 1.9.1

37	38	39	40	41	42	43	44	45	46	47

a. 38 + 1 = ___

b. 40 + 2 = ___

c. 42 + 3 = ___

Preparing for Module 10

Write the answers. You can draw jumps on the number track to help you.

1	2	3	4	5	6	7	8	9	10

a. 7 − 2 = ___

b. 10 − 2 = ___

c. 8 − 1 = ___

Addition: Exploring patterns (hundred chart)

Step In Look at these numbers.

1	2	3	4	5	6	7	8	9	10
11	12	13	14	15	16	17	18	19	20
21	22	23	24	25	26	27	28	29	30
31	32	33	34	35	36	37	38	39	40
41	42	43	44	45	46	47	48	49	50

What number is **1 more** than 37?
How do you know?

What number is **2 more** than 25?
How do you know?

What do you know about all the numbers that have 9 in the ones place?

Step Up 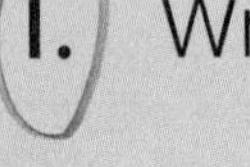 1. Write the totals.

a.	b.	c.
2 + 1 = ____	14 + 2 = ____	5 + 3 = ____
12 + 1 = ____	24 + 2 = ____	15 + 3 = ____
22 + 1 = ____	34 + 2 = ____	25 + 3 = ____
32 + 1 = ____	44 + 2 = ____	35 + 3 = ____
52 + 1 = ____	64 + 2 = ____	75 + 3 = ____
72 + 1 = ____	84 + 2 = ____	95 + 3 = ____

2. Write numbers **between 1 and 50** to match.

a. All the numbers that have 3 in the ones place.

b. The numbers that are **2 more** than each number above.

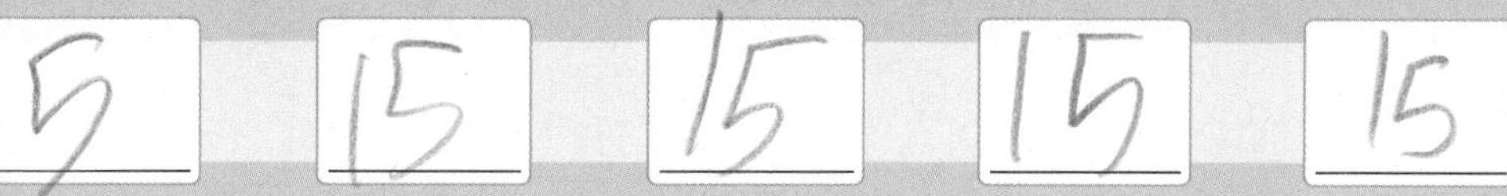

3. Write numbers **between 50 and 100** to match.

a. All the numbers that have 6 in the ones place.

b. The numbers that are **2 more** than each number above.

4. Write numbers **between 11 and 50** to complete these to show different equations.

a.

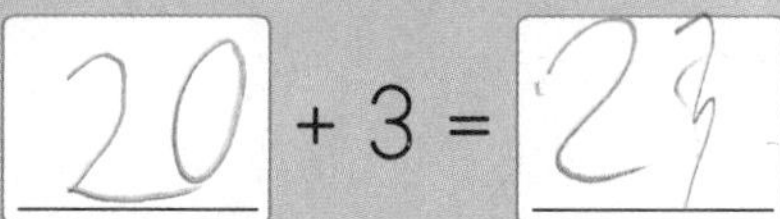

___ + 3 = ___

b.

___ + 2 = ___

c.

___ + 1 = ___

Step Ahead

John has 55 cents. He finds 4 cents more. Teresa has 56 cents. Her mom gives her 2 cents more. Riku has 58 cents.

a. Who has the most money in total? ___

b. Write the equations you used to help you.

___

___

9.4 Addition: Any two-digit number and 1, 2, 3 or 10, 20, 30 (hundred chart)

Step In **Look at this part of a hundred chart.**

1	2	3	4	5	6	7	8	9	10
11	12	13	14	15	16	17	18	19	20

What happens to the numbers as you move from left to right?

What happens to the numbers as you move down the rows?

Look at this part of the same hundred chart.
What numbers are missing? How do you know?

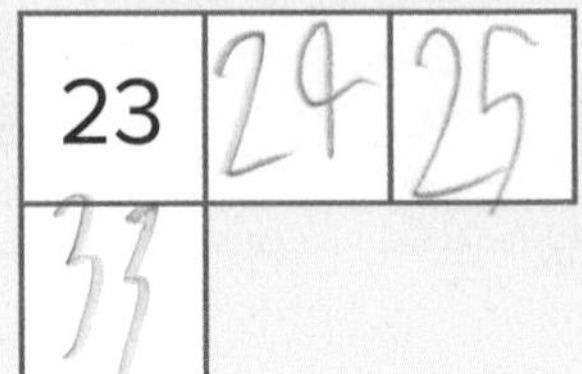

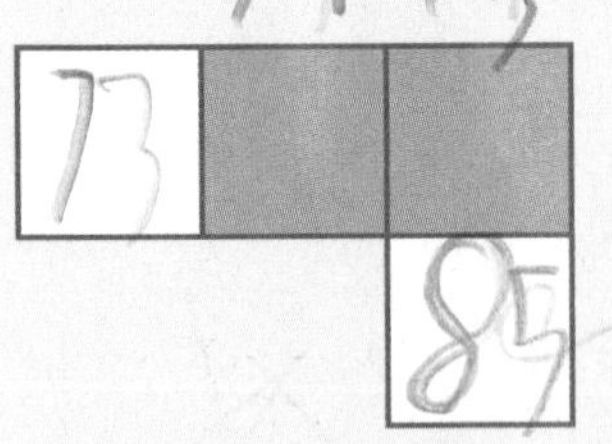

Look at this part of the hundred chart.
What numbers could you write in the white spaces?
How do you know?

Step Up 1. Write the totals. You can use the chart to help.

a. 63 + 1 = ____

b. 47 + 10 = ____

c. 78 + 2 = ____

41	42	43	44	45	46	47	48	49	50
51	52	53	54	55	56	57	58	59	60
61	62	63	64	65	66	67	68	69	70
71	72	73	74	75	76	77	78	79	80
81	82	83	84	85	86	87	88	89	90

d. 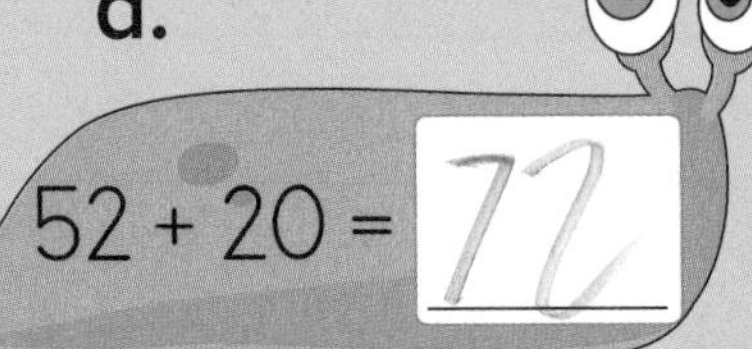

e. 74 + 10 = ____

f. 59 + 20 = ____

2. Figure out and write the totals.

a. 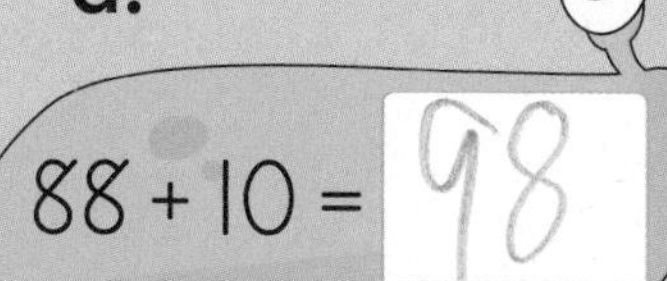
88 + 10 = ____

b. 27 + 2 = ____

c. 31 + 20 = ____

d. 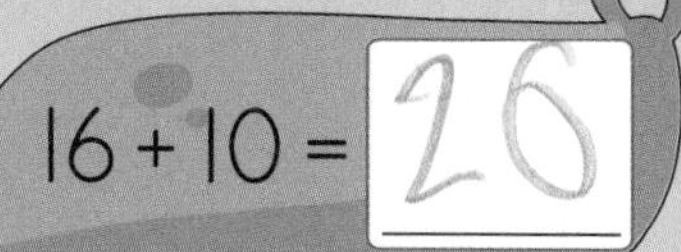
16 + 10 = ____

e. 36 + 2 = ____

f. 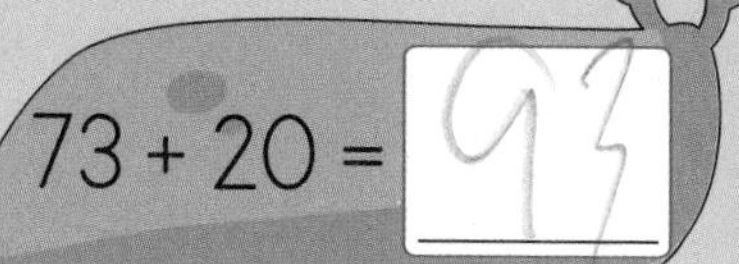
73 + 20 = ____

g. 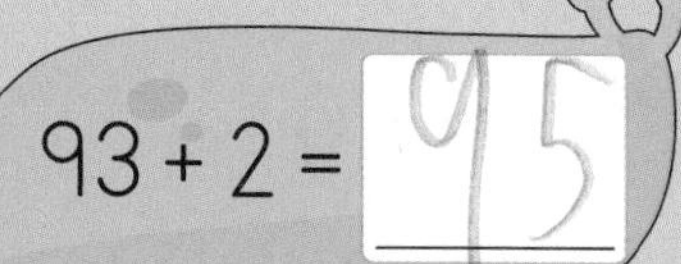
93 + 2 = ____

h. 42 + 30 = ____

i. 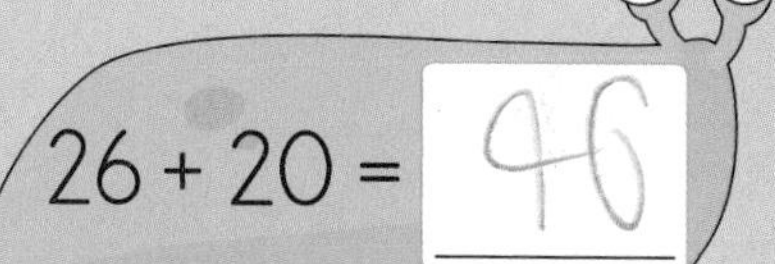
26 + 20 = ____

j. 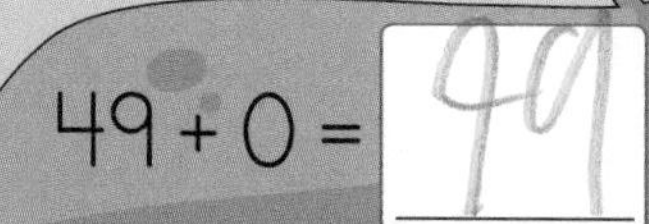
49 + 0 = ____

k. 10 + 56 = ____

l. 30 + 61 = ____

Step Ahead Write the missing numbers along the trail.

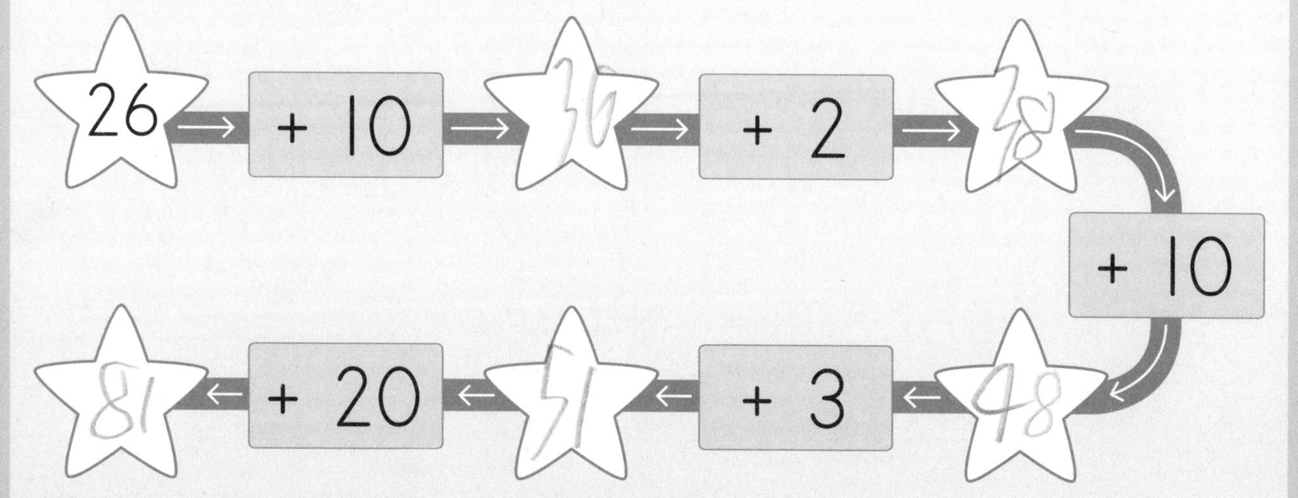

Maintaining concepts and skills

Think and Solve

Write a number to make each balance picture true.

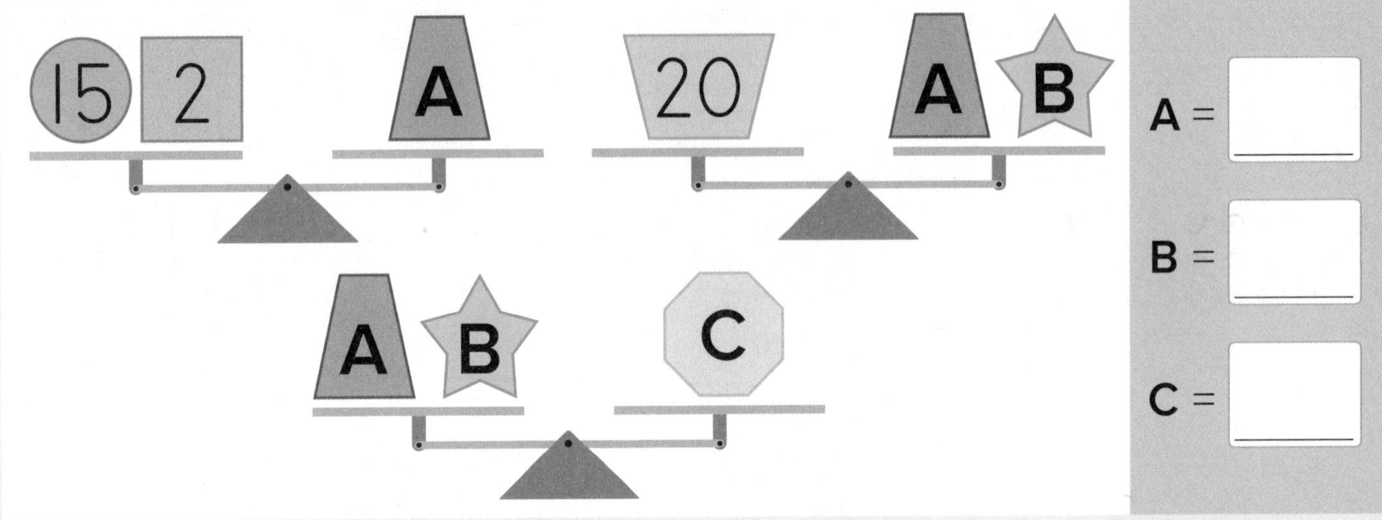

A = ____

B = ____

C = ____

Words at Work

Write about **adding on a hundred chart**. You can use words from the list to help you.

up	down	across
tens	ones	add
total	move	count on

1	2	3	4	5	6	7	8	9	10
11	12	13	14	15	16	17	18	19	20
21	22	23	24	25	26	27	28	29	30
31	32	33	34	35	36	37	38	39	40
41	42	43	44	45	46	47	48	49	50
51	52	53	54	55	56	57	58	59	60
61	62	63	64	65	66	67	68	69	70
71	72	73	74	75	76	77	78	79	80
81	82	83	84	85	86	87	88	89	90
91	92	93	94	95	96	97	98	99	100

Ongoing Practice

1. Write an addition fact to match each picture. Then write the turnaround fact.

FROM 1.8.5

a.

___ + ___ = ___

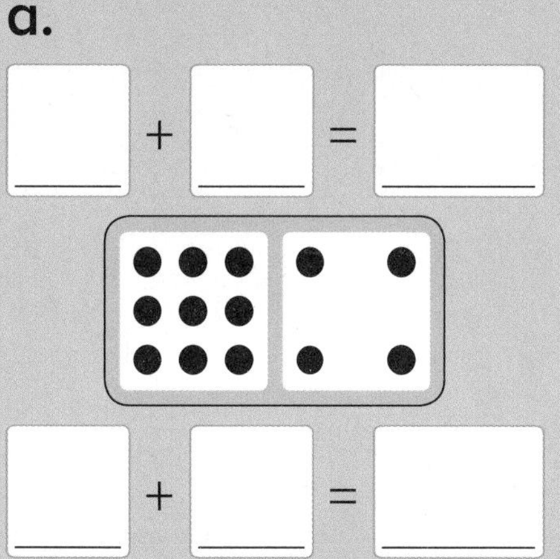

___ + ___ = ___

b.

___ + ___ = ___

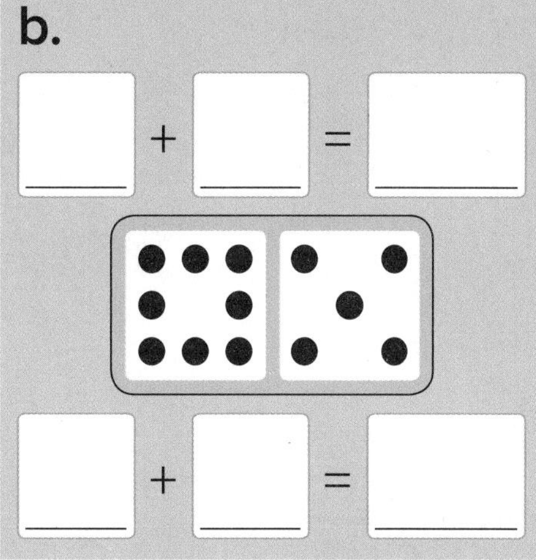

___ + ___ = ___

c.

___ + ___ = ___

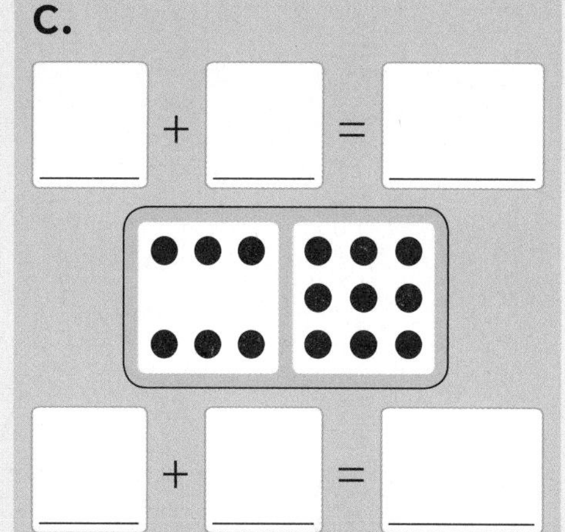

___ + ___ = ___

2. These are parts of a hundred chart. Write the missing numbers.

FROM 1.9.2

a. ___ 57 ___

b. ___ (above); ___ 35 ___

c. ___ (above); 69 ___; ___ (below)

d. ___ (above); 42; ___ (below)

Preparing for Module 10

Complete the addition fact to figure out the carrots that were taken. Then complete the subtraction fact.

a.

___ + ___ = ___

___ − ___ = ___

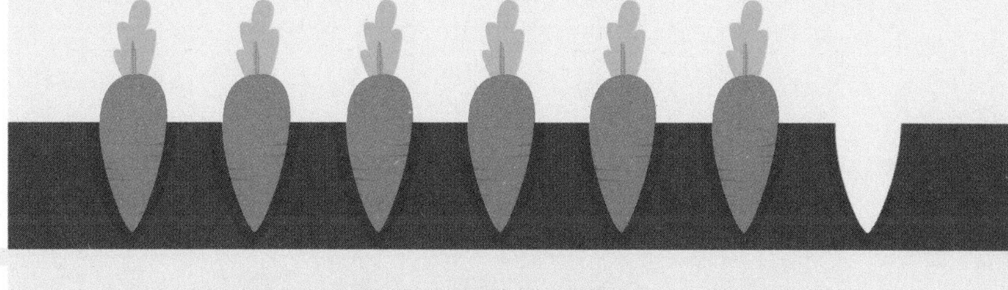

b.

___ + ___ = ___

___ − ___ = ___

9.5 Addition: Any two-digit number and a multiple of ten (hundred chart)

Step In **Look at this part of a hundred chart.**

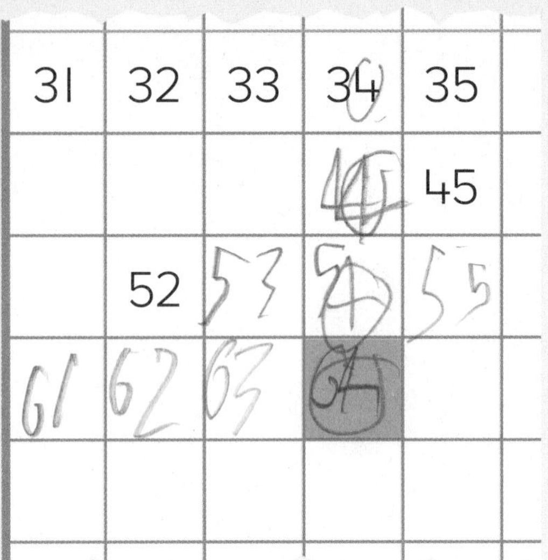

How can you figure out what number is behind the shaded tile?

I would start at 34 and add groups of 10 to the shaded tile.

How many groups of 10 would you add?

What equation could you write to match?

____ + ____ = ____

How could you use the hundred chart to figure out 52 + 20?

Step Up 1. Write the totals. You can use this part of a hundred chart to help.

1	2	3	4	5	6	7	8	9	10
11	12	13	14	15	16	17	18	19	20
21	22	23	24	25	26	27	28	29	30
31	32	33	34	35	36	37	38	39	40
41	42	43	44	45	46	47	48	49	50
51	52	53	54	55	56	57	58	59	60

a. 29 + 20 = ____

b. 16 + 30 = ____

c. 14 + 40 = ____

2. Write the totals. Use this part of a hundred chart to help.

51	52	53	54	55	56	57	58	59	60
61	62	63	64	65	66	67	68	69	70
71	72	73	74	75	76	77	78	79	80
81	82	83	84	85	86	87	88	89	90
91	92	93	94	95	96	97	98	99	100

a. 87 + 10 = ____

b. 54 + 40 = ____

c. 69 + 30 = ____

d. 73 + 20 = ____

e. 57 + 30 = ____

f. 55 + 40 = ____

3. Write these totals.

a. 33 + 50 = ____

b. 25 + 40 = ____

c. 38 + 60 = ____

d. 57 + 30 = ____

e. 15 + 70 = ____

f. 21 + 50 = ____

Step Ahead Leila has 90 cents. She wants to buy two pieces of fruit. Write equations to show all the possible combinations she can buy.

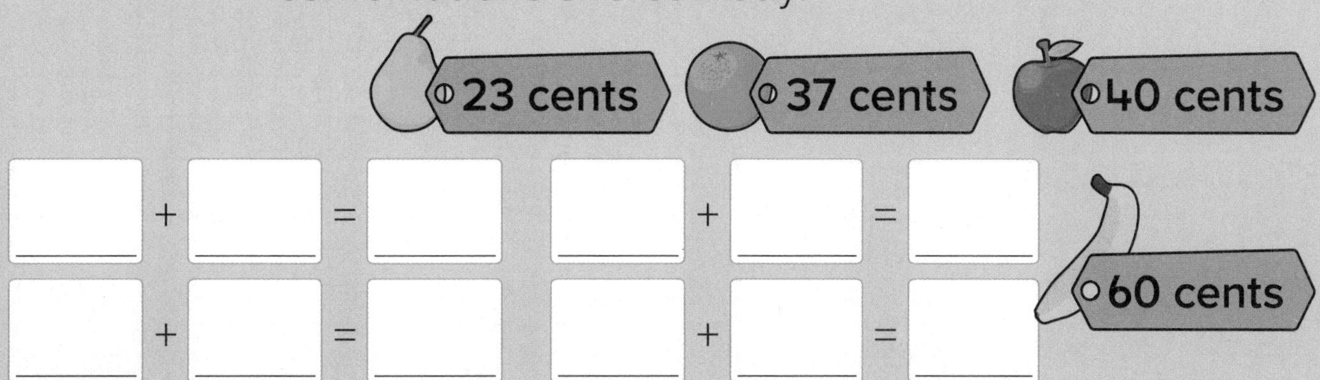

9.6 Addition: Two-digit numbers (hundred chart)

Step In **Look at this part of a hundred chart.**

1	2	3	4	5	6
11	12	13	14	15	16
21	22	23	24	25	26
31	32	33	34	35	36
41	42	43	44	45	46

How would you move the counter to show 12 + 10?

How would you move the counter to show 12 + 2?

How would you move the counter to show 12 + 12?

How would you use the hundred chart to figure out 23 + 21?

Step Up 1. Draw arrows on this hundred chart to show how you add. Then write the totals. The first one has been done for you.

a. 31 + 12 = 43

b. 52 + 21 = ____

c. 27 + 32 = ____

d. 45 + 11 = ____

e. 64 + 23 = ____

f. 57 + 21 = ____

g. 83 + 13 = ____

h. 69 + 21 = ____

1	2	3	4	5	6	7	8	9	10
11	12	13	14	15	16	17	18	19	20
21	22	23	24	25	26	27	28	29	30
31	32	33	34	35	36	37	38	39	40
41	42	43	44	45	46	47	48	49	50
51	52	53	54	55	56	57	58	59	60
61	62	63	64	65	66	67	68	69	70
71	72	73	74	75	76	77	78	79	80
81	82	83	84	85	86	87	88	89	90
91	92	93	94	95	96	97	98	99	100

2. Write the number at the end of each part of a hundred chart. Then complete the matching equation.

a.

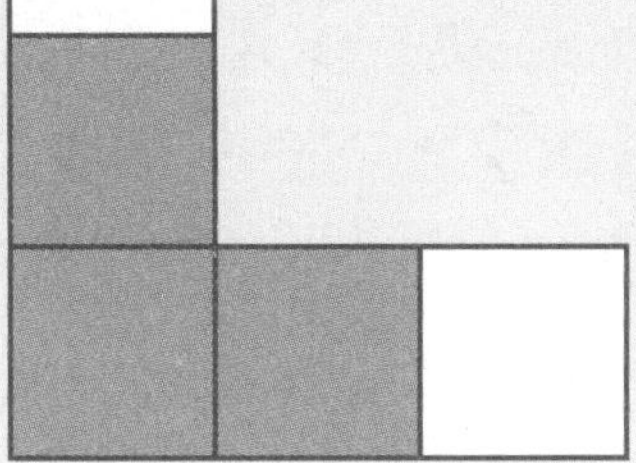

37 + 22 = ____

b.

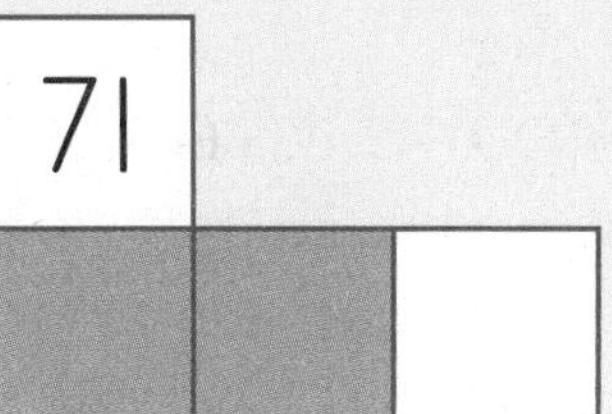

____ + ____ = ____

c.

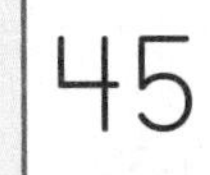

____ + ____ = ____

d.

52

____ + ____ = ____

Step Ahead Thomas added tens and then ones to figure out 35 + 13. Use his strategy to figure out 46 + 21.

35 + 13 = 48	46 + 21 = ?
35 45	  46 ____ ____
46 47 48	 ____

Maintaining concepts and skills

Computation Practice

What does an egg do if you tell it a joke?

★ Complete the equations. Then write each letter above its matching answer in the box below. One letter appears more than once.

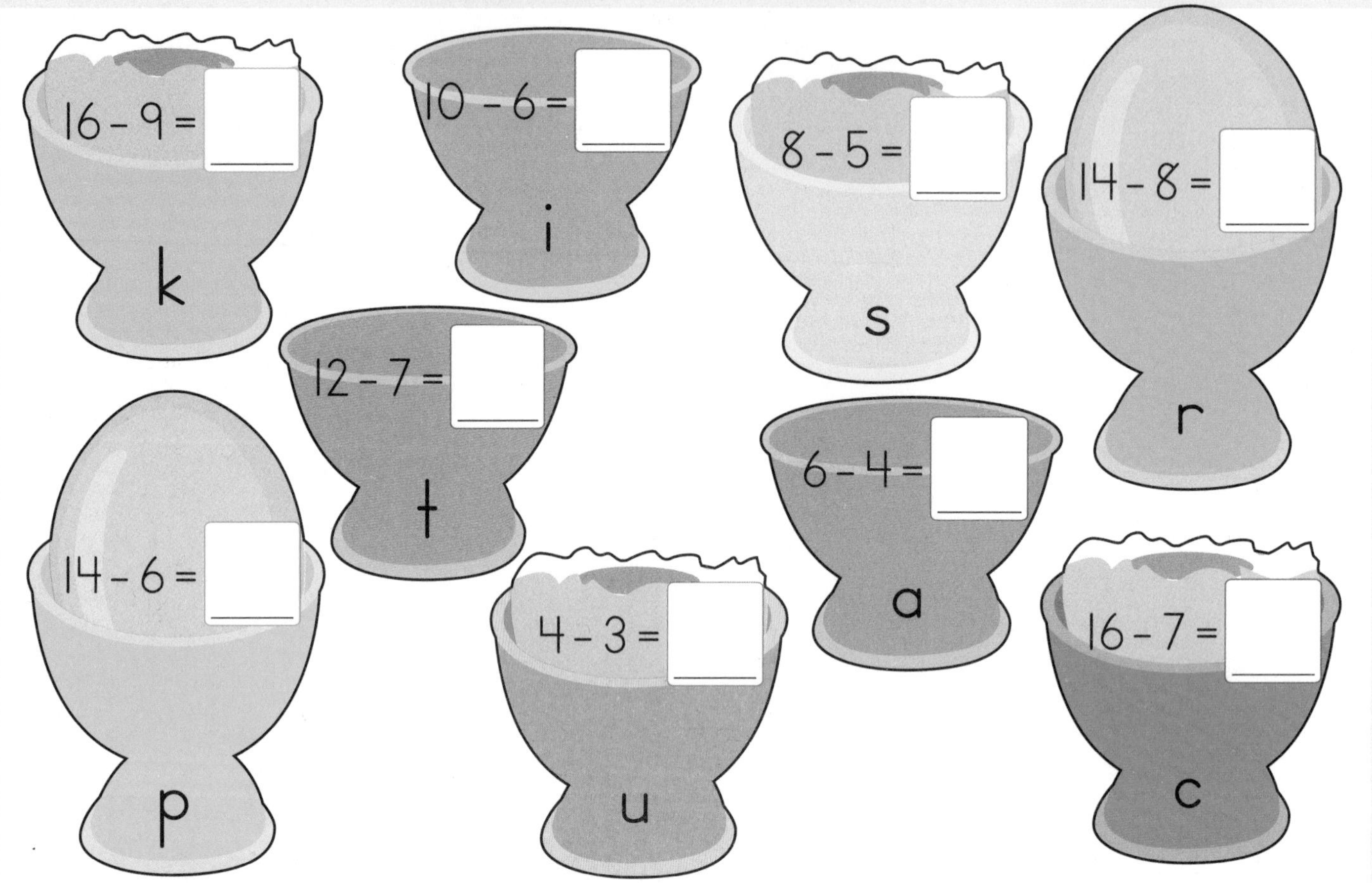

k: 16 - 9 = ☐

i: 10 - 6 = ☐

s: 8 - 5 = ☐

r: 14 - 8 = ☐

t: 12 - 7 = ☐

a: 6 - 4 = ☐

p: 14 - 6 = ☐

u: 4 - 3 = ☐

c: 16 - 7 = ☐

☐	☐		☐	☐	☐	☐	☐	☐		☐	☐
4	5		9	6	2	9	7	3		1	8

Complete the equations as fast as you can.

10 - 7 = ☐	10 - 4 = ☐	8 - 3 = ☐
9 - 5 = ☐	4 - 1 = ☐	6 - 2 = ☐

Ongoing Practice

1. Write an addition fact to match each picture. Then write the turnaround fact.

FROM 1.8.5

a. ___ + ___ = ___

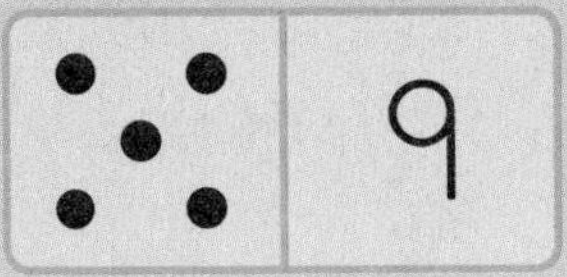

(domino: 5 dots | 9)

___ + ___ = ___

b. ___ + ___ = ___

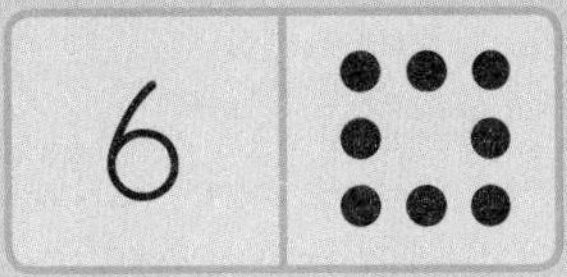

(domino: 6 | 8 dots)

___ + ___ = ___

c. ___ + ___ = ___

(domino: 9 dots | 3)

___ + ___ = ___

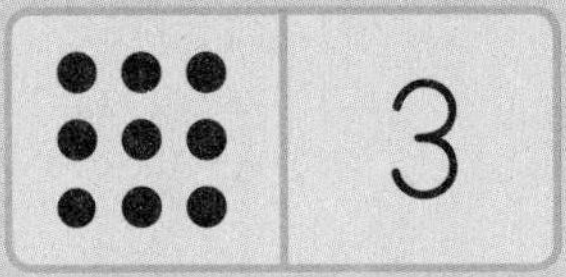

2. Write the totals. Use the chart to help.

FROM 1.9.5

41	42	43	44	45	46	47	48	49	50
51	52	53	54	55	56	57	58	59	60
61	62	63	64	65	66	67	68	69	70
71	72	73	74	75	76	77	78	79	80
81	82	83	84	85	86	87	88	89	90

a. 65 + 10 = ___

b. 42 + 40 = ___

c. 59 + 20 = ___

d. 45 + 20 = ___

Preparing for Module 10

Count on or count back to figure out these. Draw jumps on the number track to show your thinking.

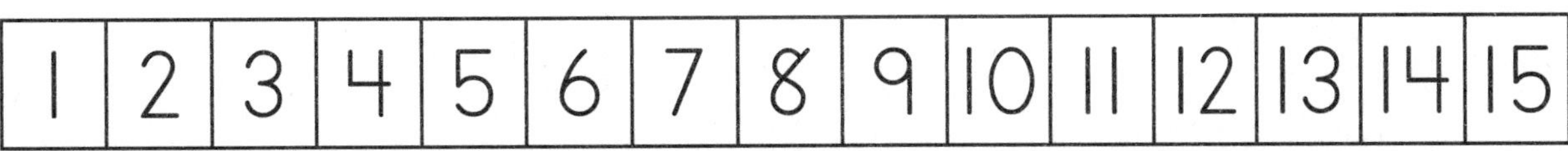

a. 4 - 1 = ___

b. 11 - 7 = ___

c. 15 - 3 = ___

9.7 Addition: Introducing place-value methods

Step In How can you figure out the total cost of these two pieces of fruit?

Mia used this chart.

50 + 30 = → 50 + 30 = 80

How do the blocks on the chart match the price tags?

How do you think she figured out the total cost?

How would you use this chart to figure out 42 + 5?

Draw tens and ones blocks on the right to show the total.

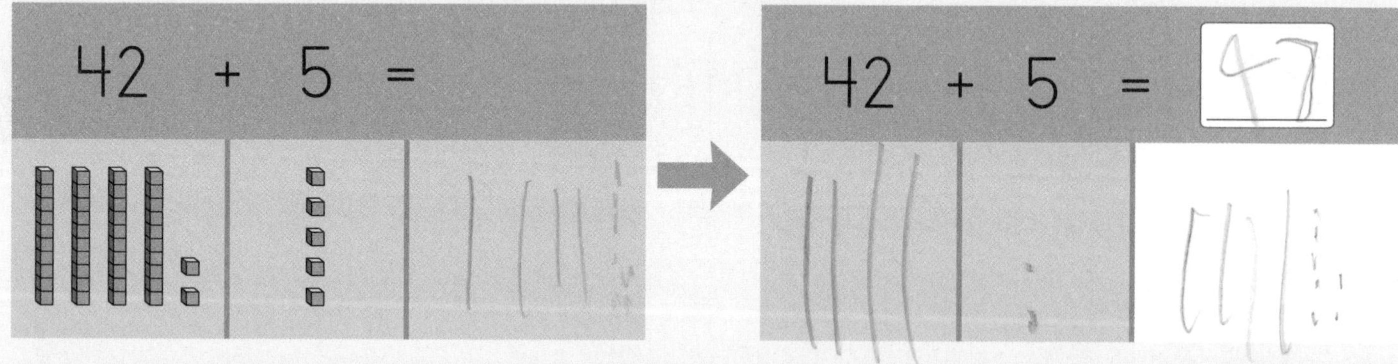

Step Up 1. Add the two groups. Then write the matching equation. Use blocks to help you.

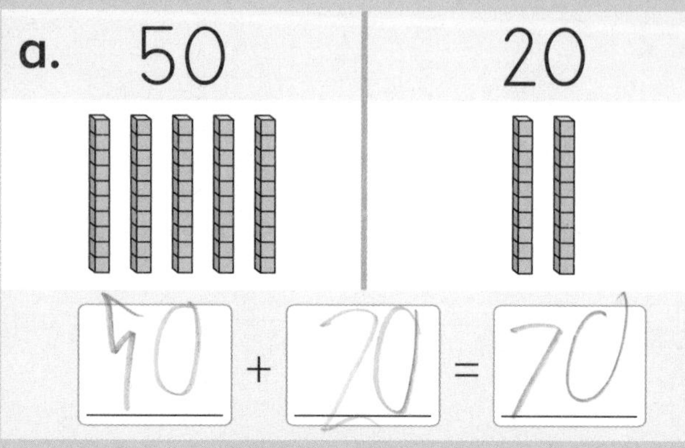

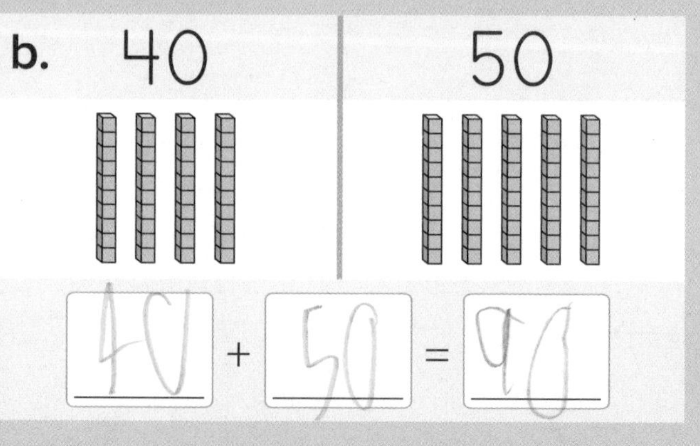

2. Add the two groups. Then write the matching equation. Use blocks to help you.

a. 30 | 4

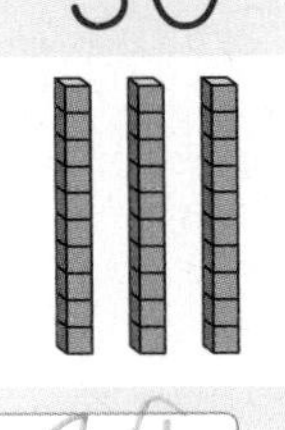

___ + ___ = ___

b. 51 | 7

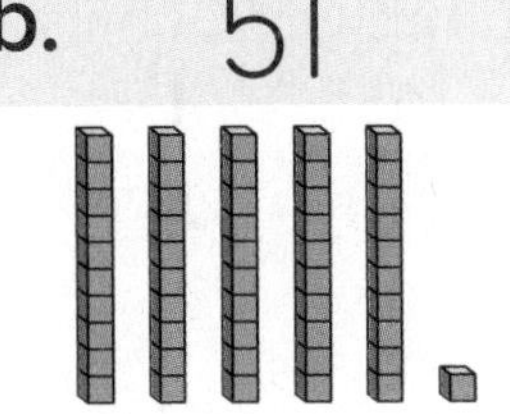

___ + ___ = ___

c. 63 | 5

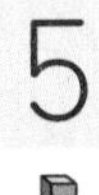

___ + ___ = ___

d. 6 | 21

___ + ___ = ___

3. Write each total. Use blocks to help your thinking.

a. 30 + 30 = ___

b. 10 + 60 = ___

c. 40 + 9 = ___

d. 3 + 50 = ___

e. 25 + 3 = ___

f. 72 + 6 = ___

Step Ahead

Write equations to show four different ways these coins could be split between two people.

___ + ___ = 90

___ + ___ = 90

___ + ___ = 90

___ + ___ = 90

9.8 Addition: Two-digit numbers

Step In **Look at these scoreboards.**

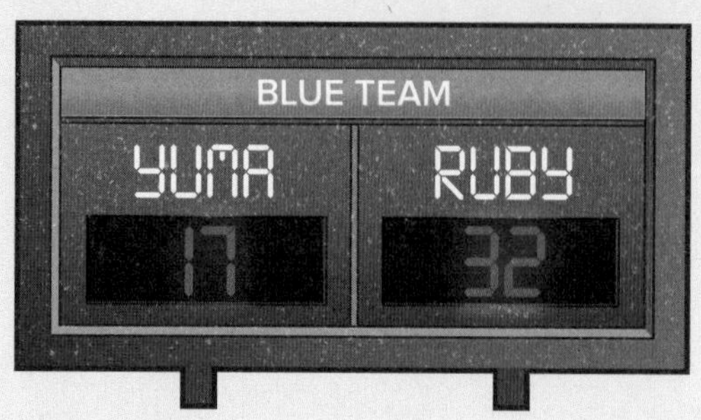

How can you figure out the total number of points scored by the Blue Team?

Andrew used this chart.

17 + 32 =

→

17 + 32 = 49

What steps do you think he used?

How would you use the chart to figure out the total for the Red Team?

How could you figure out the total in your head?

I would start with 23 then add the tens and ones of the other number. 23 + 25 **is the same value as** 23 + 20 + 5.

I would add the tens first, then the ones. 23 + 25 **is the same value as** 20 + 20 + 3 + 5.

What other way could you add to find the total?

Step Up

1. Figure out the total for each team. Use blocks to help. Then write a matching equation.

Team A		Team B		Team C	
Peta 51	Nathan 14	Oscar 45	Sheree 34	Carlos 26	Nicole 33
51 + 14 = 65		45 + 34 = 79		26 + 33 = 59	

2. Figure out the total for each team in your head. Write an equation to show your thinking.

Team A		Team B		Team C	
Stella 43	Dixon 24	Beatrice 31	Gabriel 32	Shiro 52	Grace 17
43+24=67		31 +32=63		52 + 17=69	

Team D		Team E		Team F	
Owen 23	Camila 22	Allan 26	Ashley 12	Fiona 16	Hugo 11

Step Ahead

Look at the total points scored by these teams. Write a pair of possible scores on each board. Then write the matching equation.

Green Team 84 total points		Blue Team 67 total points		Yellow Team 76 total points	
Mateo ____	Charlotte ____	Cathy ____	Carey ____	Carmen ____	Ethan ____
____ + ____ = ____		____ + ____ = ____		____ + ____ = ____	

9.8 Maintaining concepts and skills

Think and Solve  Look at this rectangle.

Draw one more line to make 2 equal parts.

What shape is each part?

Words at Work Write the answer for each clue in the grid. Use words from the list.

Clues Across	Clues Down
1. 39 plus 23 __ 62.	**2.** 47 __ 17 makes a total of 64.
4. You can show __ on a hundred chart.	**3.** 8 tens and 14 ones shows the same number as __ tens and 4 ones.
6. You can draw __ on a number track to show how to add.	**5.** Ten ones blocks is the same value as one __ block.

add
addition
jumps
equals
nine
tens

Ongoing Practice

1. Draw tally marks in the chart to show the number of socks in each group. Then write the total number of tally marks beside each group.

FROM 1.8.10

Socks	Tally	Total
Plain		
Striped		
Spotted		

2. Add the two groups. Write the matching equation.

FROM 1.9.7

a. 60 | 30

___ + ___ = ___

b. 20 | 70

___ + ___ = ___

Preparing for Module 10

Count on to 10. Write the addition fact.

a.

9 + ___ = 10

b.

7 + ___ = 10

9.9 Addition: One- and two-digit numbers (composing tens)

Step In Jennifer uses this chart to figure out 39 + 3.

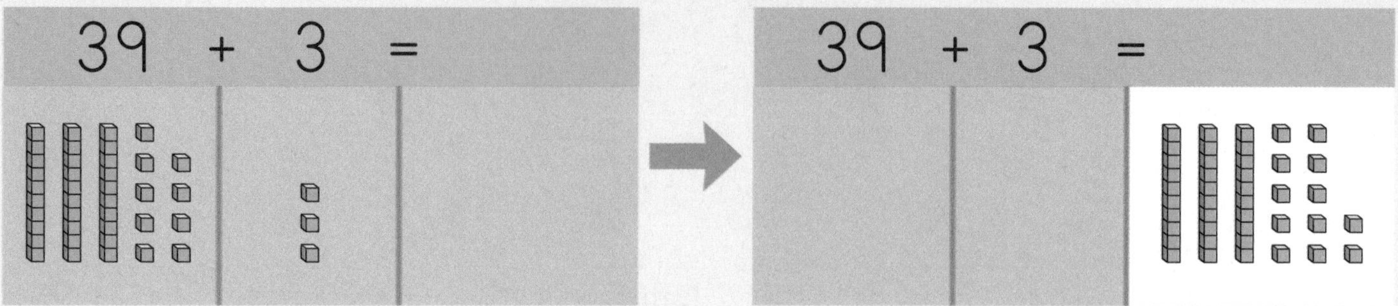

What does Jennifer need to do to figure out the total?

The 12 ones blocks can be regrouped as 1 ten and 2 ones.

Jennifer regroups the ones blocks.

39 + 3 =

39 + 3 = 42

How does she regroup the ones blocks? What is the total?

Step Up 1. Write the number of ones blocks. Circle 10 ones. Then write the number of tens and ones.

a. ____ ones

____ ten ____ ones

b. ____ ones

____ ten ____ ones

2. Add the two groups. Write the matching equation. Use blocks to help you.

a. 29 | 2

___ + ___ = ___

b. 48 | 5

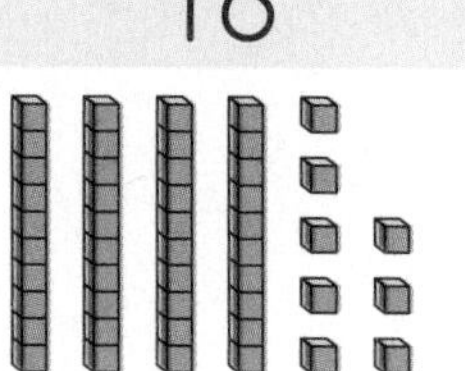

___ + ___ = ___

c. 35 | 6

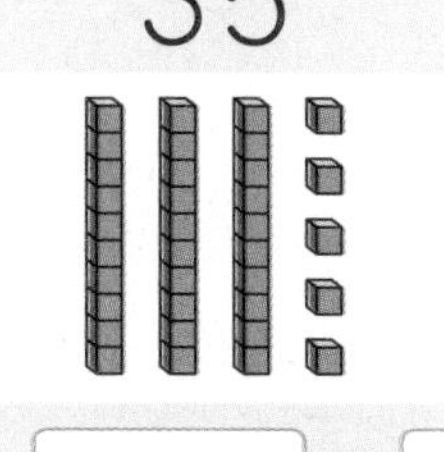

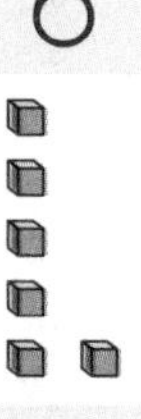

___ + ___ = ___

d. 4 | 57

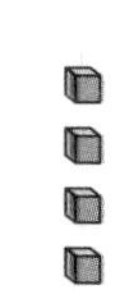

___ + ___ = ___

3. Write each total. You can use blocks to help your thinking.

a. 19 + 3 = ___

b. 47 + 5 = ___

c. 27 + 4 = ___

d. 6 + 55 = ___

e. 3 + 37 = ___

f. 79 + 5 = ___

Step Ahead Color the statements that are true. Use blocks to help your thinking.

3 tens 14 ones **shows the same number as** 4 tens and 4 ones	5 tens 12 ones **shows the same number as** 7 tens and 2 ones
4 tens 10 ones **shows the same number as** 5 tens and 0 ones	7 tens 17 ones **shows the same number as** 9 tens and 7 ones

Addition: Two-digit numbers (composing tens)

Step In **Imagine you have 70 cents.**

Do you have enough money to buy both toys?

How could you figure out the total cost of the two toys?

Antonio uses this chart to figure out the total.

47 + 25 =

47 + 25 =

There are 6 tens and 12 ones. I can figure out the total by adding 60 + 12, or I can regroup some of the ones blocks.

Antonio regroups the ones blocks.

47 + 25 =

47 + 25 = 72

How does Antonio regroup the ones blocks? What is the total?
What is another way to figure out the total?

Step Up

1. Add the two groups. Write the matching equation. Use blocks to help you.

a. 39 | 12

____ + ____ = ____

b.

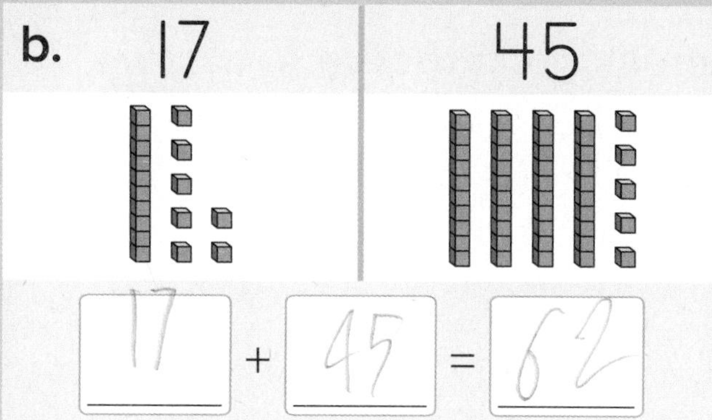

____ + ____ = ____

c. 35 | 28

____ + ____ = ____

d.

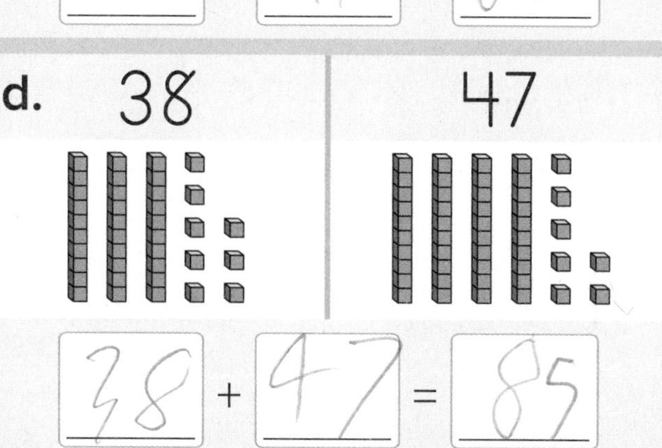

____ + ____ = ____

2. Write each total. You can use blocks to help your thinking.

a. 29 + 22 = ____

b. 32 + 18 = ____

c. 46 + 26 = ____

d. 23 + 58 = ____

e. 37 + 24 = ____

f. 36 + 27 = ____

Step Ahead

Each brick in this wall shows the total of the two numbers directly below. Write the missing numbers.

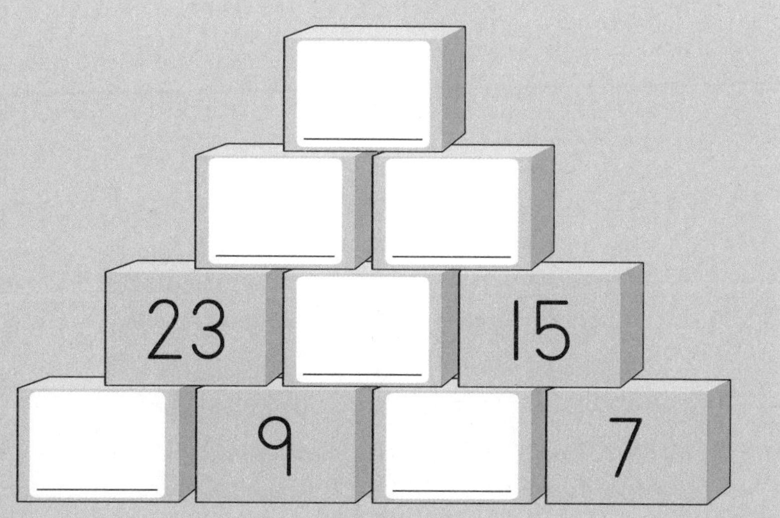

Maintaining concepts and skills

Computation Practice

★ Complete each equation. Color each matching pair with a different color.

★ Then draw an anchor line from each ship to the anchor with the same answer.

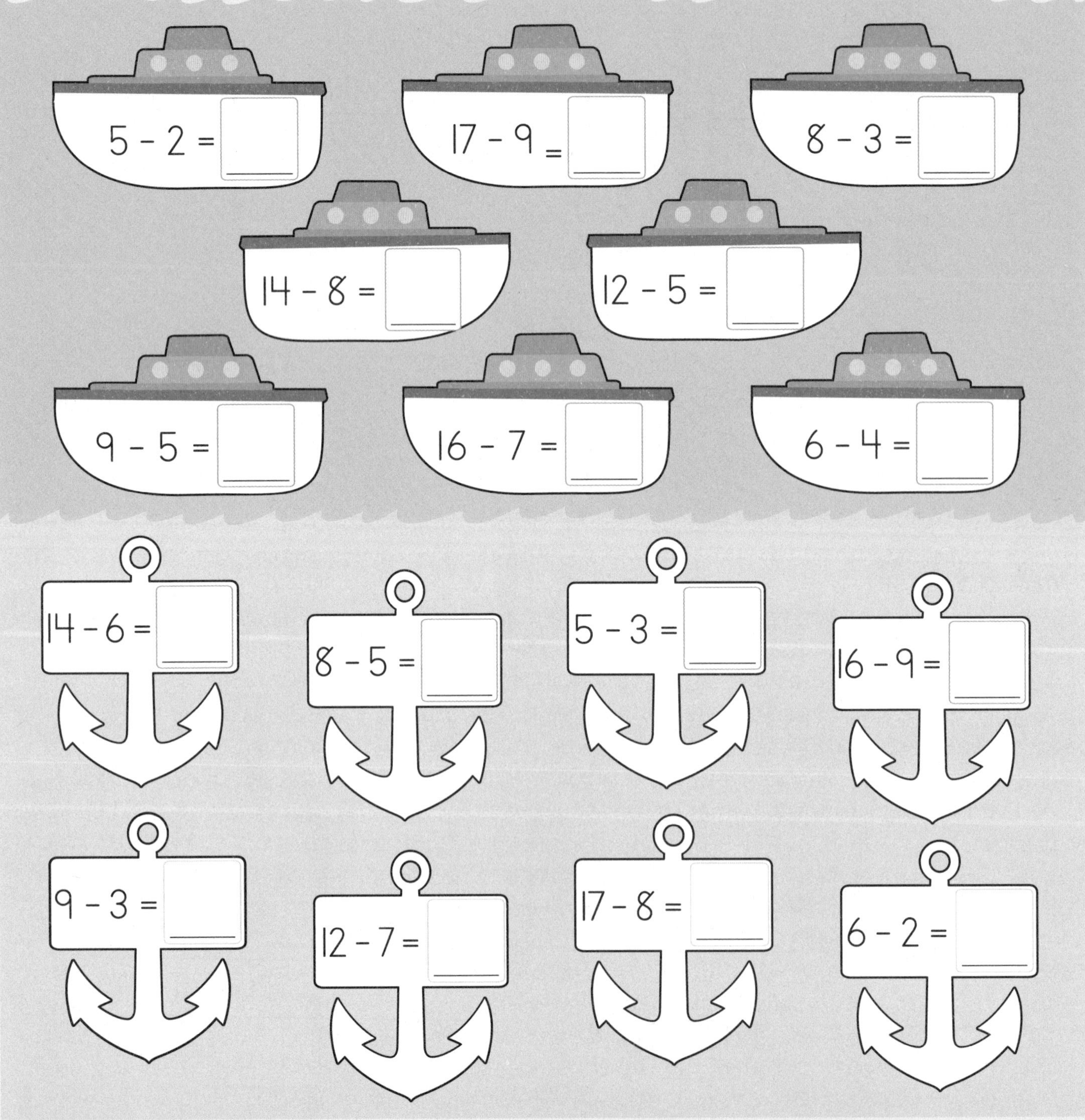

Ongoing Practice

1. a. Write the total number of tally marks for each.

FROM 1.8.11

Favorite Sea Creature		
Creature	**Tally**	**Total**
Whale	𝍸 III	
Octopus	III	
Crab	𝍸 𝍸 II	
Shark	𝍸 𝍸 𝍸 I	

b. Which creature was the most popular? ______

c. How many people voted for the Whale? ______

2. Draw blocks to show the total. Then write a matching equation.

FROM 1.9.9

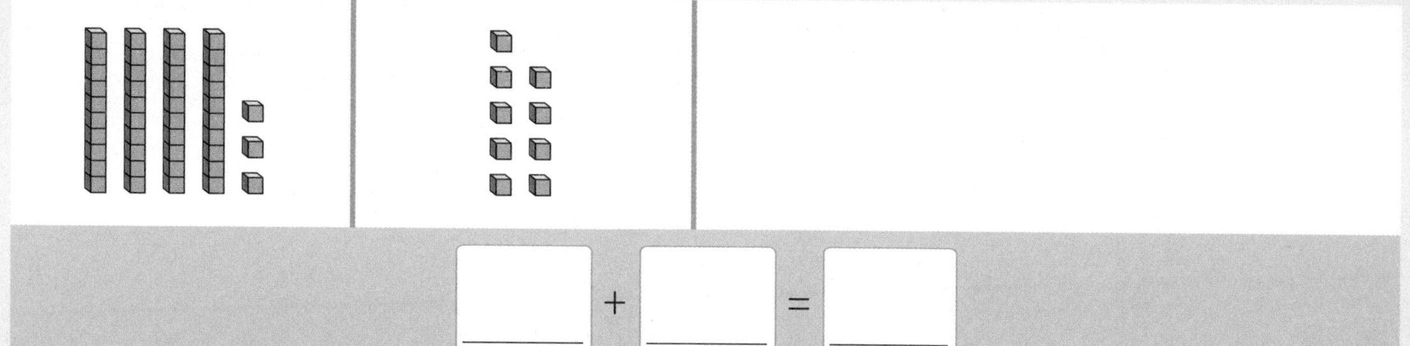

___ + ___ = ___

Preparing for Module 10

Circle the pictures of 3D objects that have all flat surfaces.

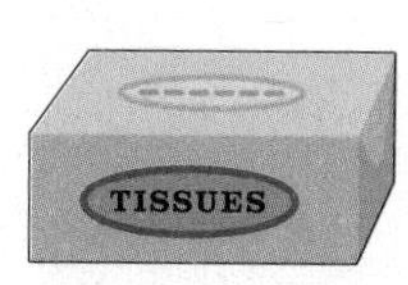

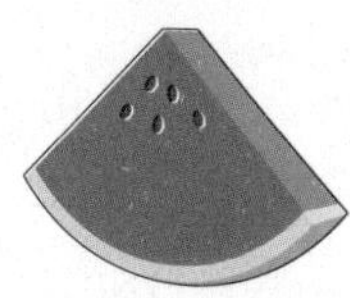

Addition: Reinforcing place-value strategies (composing tens)

Step In

What numeral would you write to match this picture of blocks?

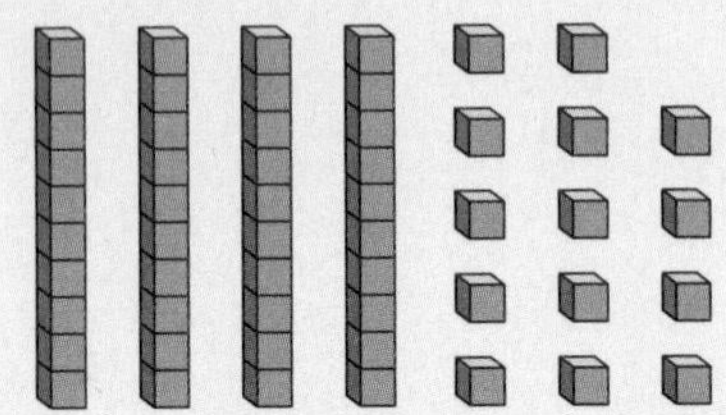

Some of these ones blocks can be regrouped for a tens block.

Circle 10 ones blocks.
Then complete this statement.

4 tens 14 ones
shows the same number as
___ tens ___ ones

This chart was used to figure out 39 + 34.

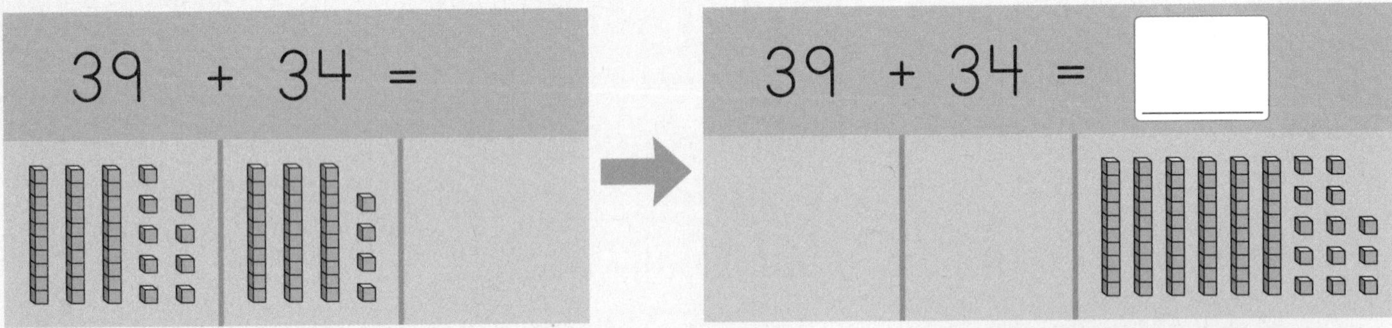

Describe the steps that were followed.

How would you regroup the ones blocks to write the total?

Complete this statement.

6 tens 13 ones
shows the same number as
___ tens ___ ones

Step Up

1. Complete each statement.
   Use blocks to help you.

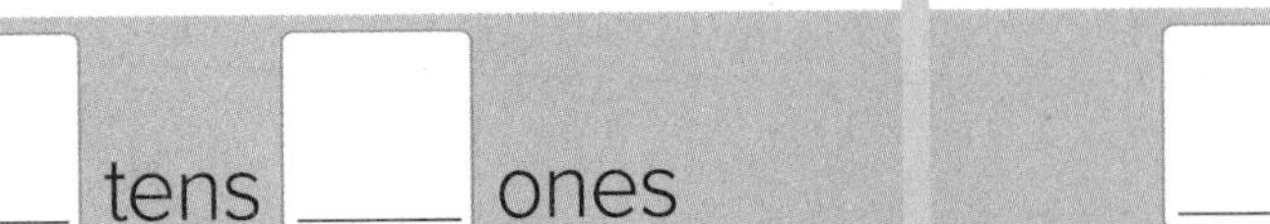

a. 5 tens 12 ones	**b.** 3 tens 17 ones
shows the same number as	**shows the same number as**
___ tens ___ ones	___ tens ___ ones

2. Add the two groups. Write the matching equation. Write the greater number first. Use blocks to help you.

a. 55 | 7

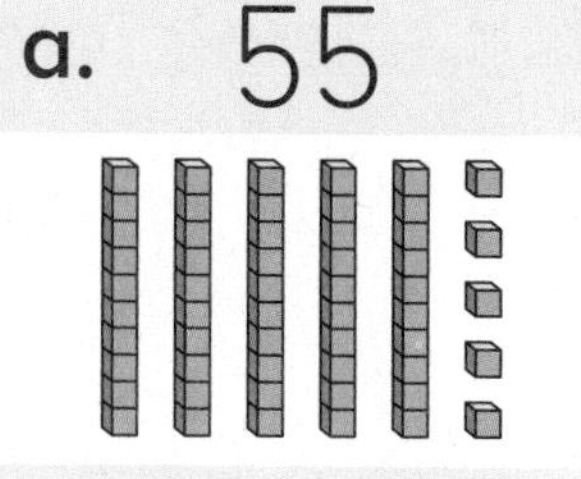

☐ + ☐ = ☐

b. 63 | 29

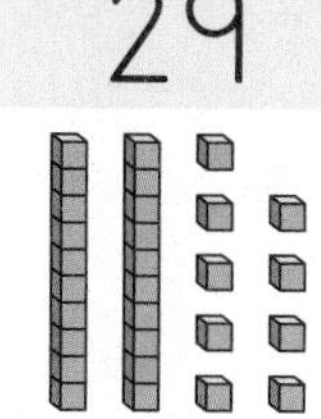

☐ + ☐ = ☐

c. 8 | 54

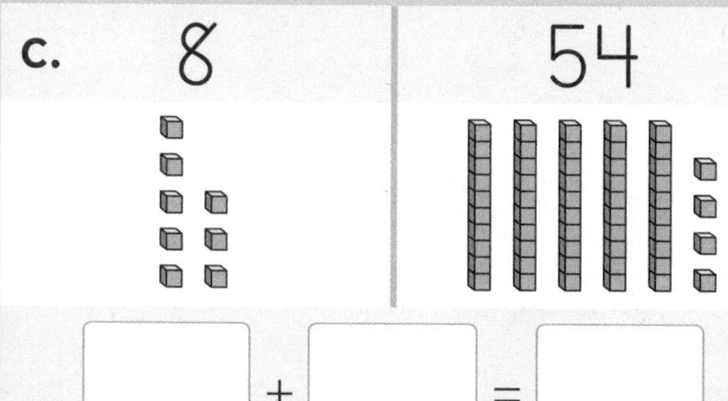

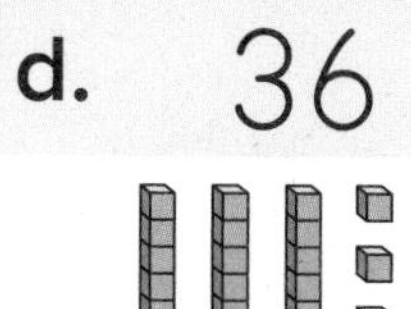

☐ + ☐ = ☐

d. 36 | 39

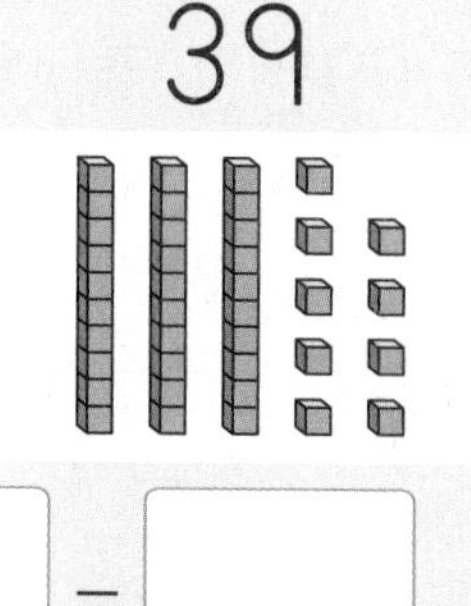

☐ + ☐ = ☐

3. Write each total. Use blocks to help you.

a. 47 + 5 = ☐

b. 29 + 15 = ☐

c. 7 + 34 = ☐

d. 61 + 19 = ☐

e. 4 + 89 = ☐

f. 27 + 25 = ☐

Step Ahead Jacinta added these two groups. Write the correct total. ☐

Then talk about the mistake that was made with the student beside you.

27 + 14 =

27 + 14 = 311

Addition: Solving word problems

Step In What addition story could you write about this picture?

What equation could you write to match your story?

Harvey puts some money in his pocket. He then finds another two dimes under the sofa. He now has a total of 65 cents. How much money was in his pocket before his find?

Step Up

1. Draw a picture of coins to represent this story. Then write an equation to match.

Emily has 6 dimes. Each dime is 10 cents. She finds one more dime and 2 pennies. How much money does she have now?

60 + ______

2. Solve each problem. Show your thinking.

a. Michelle has 40 cents. She finds more money under the bed. She now has 90 cents. How much money did she find?

☐ cents

b. Juan has 48 cents and his friend has 27 cents. Juan's aunt gives him 30 cents. How much money does Juan have now?

☐ cents

c. Ringo has saved 75 cents. His sister has saved 40 cents. How much more money has Ringo saved?

☐ cents

d. A small pencil costs 49 cents. A large pencil costs 25 cents more. What is the cost of a large pencil?

☐ cents

Step Ahead

Corey finds two quarters on the ground. Each quarter is 25 cents. He now has 90 cents in total. How much money did he have before?

☐ cents

Maintaining concepts and skills

Think and Solve  Imagine this pattern keeps going.

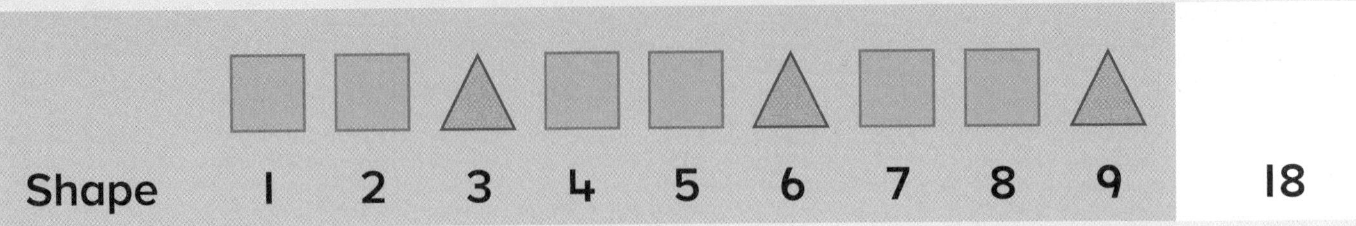

Shape	1	2	3	4	5	6	7	8	9	18

a. Draw Shape 18 in the white box.

b. Circle the repeating part.

c. Imagine the pattern showed seven repeating parts.
Write the number of squares and triangles there would be.

_____ squares _____ triangles

Words at Work

a. Write a word problem to solve using addition.
Use numbers that have some tens and ones.

b. Draw a picture to show your problem.

Ongoing Practice

1. Use the tally chart to answer the questions.

FROM 1.8.12

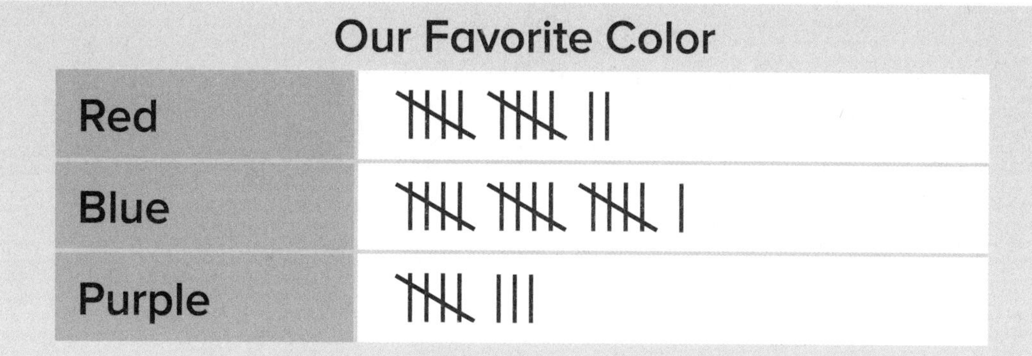

a. Which color is the most popular? ____________

b. Which color is the least popular? ____________

2. Figure out the total. Write an equation to match.

FROM 1.9.10

a.

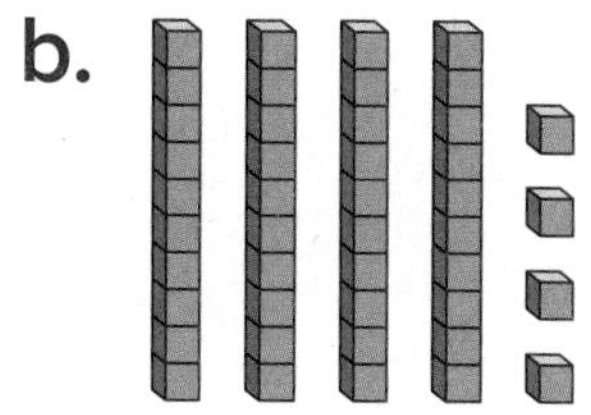

____

b.

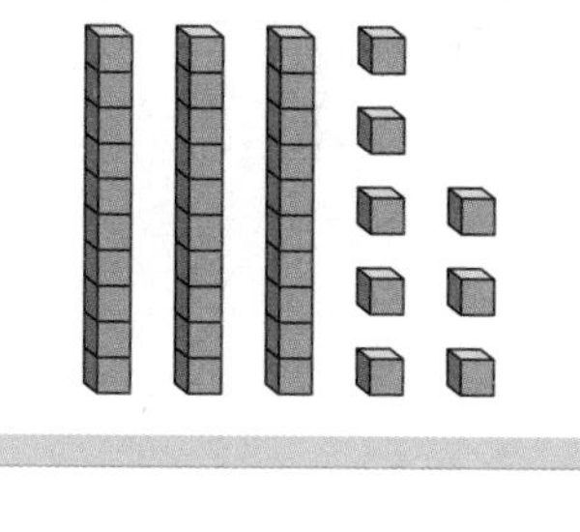

____

Preparing for Module 10

Draw a line from each shape to its matching name.

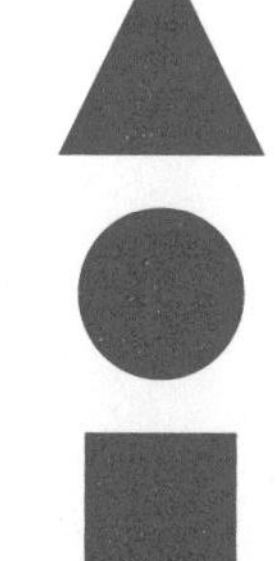

circle

square

triangle

Working Space

Subtraction: Writing related facts

Step In **Look at this picture. What do you see?**

$6 - 1 = 5$

$6 - 5 = 1$

How does each equation match the picture?

What do the numbers in each equation tell you?

What stays the same in each equation?

What changes?

A subtraction fact does not have a turnaround fact. It has a **related** fact.

Step Up **1.** Write numbers to match each picture.

a.

☐ frogs in total

☐ frogs are out

☐ frogs are in

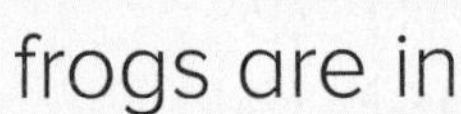

$7 - 2 =$ ☐

☐ frogs in total

☐ frogs are in

☐ frogs are out

$7 - 5 =$ ☐

b.

☐ sheep in total

☐ sheep are out

☐ sheep are in

$9 - 4 =$ ☐

☐ sheep in total

☐ sheep are in

☐ sheep are out

$9 - 5 =$ ☐

2. Write the missing numbers.

a.

5 - 1 = ____

5 - 4 = ____

b.

8 - 5 = ____

8 - 3 = ____

c.

12 - 9 = ____

12 - 3 = ____

d.

11 - 4 = ____

11 - 7 = ____

Step Ahead Draw a subtraction picture.
Then write two related subtraction facts to match.

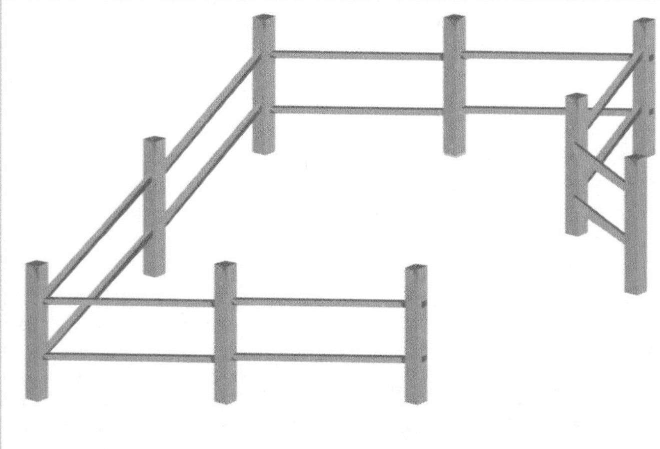

____ - ____ = ____

____ - ____ = ____

10.2 Subtraction: Reinforcing related facts

Step In What do you notice about this picture?

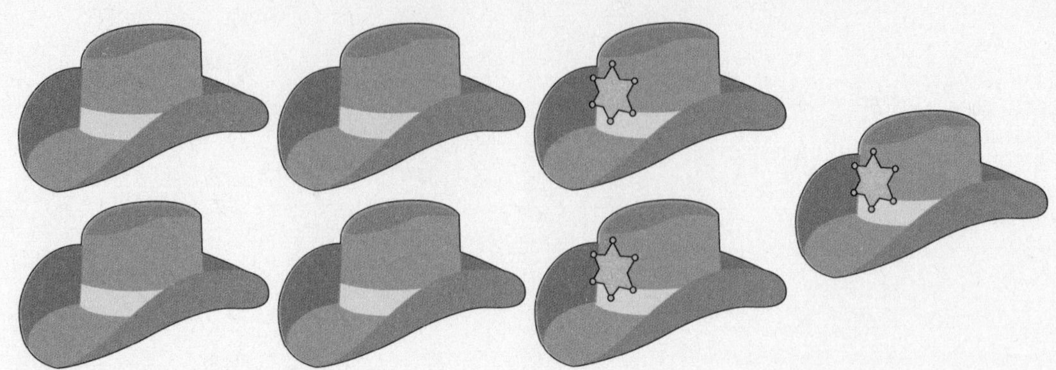

What is the total number of hats?
How many hats have a star?
How many hats do not have a star?

How does each of these subtraction facts match the picture?

What does each number in the equations tell you?

$7 - 3 = 4$

$7 - 4 = 3$

Step Up I. Write two subtraction facts to match each picture.

a.

$5 - 2 = 3$

$5 - 3 = 2$

b.

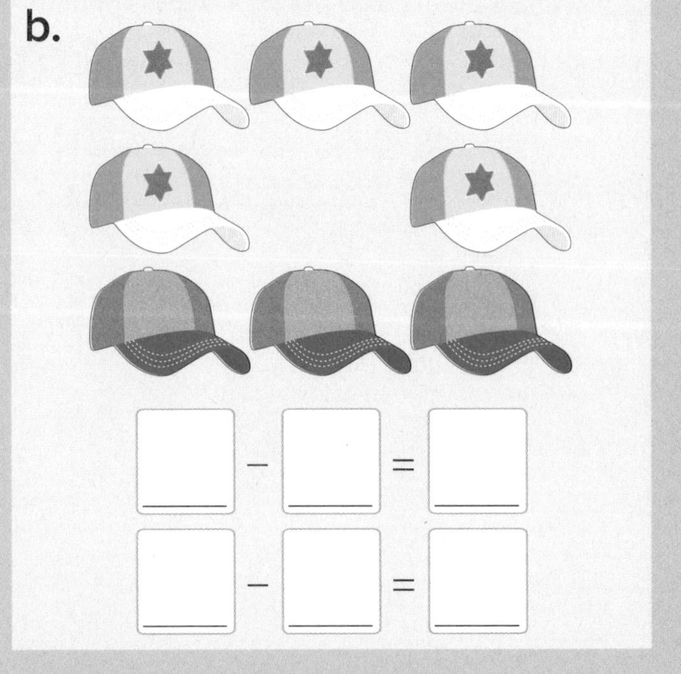

2. Color some of the pictures. Then write the two subtraction facts to match.

a.

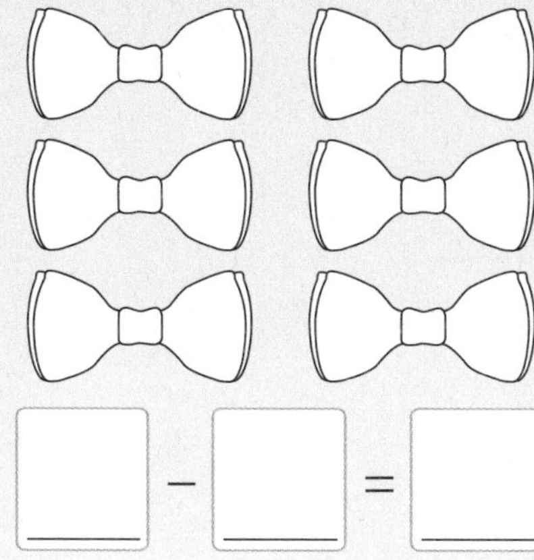

☐ – ☐ = ☐

☐ – ☐ = ☐

b.

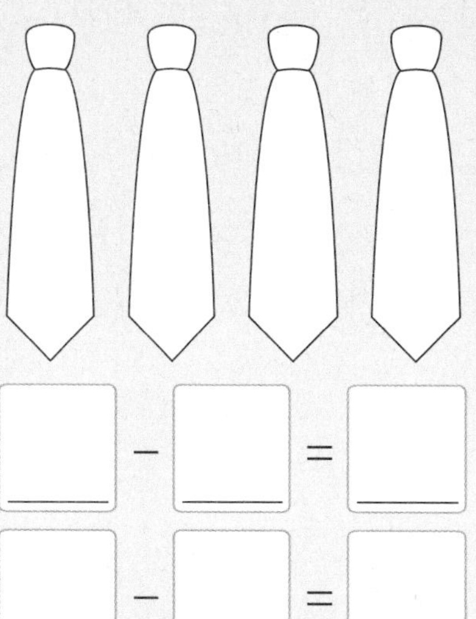

☐ – ☐ = ☐

☐ – ☐ = ☐

c.

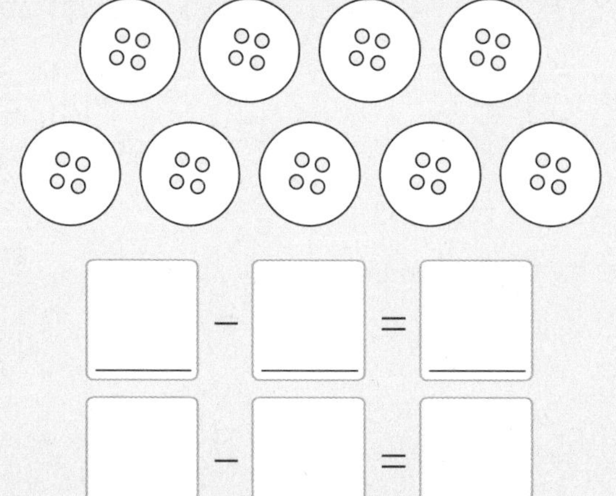

☐ – ☐ = ☐

☐ – ☐ = ☐

d.

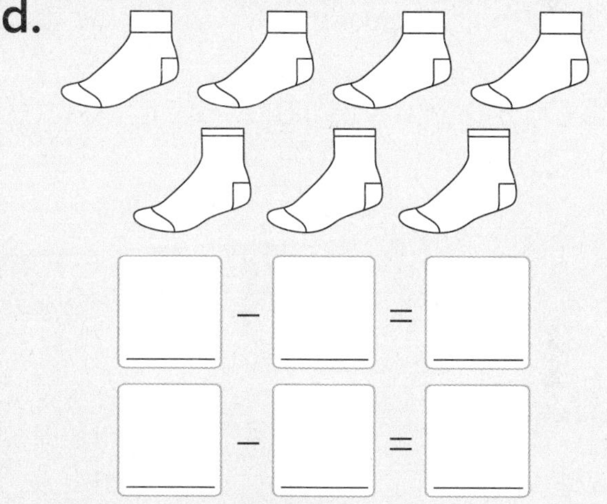

☐ – ☐ = ☐

☐ – ☐ = ☐

Step Ahead Write the related subtraction fact for each of these.

a. 9 - 7 = 2

9 – 2 = 7

b. 5 - 1 = 4

☐ – ☐ = ☐

c. 9 - 3 = 6

☐ – ☐ = ☐

d. 10 - 4 = 6

☐ – ☐ = ☐

e. 6 - 0 = 6

☐ – ☐ = ☐

f. 13 - 6 = 7

☐ – ☐ = ☐

Computation Practice

Why can't elephants drive cars?

- ★ Complete the equations.
- ★ Write each letter in the box above its matching total at the bottom of the page. Some letters are used more than once.

10 + 2 = ____	b	3 + 14 = ____	r 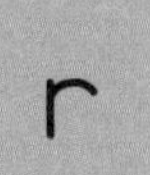	6 + 1 = ____	s
2 + 11 = ____	o	6 + 3 = ____	t	3 + 2 = ____	h
18 + 2 = ____	d	1 + 10 = ____	f	1 + 15 = ____	a
2 + 6 = ____	i	7 + 3 = ____	g	17 + 1 = ____	l
13 + 1 = ____	e	3 + 16 = ____	p		

Ongoing Practice

1. Write **<**, **>**, or **=** to make true comparisons.

FROM 1.5.11

a. 12 + 3 ◯ 2 + 14	**b.** 9 + 3 ◯ 6 + 8	**c.** 8 + 5 ◯ 9 + 2
d. 6 + 7 ◯ 7 + 8	**e.** 7 + 4 ◯ 9 + 2	**f.** 1 + 12 ◯ 9 + 9
g. 4 + 6 ◯ 7 + 3	**h.** 2 + 7 ◯ 5 + 1	**i.** 5 + 7 ◯ 8 + 8

2. Write the missing numbers.

FROM 1.10.1

a.

6 − 1 = ____

6 − 5 = ____

b.

7 − 2 = ____

7 − 5 = ____

Preparing for Module 11

Draw more counters to figure out the total. Fill the ten-frame first. Then write the tens fact to match the picture.

a. 9 + 4 = ____

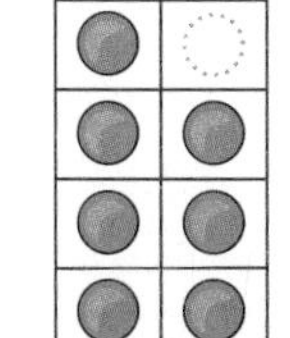

____ + ____ = ____

b. 9 + 7 = ____

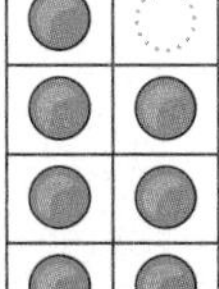

____ + ____ = ____

c. 8 + 5 = ____

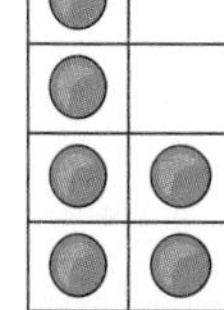

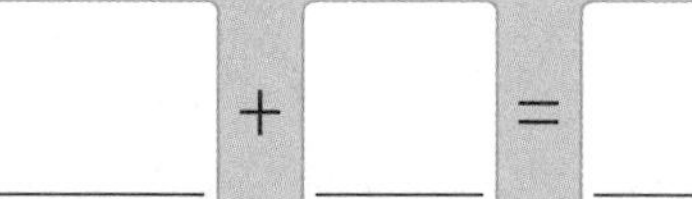

____ + ____ = ____

Subtraction: Writing related equations (multiples of ten)

Step In

How could you figure out 50 – 20?

I can use my basic subtraction facts.

5 tens take 2 tens is 3 tens.
3 tens is the same value as 30.

I count back in jumps of 10.

50 take 10 is 40... 40 take 10 is 30.

What are two subtraction equations that involve 30 and 70?

What story would match?

I could write 70 – 30 = 40 and 70 – 40 = 30.

Bella had 70 cents and gave 30 cents to Paul.
Now she has 40 cents left.

Step Up

1. Write two subtraction equations to match each picture.

a.

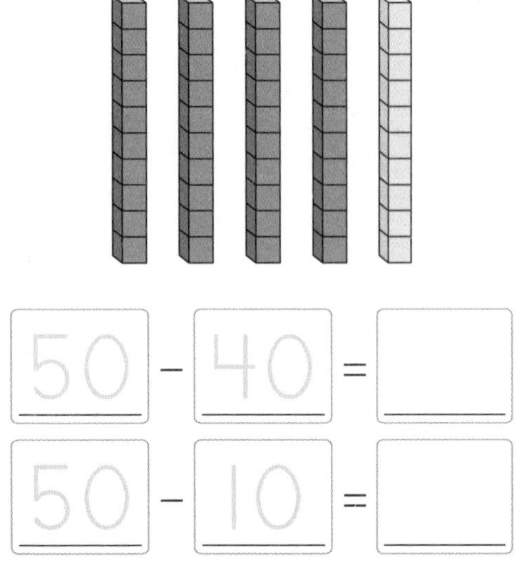

50 – 40 = ___

50 – 10 = ___

b.

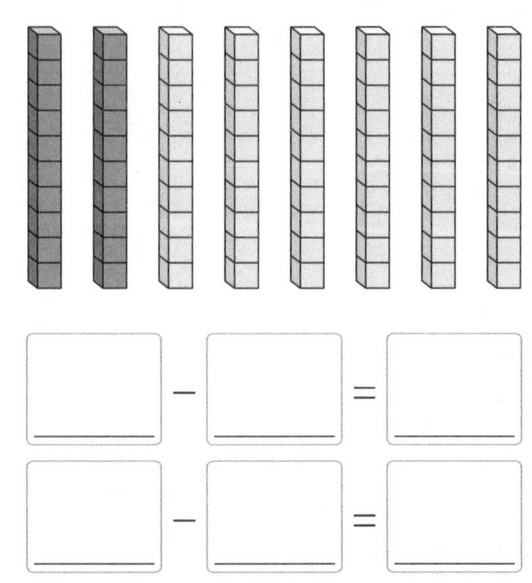

___ – ___ = ___

___ – ___ = ___

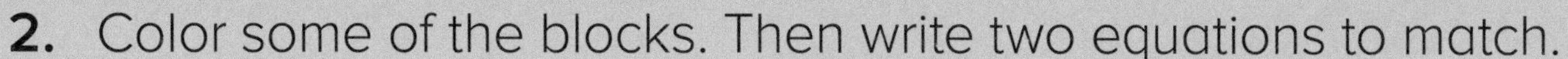

2. Color some of the blocks. Then write two equations to match.

a.

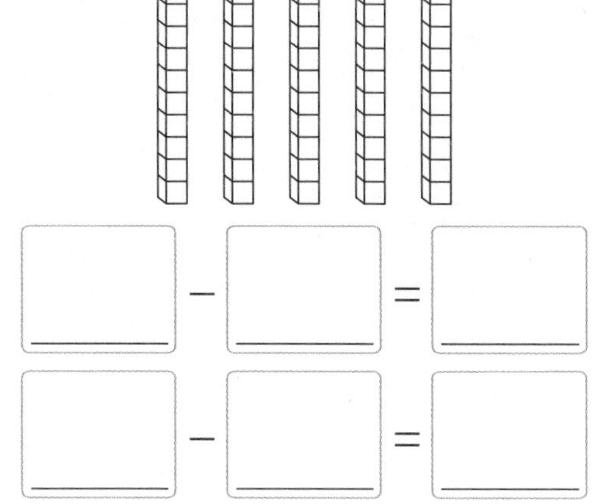

___ – ___ = ___

___ – ___ = ___

b.

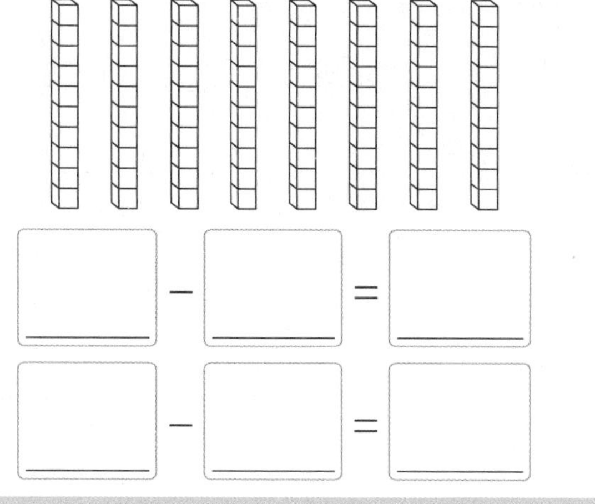

___ – ___ = ___

___ – ___ = ___

c.

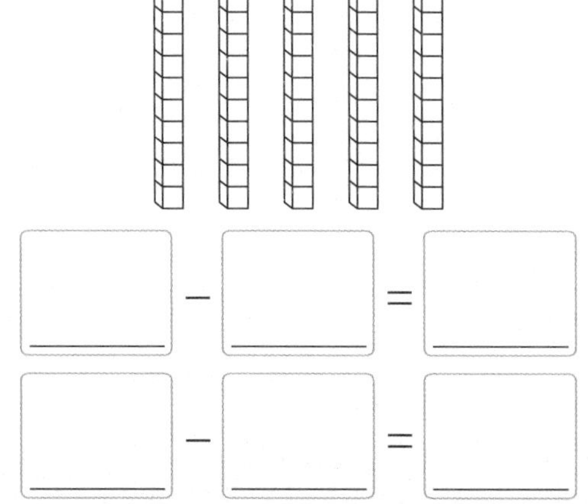

___ – ___ = ___

___ – ___ = ___

d.

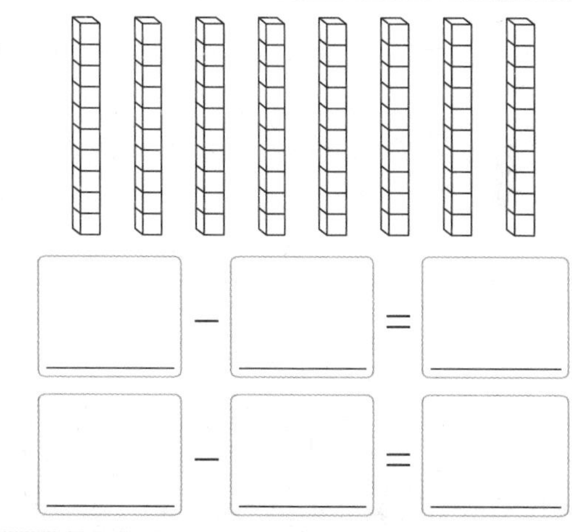

___ – ___ = ___

___ – ___ = ___

3. Complete each equation.
Then write a related subtraction equation.

a. 90 – 40 = ___

___ – ___ = ___

b. 80 – 70 = ___

___ – ___ = ___

Step Ahead Write the missing numbers along the trail.

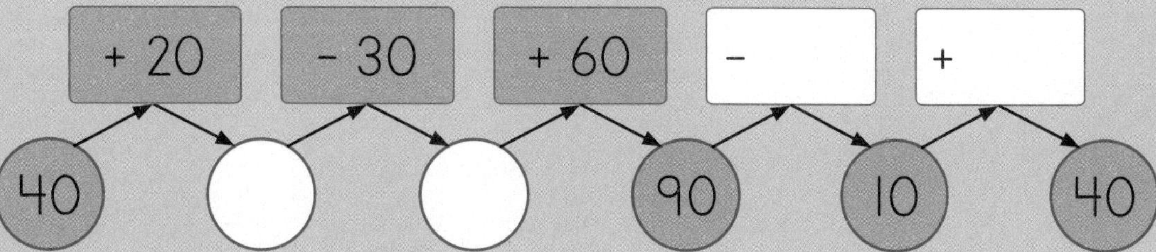

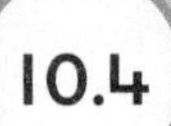

10.4 Subtraction: Writing related addition and subtraction facts

Step In Look at this picture.

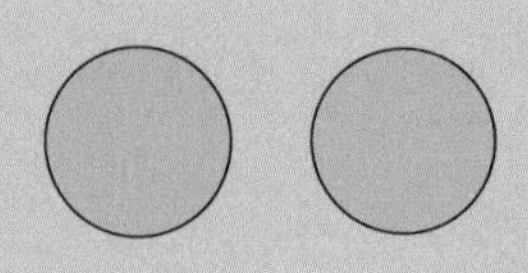

What is an addition fact that matches the picture?

What is the **turnaround** fact?

What is a subtraction fact that matches?

What is the **related** subtraction fact?

6 - 2 = 4 is related to 6 - 4 = 2.

Step Up 1. Color the animals to show two groups. Then write an addition fact and a subtraction fact to match each picture.

a.

☐ + ☐ = ☐

☐ − ☐ = ☐

b.

☐ + ☐ = ☐

☐ − ☐ = ☐

2. Color the animals to show two groups. Then write two addition facts and two related subtraction facts to match each picture.

a.

☐ + ☐ = ☐

☐ + ☐ = ☐

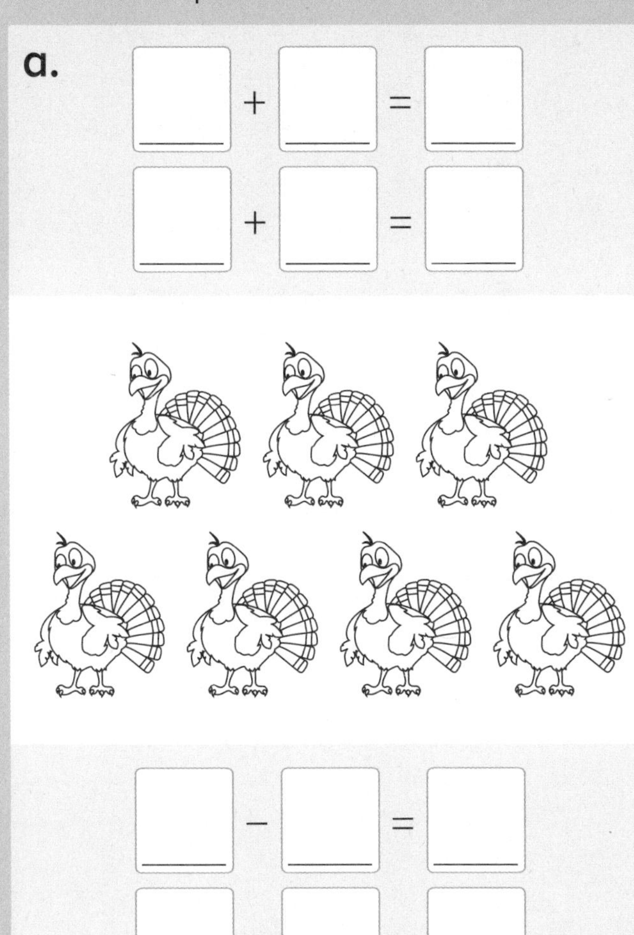

☐ − ☐ = ☐

☐ − ☐ = ☐

b.

☐ + ☐ = ☐

☐ + ☐ = ☐

☐ − ☐ = ☐

☐ − ☐ = ☐

Step Ahead Write two addition facts and two subtraction facts to match this picture.

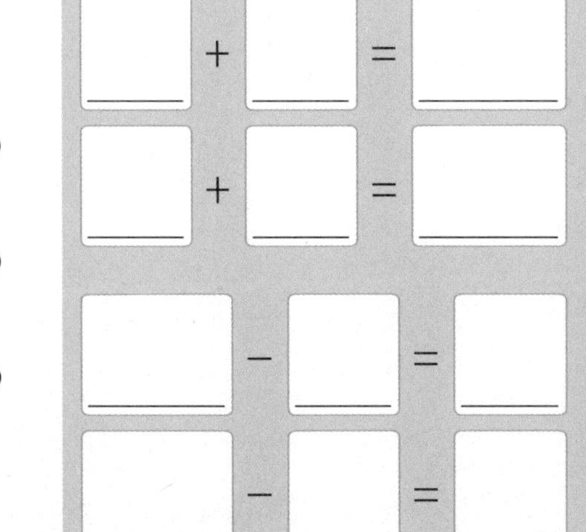

☐ + ☐ = ☐

☐ + ☐ = ☐

☐ − ☐ = ☐

☐ − ☐ = ☐

Maintaining concepts and skills

Think and Solve 

The same shapes are the same number. Write the missing number inside each triangle to complete the equation.

Words at Work

Imagine you had some money and then you spent 10 dollars.

a. Draw a picture to show how much money you could have had at the start.

b. Write about how you figured it out.

c. Write an equation to show how much money you have left.

☐ − ☐ = ☐

Ongoing Practice

1. Write the totals.

a.

27 + 1 = ____

37 + 1 = ____

47 + 1 = ____

b.

16 + 2 = ____

26 + 2 = ____

36 + 2 = ____

c.

4 + 3 = ____

14 + 3 = ____

24 + 3 = ____

FROM 1.9.3

2. Color some of the blocks. Then write two equations to match.

a.

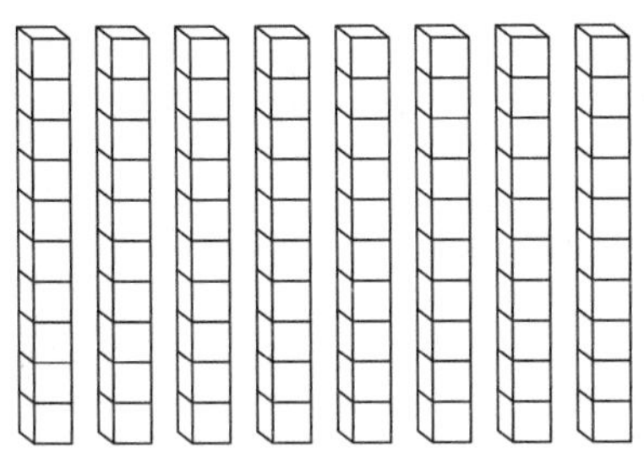

____ – ____ = ____

____ – ____ = ____

b.

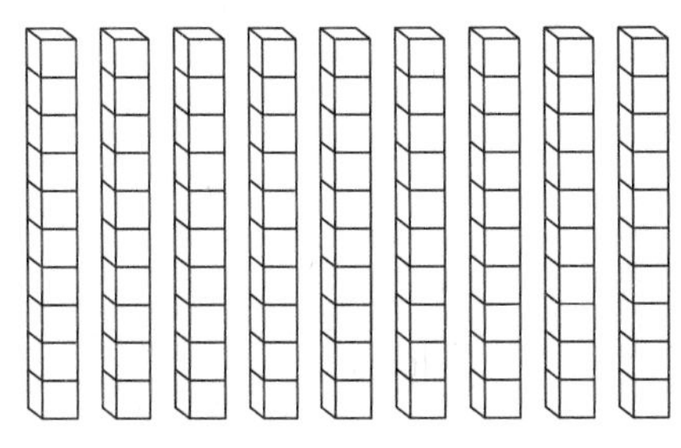

____ – ____ = ____

____ – ____ = ____

FROM 1.10.3

Preparing for Module 11

Complete each fact. Then color the facts to show the thinking you used.

Strategy used
Doubles (blue)
Count on or back (red)
Make ten (green)
Think addition (yellow)

a. 6 + 1 = ____

b. 9 + 5 = ____

c. 7 – 3 = ____

d. 12 – 4 = ____

e. 8 – 2 = ____

f. 7 + 8 = ____

10.5 Subtraction: Writing fact families

Step In Imagine this cube train is broken into two parts.

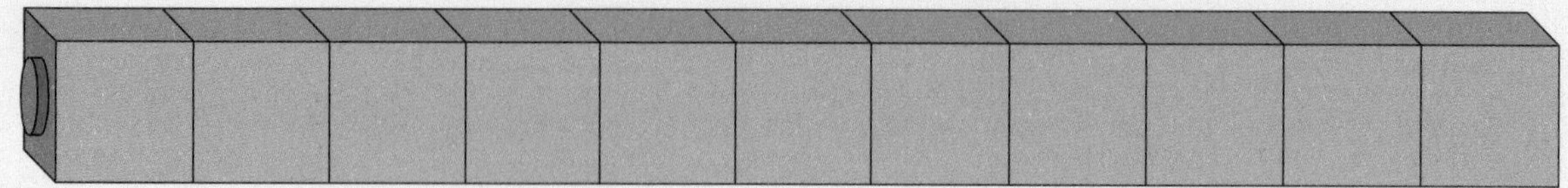

What two addition facts could you write about the two parts?

What two subtraction facts could you write to match?

The two addition facts and the two related subtraction facts make a **fact family**.

What is another fact family you know that goes with this cube train?

Step Up **1.** Write the fact family to match each picture.

a.

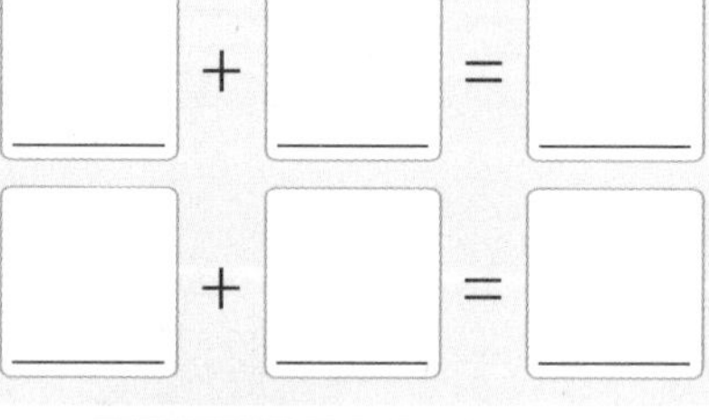

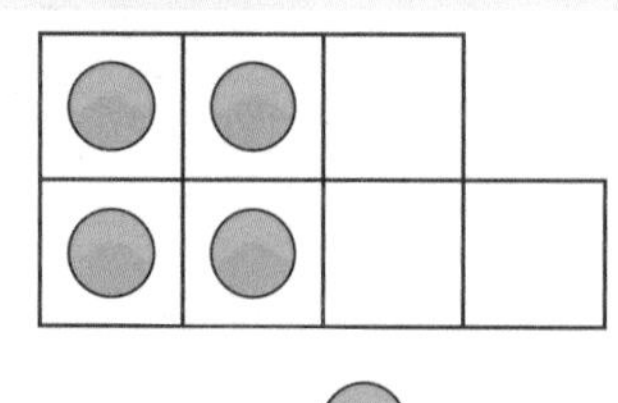

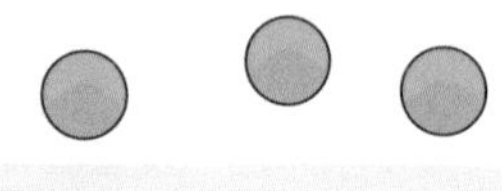

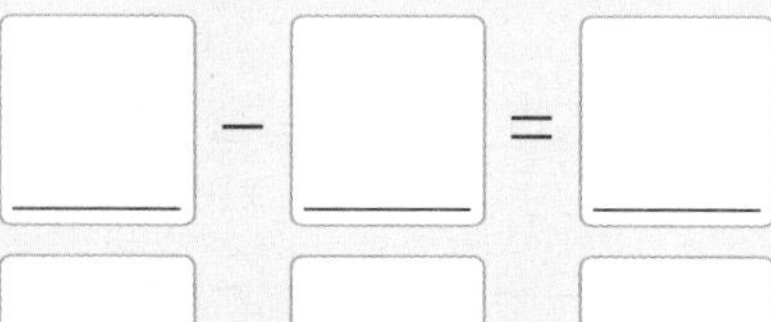

b.

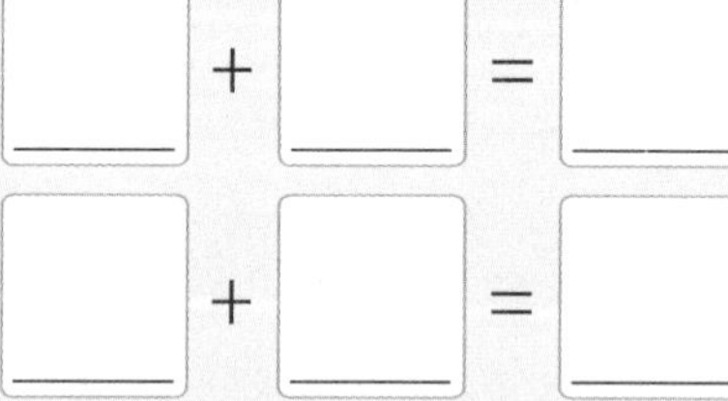

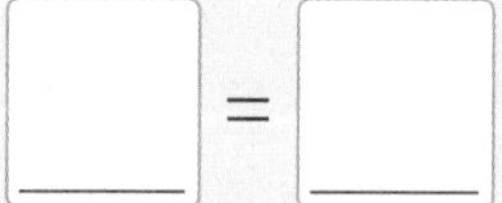

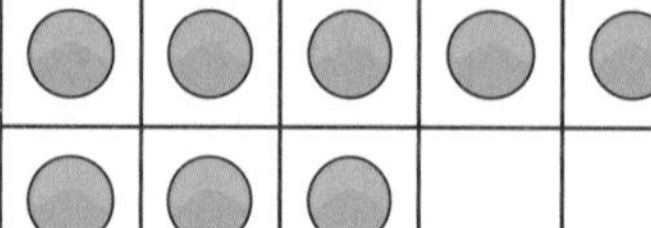

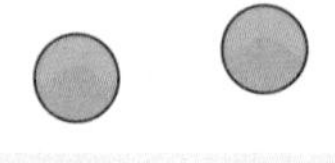

c.

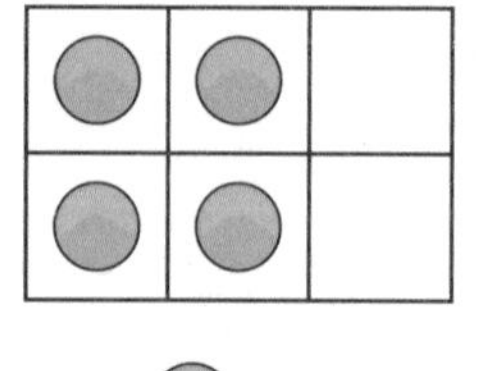

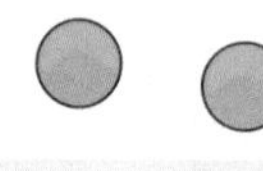

2. Draw a line from each fact to a matching picture.
Cross out the two facts that do not have a match.

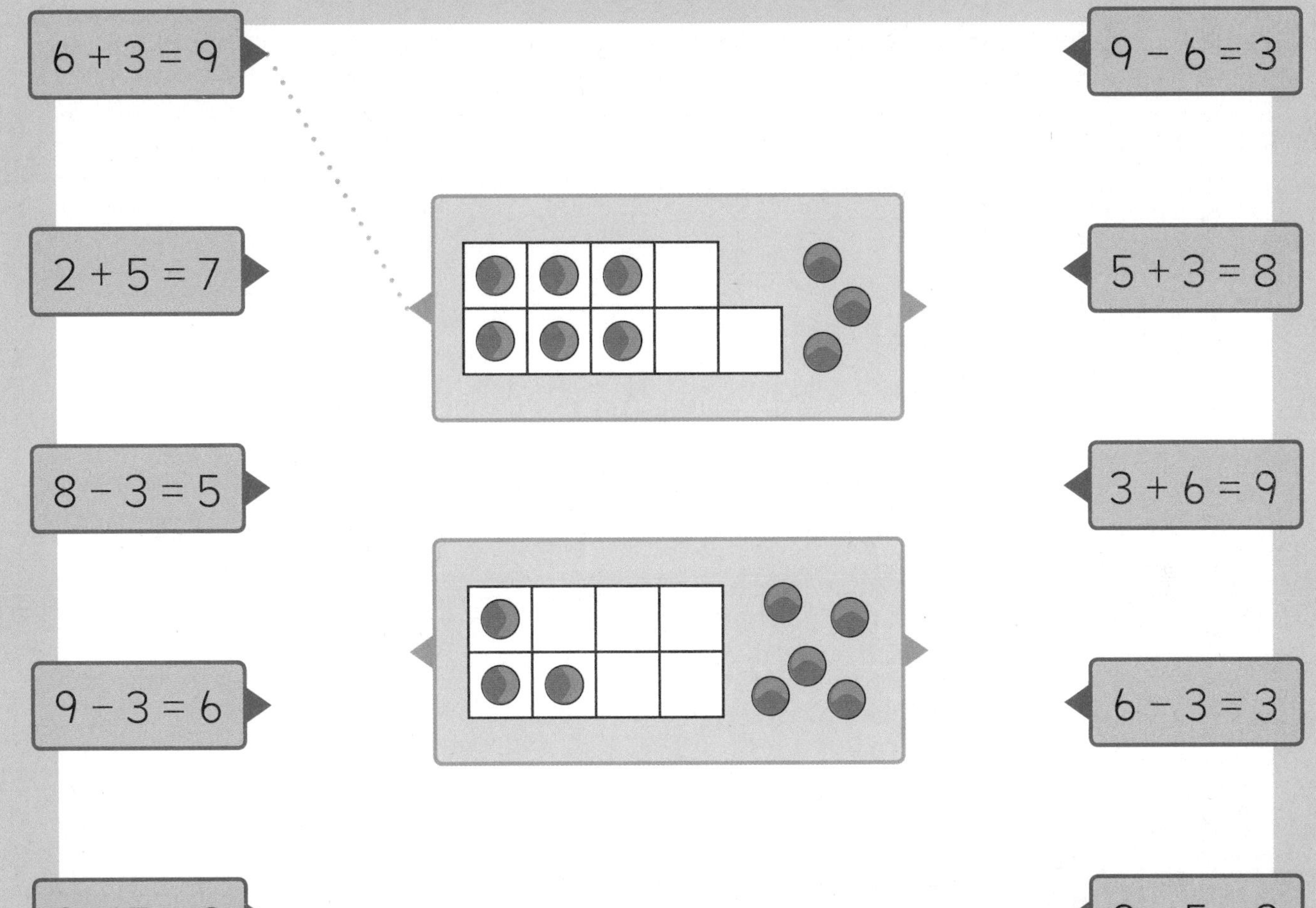

Step Ahead Write the missing facts to complete each fact family.

a.	b.	c.
6 + 5 = 11	___ + ___ = ___	___ + ___ = ___
5 + 6 = 11	6 + 7 = 13	___ + ___ = ___
___ − ___ = ___	___ − ___ = ___	17 − 8 = 9
11 − 6 = 5	13 − 7 = 6	___ − ___ = ___

Subtraction: Exploring the comparison model

Step In **Look at this picture of cubes.**

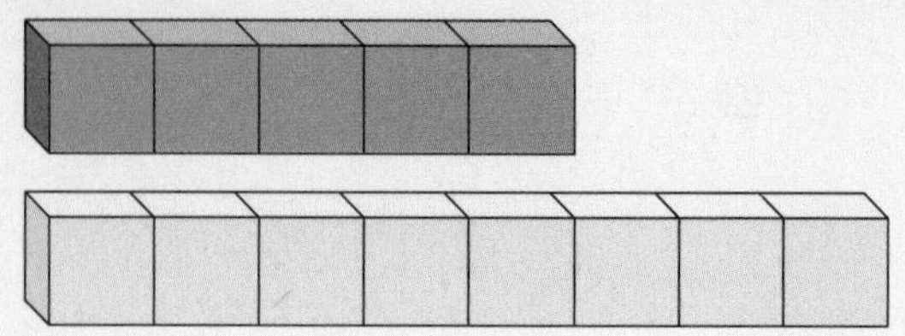

How many purple cubes are there?
How many yellow cubes are there?

How many more yellow cubes are there than purple cubes?
How could you figure it out?

How could you show your thinking on a number track?

I can count on or count back. The **difference** between the numbers is always three jumps.

Step Up

1. Figure out the **difference** between each pair of cube trains. Then complete the equation.

a.

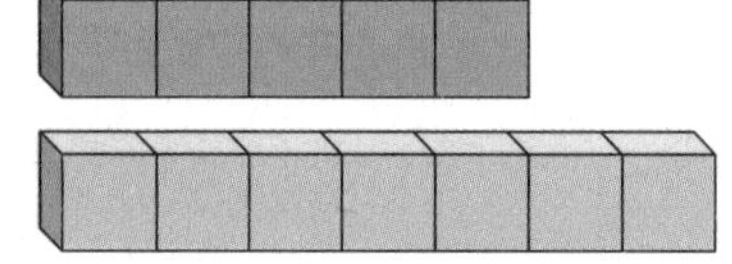

The difference is ____

so 7 − 5 = ____

b.

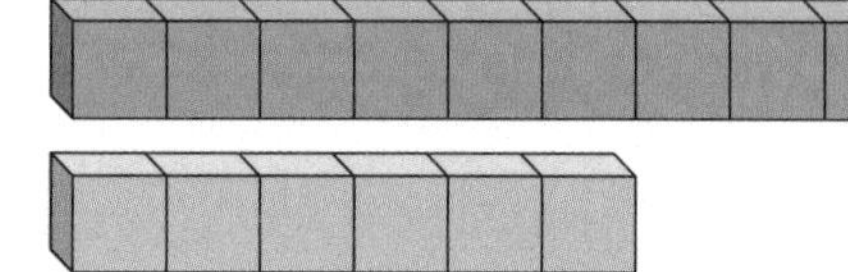

The difference is ____

so 9 − 6 = ____

c.

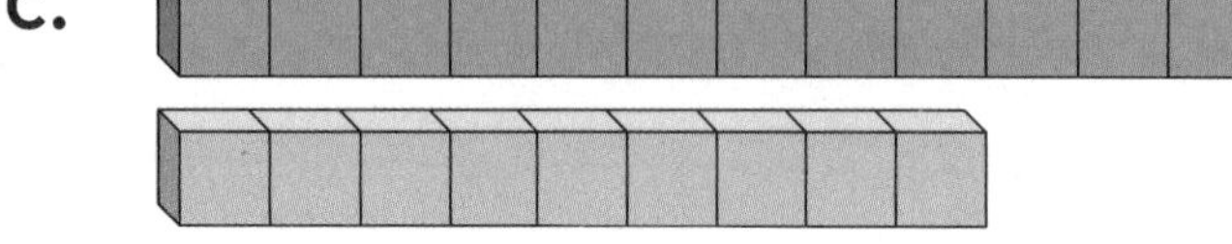

The difference is ____

so 17 − 9 = ____

2. Count the jumps to figure out the difference for each pair of shaded numbers. Then complete the equation.

a.

1	2	3	4	5	6	7

The difference is ____

so ____ – ____ = ____

b.

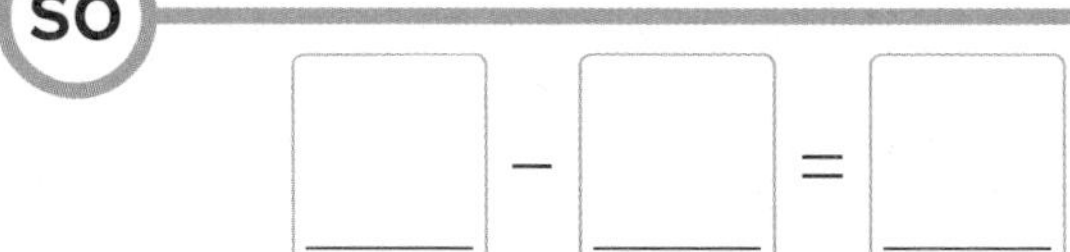

1	2	3	4	5	6	7	8

The difference is ____

so ____ – ____ = ____

3. Draw jumps to figure out the difference for each pair of shaded numbers. Then complete the equation.

a.

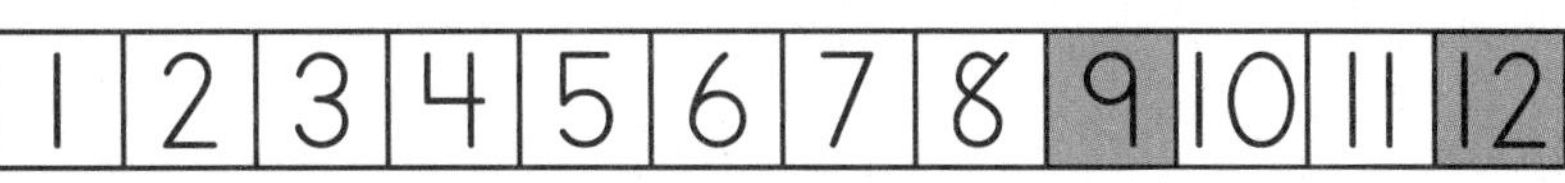

1	2	3	4	5	6	7	8	9	10	11	12

The difference is  so  ____ – ____ = ____

b.

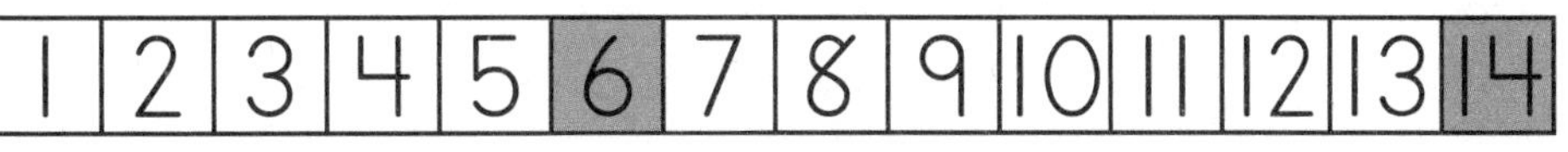

1	2	3	4	5	6	7	8	9	10	11	12	13	14

The difference is ____ so  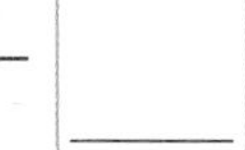 – ____ = ____

c.

1	2	3	4	5	6	7	8	9	10	11	12	13	14	15	16	17	18

The difference is  so   – ____ = ____

Step Ahead

Three students each find and measure a worm. Circle the two lengths that have the greatest difference.

13 blocks long	11 blocks long	4 blocks long

Computation Practice

What does a baby elephant suck with?

- ★ Complete the equations.
- ★ Write each letter above its matching answer below. Some letters appear more than once.

0 - 0 = ___	i
4 - 2 = ___	c
14 - 7 = ___	w
8 - 4 = ___	u
16 - 8 = ___	o
18 - 9 = ___	t
2 - 1 = ___	h
12 - 6 = ___	m
10 - 5 = ___	s
6 - 3 = ___	k

0 9   5 4 2 3 5   7 0 9 1

0 9 5   6 8 4 9 1

Write these answers as fast as you can.

10 - 2 = ___ 8 - 3 = ___ 6 - 1 = ___

2 - 0 = ___ 4 - 3 = ___ 7 - 2 = ___

5 - 3 = ___ 9 - 3 = ___ 9 - 2 = ___

Ongoing Practice

1. Write the answers. Use this chart to help.

FROM 1.9.5

a. 68 + 30 = ____

b. 75 + 20 = ____

c. 83 + 10 = ____

61	62	63	64	65	66	67	68	69	70
71	72	73	74	75	76	77	78	79	80
81	82	83	84	85	86	87	88	89	90
91	92	93	94	95	96	97	98	99	100

d. 79 + 20 = ____

e. 61 + 20 = ____

f. 89 + 10 = ____

2. Write the fact family to match each picture.

FROM 1.10.4

a. ____ + ____ = ____
____ + ____ = ____

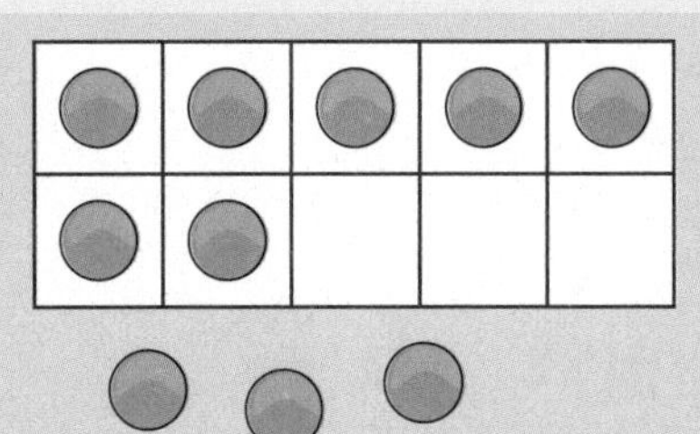

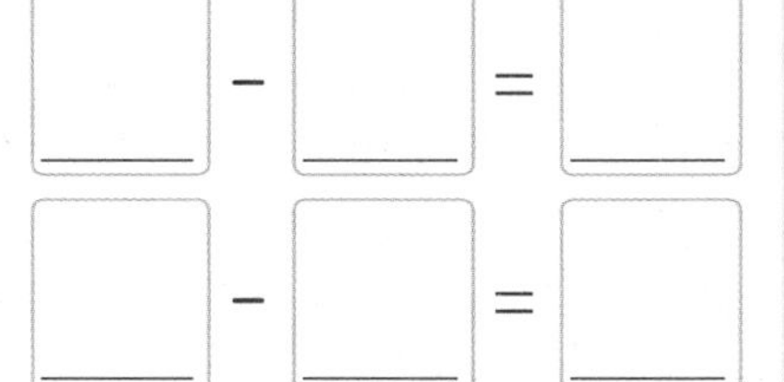

____ – ____ = ____
____ – ____ = ____

b. ____ + ____ = ____
____ + ____ = ____

____ – ____ = ____
____ – ____ = ____

Preparing for Module 11

Draw a line from each coin name to its matching value.

penny	10 cents
dime	5 cents
nickel	1 cent

Subtraction: Counting on and back

Step In **This chipmunk has 9 acorns.**

Imagine it eats 2 acorns.

How many acorns will it have left?

How can you use this number track to figure out the answer?

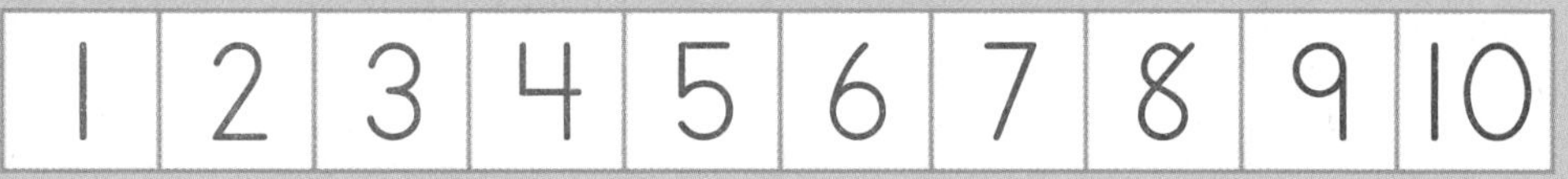

I would start at 9 and jump **back** 2.
9 take 2 is 7, so there would be 7 acorns left.

Imagine the chipmunk has 9 acorns and eats 6 of them.

How could you use a number track to figure out the number of acorns it has left?

I would start at 6 and jump **on** to 9.
6 add 3 is 9, so there would be 3 acorns left.

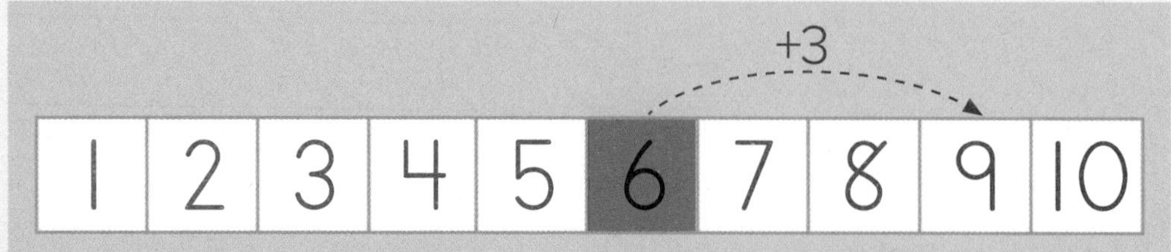

Step Up Write an equation to show how many acorns will be left. Use a number track on page 376 to help.

Step Ahead Solve the problem. You can draw a picture on page 394 to help.

At the zoo, we buy 10 bags of animal food. In the morning, we feed 2 bags of food to the giraffes, and 5 bags to the monkeys. How many bags do we have left?

☐ bags

Subtraction: Decomposing a number to bridge ten

Step In Imagine you have 7 pennies.

How much more money do you need to buy this toy?

How could you use a number track to figure it out?

I would start at 7 and jump on to 10.
Then I would jump on from 10 to 12.
3 add 2 is 5, so I would need 5 cents.

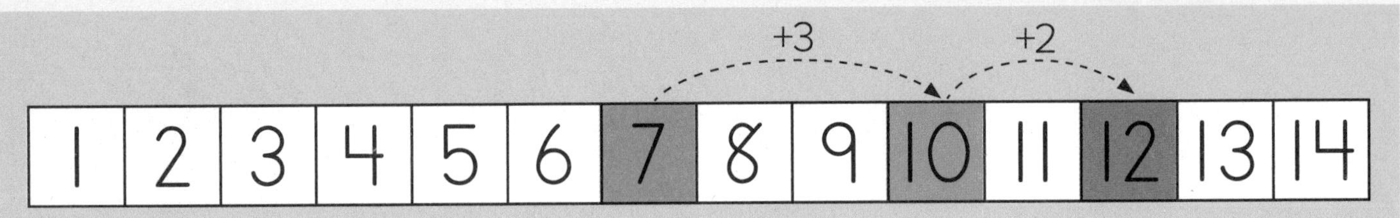

I would start at 12 and jump back to 10.
Then I would jump back from 10 to 7.
2 add 3 is 5, so I would need 5 cents.

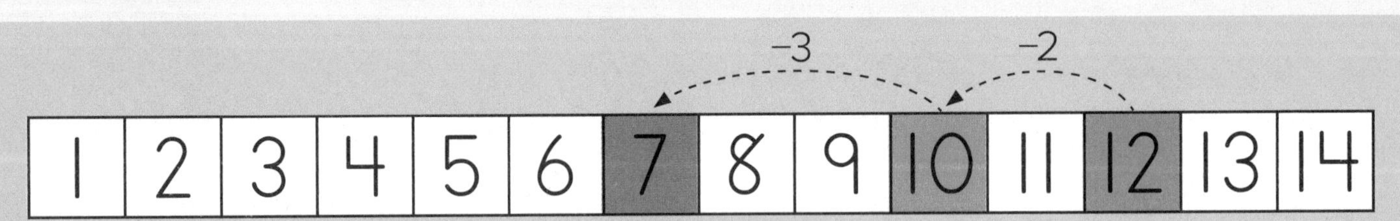

Step Up

1. Write how far each number is from 10.
You can use the number track to help you.

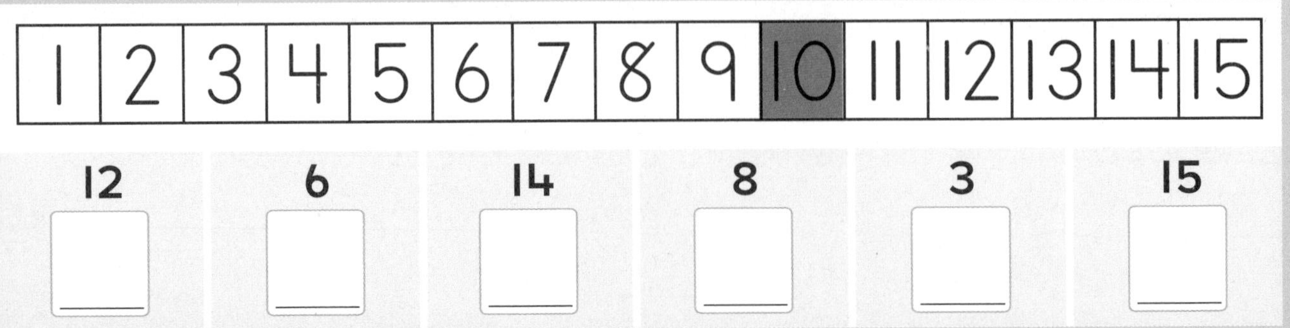

2. Figure out how much **more** money is needed to pay the price.
Draw jumps on the number track to show your thinking.

a.

13 cents

7 cents

4	5	6	7	8	9	10	11	12	13	14

Amount needed is ____ cents

b.

11 cents

8 cents

4	5	6	7	8	9	10	11	12	13	14

Amount needed is ____ cents

c.

14 cents

6 cents

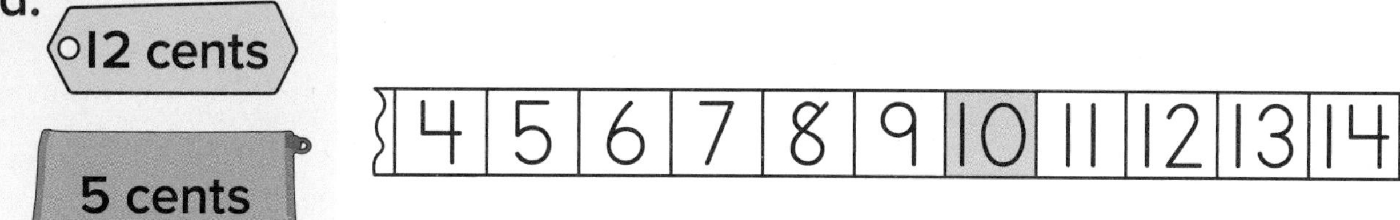

4	5	6	7	8	9	10	11	12	13	14

Amount needed is ____ cents

d.

12 cents

5 cents

4	5	6	7	8	9	10	11	12	13	14

Amount needed is ____ cents

Step Ahead Write an addition or subtraction fact to match each question above.

a. ________ = ____

b. ________ = ____

c. ________ = ____

d. ________ = ____

10.8 Maintaining concepts and skills

Think and Solve  Read the clues. Use the letters to answer.

Clues

X is heavier than **Y**.

Y is heavier than **Z**.

W is lighter than **Z**.

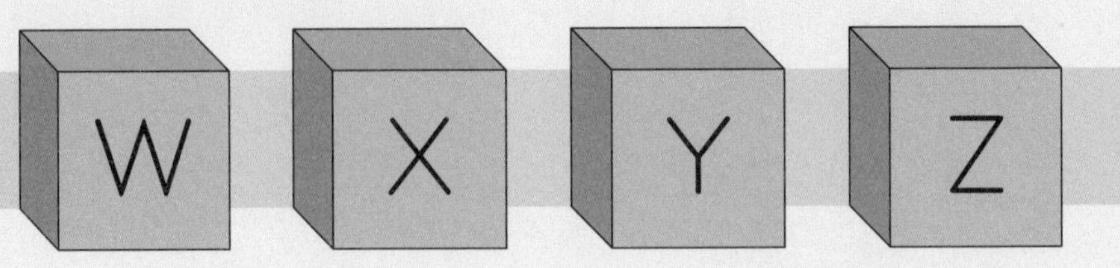

a. Which is heaviest? 

b. Which is lightest? ☐

Words at Work

a. Write about the parts and total in the fact family that uses these numbers. 7 12 5

b. Write equations to show your **fact family**.

Ongoing Practice

1. Look at each shape. Write **true** or **false** for each fact.

FROM 1.4.10

Shape A	
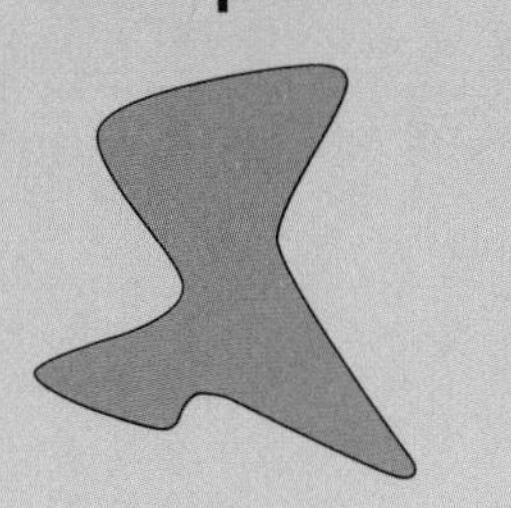	• It has no corners. ________ • It is a triangle. ________ • It is a closed shape. ________

Shape B	
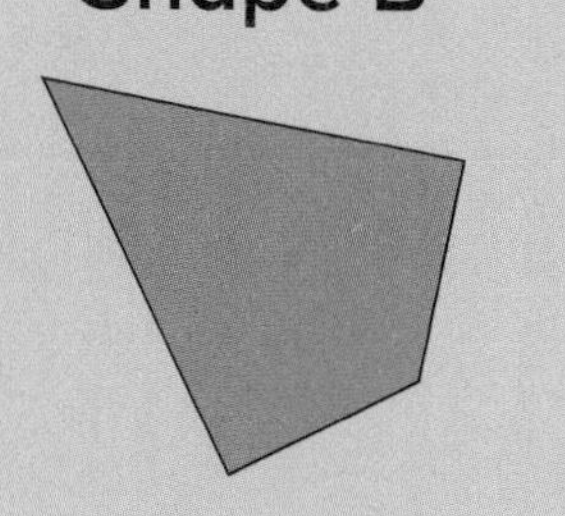	• It has 5 corners. ________ • It is a rectangle. ________ • It has 4 straight sides. ________

2. Write an equation to show how may acorns will be left.

FROM 1.10.7

a. I am going to eat **4** acorns.

8 acorns

________________ = ____

b. I am going to eat **2** acorns.

6 acorns

________________ = ____

Preparing for Module 11

Circle the repeating part in each pattern.

a.

b.

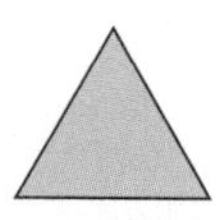 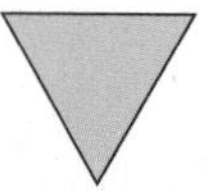 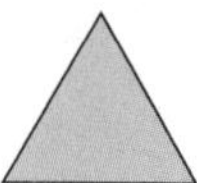 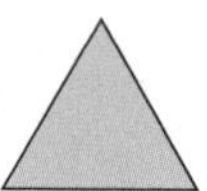 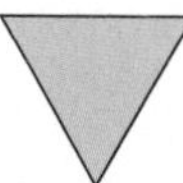 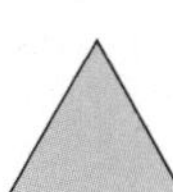 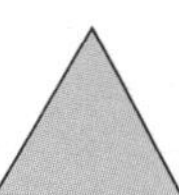 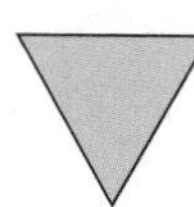 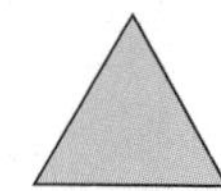

Subtraction: Solving word problems (with comparisons)

Step In **Manuel compares the number of blocks in each box.**

How many more blocks does the bigger box hold? What equation could you write to figure out the difference?

Hannah buys the bigger box of blocks.
She takes out 5 blocks.

How many blocks are left in the box? What equation could you write?

Step Up 1. Solve each problem. Draw pictures or write equations to show your thinking.

a. There are 16 blocks in a box. 3 blocks are taken out. How many blocks are left in the box?	**b.** Mika has 3 blocks. Megan has 10 blocks. How many fewer blocks does Mika have than Megan?
blocks	 blocks

2. Solve each problem. Show your thinking.

a. A box holds 15 blocks. Jie uses some blocks. There are 7 blocks left in the box. How many blocks did Jie use?

blocks

b. Deon has 11 blocks. Andrea has 5 fewer blocks than Deon. How many blocks does Andrea have?

blocks

c. A large box of blocks is 13 dollars. That is 6 dollars more than a small box of blocks. How much is a small box of blocks?

dollars

d. Some blocks are on the table. Hunter takes 4 blocks. There are 2 blocks left. How many blocks were on the table before?

blocks

Step Ahead Color the ⬭ beside the word problem that matches this equation. $12 - 7 = 5$

- ⬭ A box holds 15 blocks. Monique takes out 7 blocks. How many blocks are left?
- ⬭ There are 12 blocks. Carter uses 5 blocks. How many are left?
- ⬭ A large box of blocks holds 12 blocks. A small box holds 7 blocks. What is the difference in the number of blocks?

10.10 3D objects: Identifying and sorting objects

Step In Look at these 3D objects.

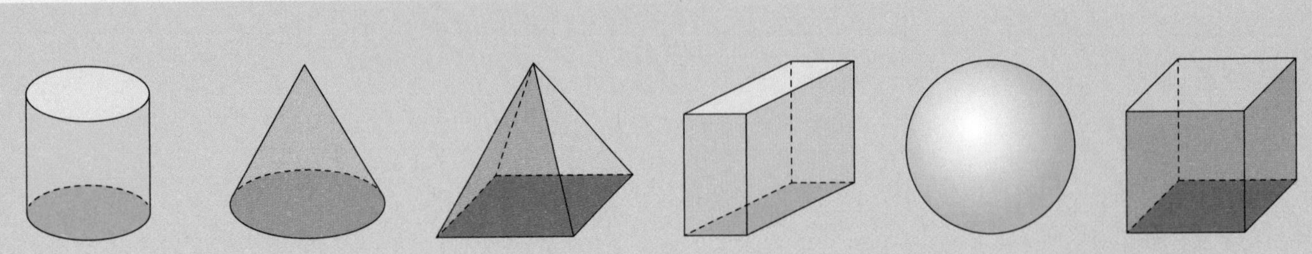

What 2D shapes were used to make these objects?

What other things do you know about these objects?

Step Up 1. Your teacher will give you a 3D object. Draw your object.

2. Write the names of **two** other things that look like your object.

a. ____________________

b. ____________________

3. My object has ☐ surfaces.

4. Color the ⬭ beside each statement that describes your object.

a.
⬭ It can roll.
⬭ It can stack.
⬭ It cannot roll or stack.

b.
⬭ It has all flat surfaces.
⬭ It has no flat surfaces.
⬭ It has some flat surfaces and some curved surfaces.

5. Draw each flat surface of your object.

Step Ahead Look at this 3D object.

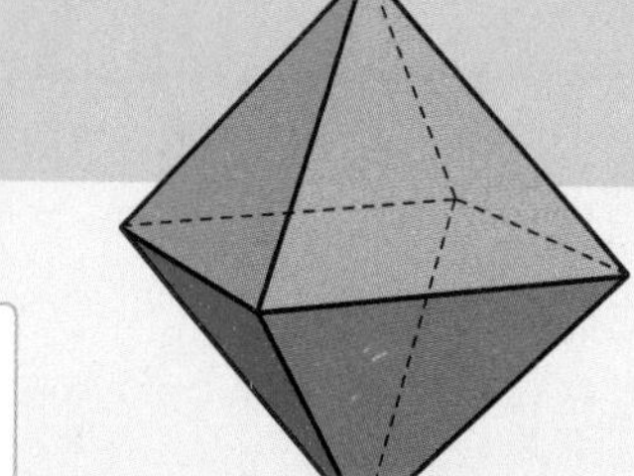

a. How many surfaces does this object have? ____

b. What shape is each surface? ____

Maintaining concepts and skills

Computation Practice **What bed does a mermaid sleep in?**

- Complete the equations.
- Use a ruler to draw a straight line to join matching totals. Each line will pass through a letter.
- Write the letter above its matching total at the bottom of the page.

9 + 4 = ☐ ▶	a	◀ ☐ = 1 + 9
8 + 2 = ☐ ▶	b e	◀ ☐ = 9 + 3
1 + 7 = ☐ ▶		◀ ☐ = 5 + 9
7 + 5 = ☐ ▶	a	◀ ☐ = 8 + 5
4 + 2 = ☐ ▶	d	◀ ☐ = 2 + 6
8 + 6 = ☐ ▶	e	◀ ☐ = 1 + 5
6 + 1 = ☐ ▶	s	◀ ☐ = 5 + 2

10   7 6 8   13 12 14

Ongoing Practice

1. Use a ruler to draw one or two straight sides to complete three triangles.

FROM 1.4.10

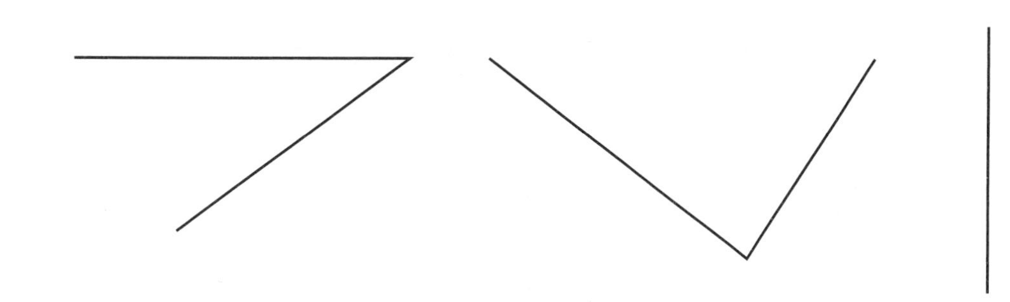

2. Color the ⬭ beside each statement that describes the object.

FROM 1.10.10

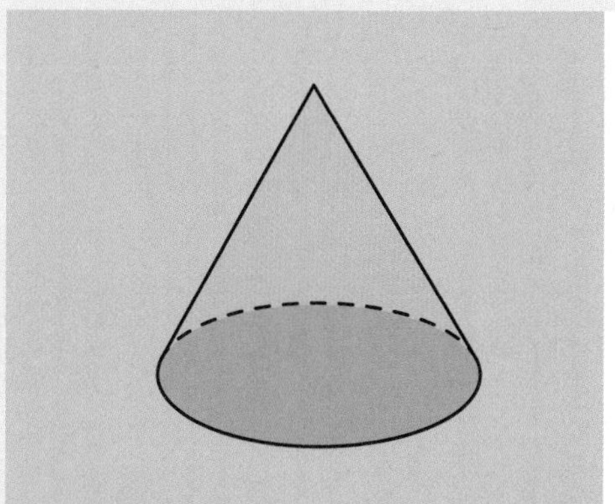

- ⬭ It can roll.
- ⬭ It has one flat surface and one curved surface.
- ⬭ It cannot roll or stack.
- ⬭ It has no flat surfaces.

Preparing for Module 11

Color coins to show the amount on each price tag.

a.

b.

3D objects: Analyzing objects

Step In **Look at these two objects.**

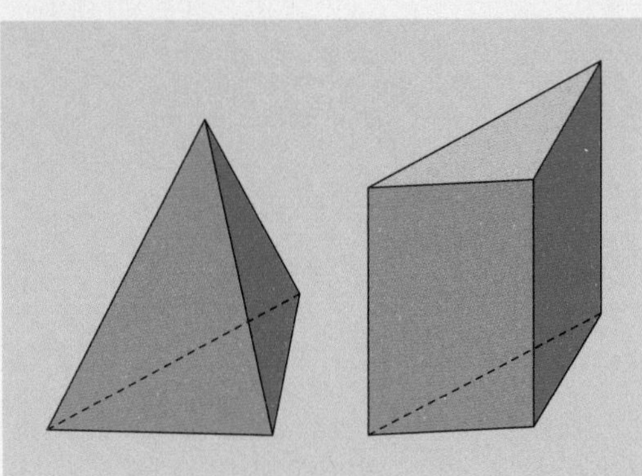

What 2D shapes were used to make these objects?

What is the same about these two objects?

What is different about the two objects?

Both objects have only flat surfaces. One object was made with triangles, and the other with triangles and non-square rectangles.

Step Up 1. Look at these pictures. Use real objects to help you answer the questions.

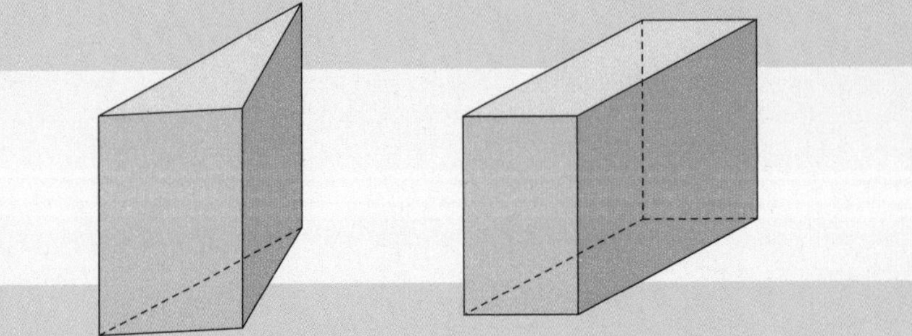

a. How are the objects the same?

____

____

b. How are the objects different?

____

____

2. Look at these pictures. Answer the questions.

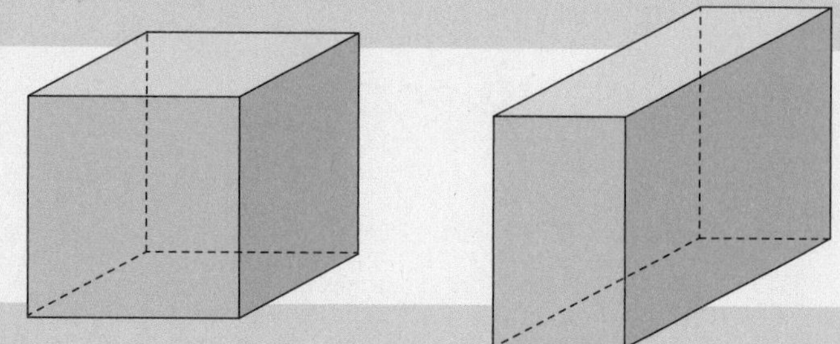

a. How are the objects the same?

____

____

b. How are the objects different?

____

____

Step Ahead Read all the clues. Circle the object that matches.

Clues

- I have six surfaces.
- I can be stacked.
- Only one of my surfaces is curved.

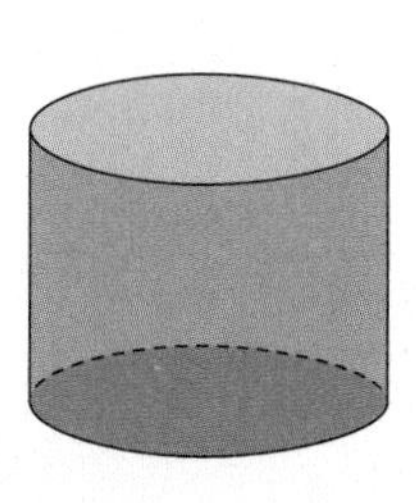 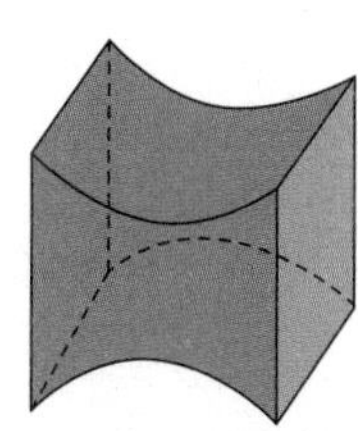 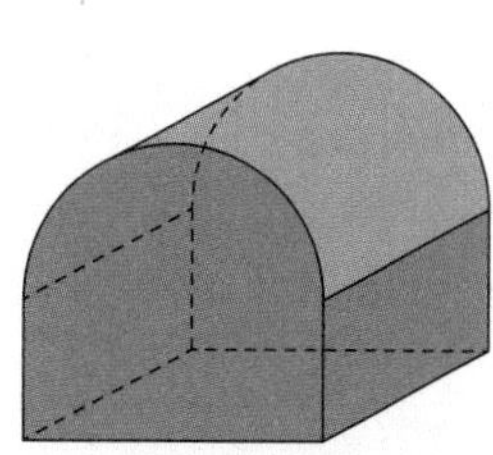 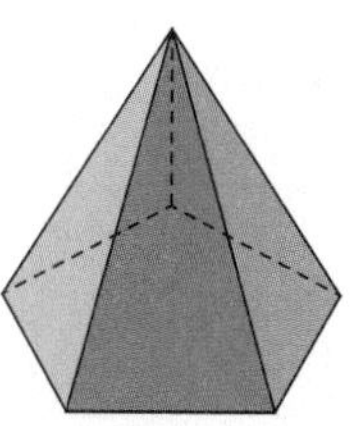

10.12 3D objects: Creating objects

Step In

Look at this building.

Which 3D objects can you see?

Think about the buildings in your neighborhood. Which 3D objects can you see in those buildings?

Think about blocks you have used at home or at school. Which blocks do you use the most? Why?

Step Up

1. Count how many of each object has been used to make each stack. The objects may be different sizes. Write the number of each object below.

a.

b.

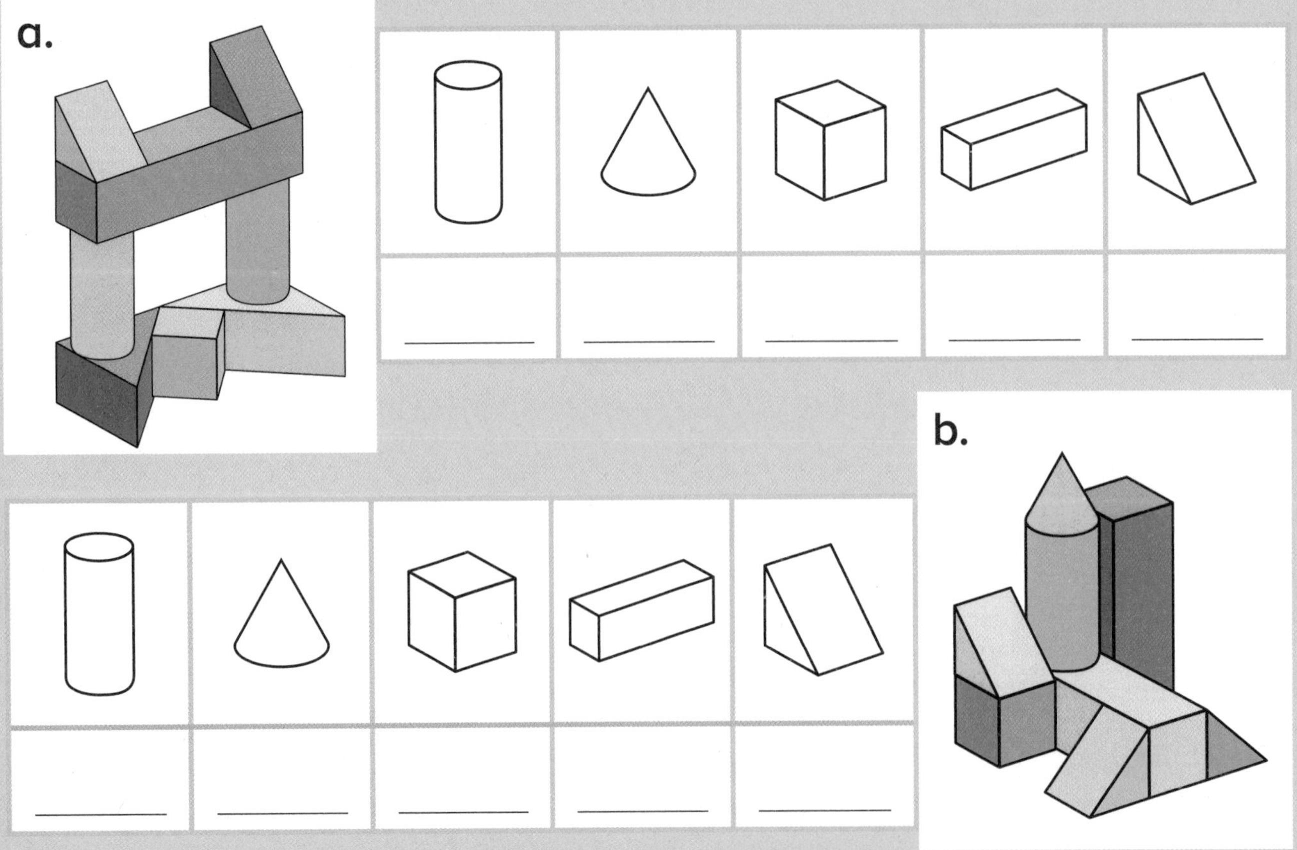

2. Circle the stacks below that can be made with these numbers of objects. The objects may be different sizes.

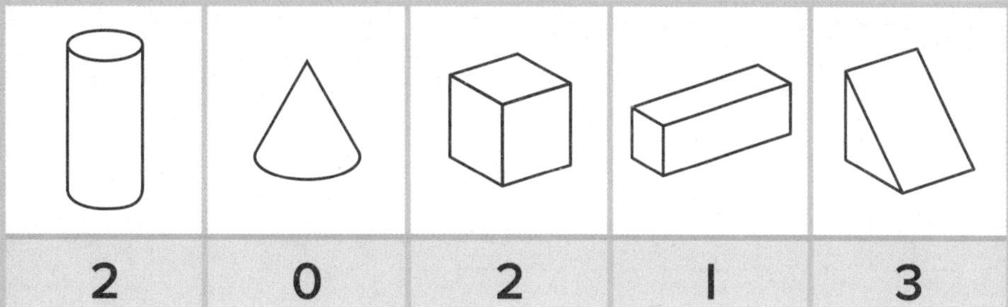

a.

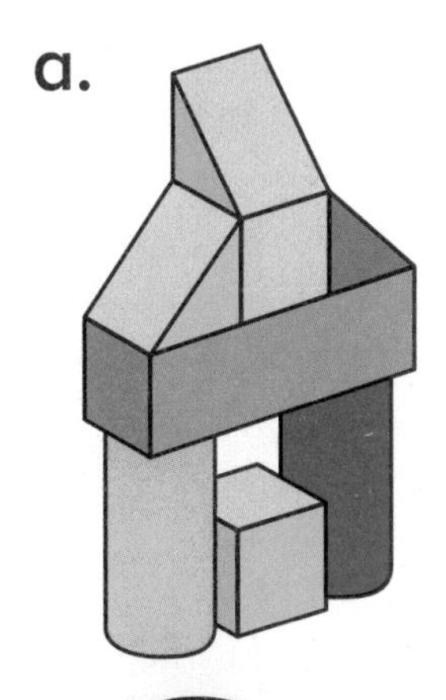

b.

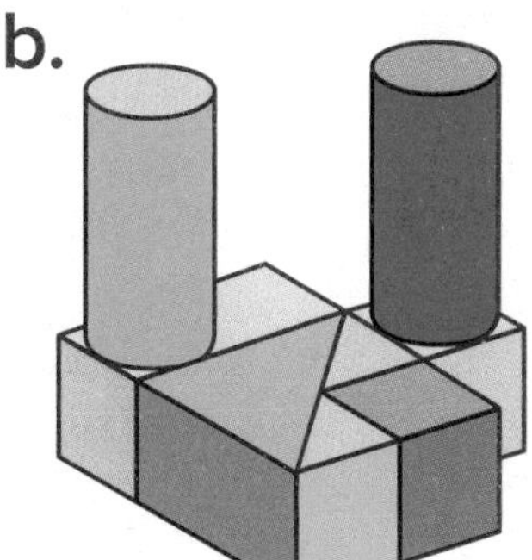

c.

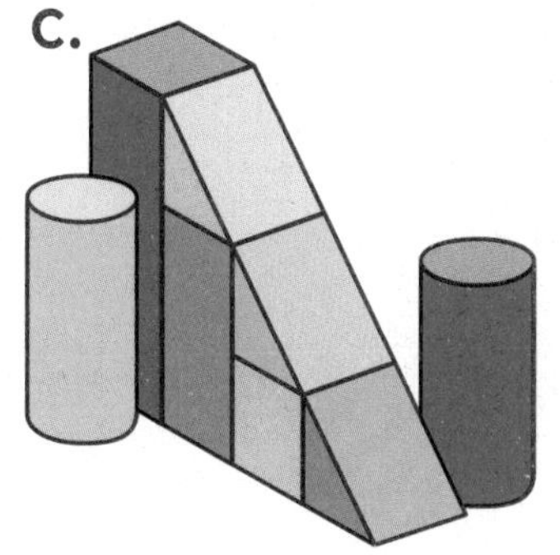

d.

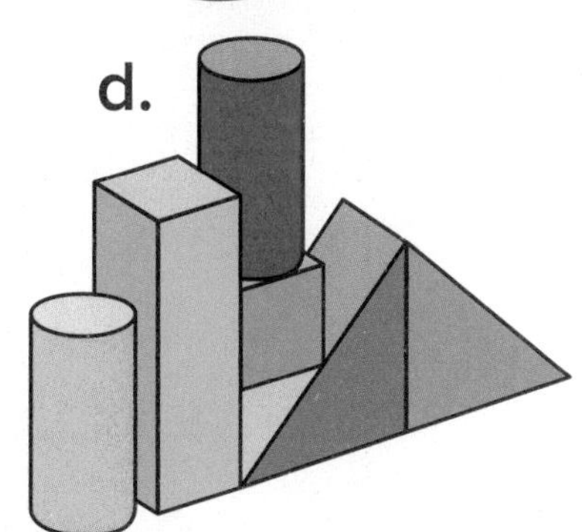

e.

f.

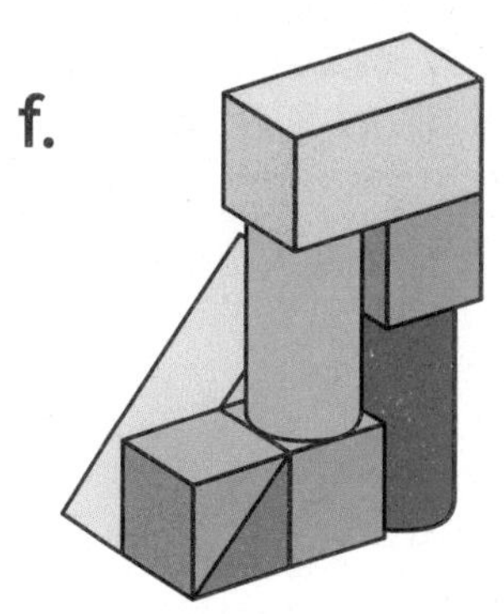

Step Ahead

Two of the stacks below match this stack.
One stack below does not match.
Circle the stack that does **not** match.

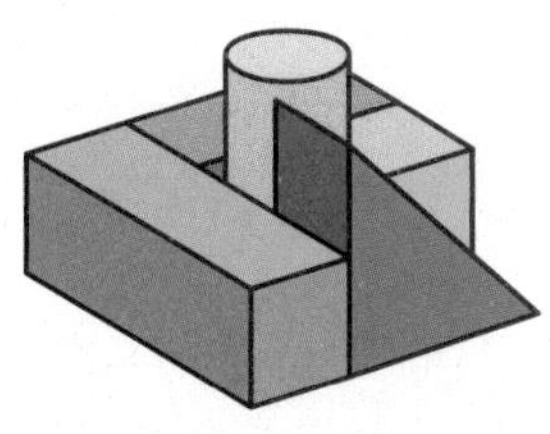

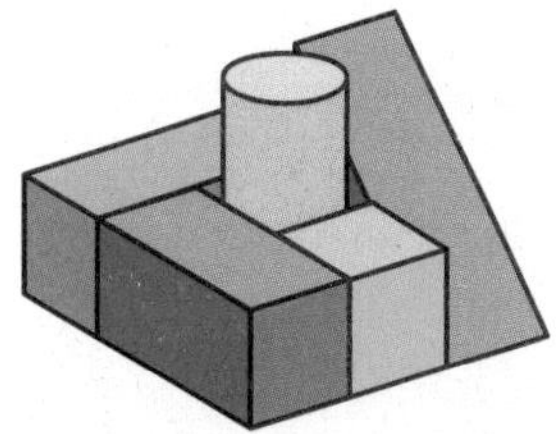

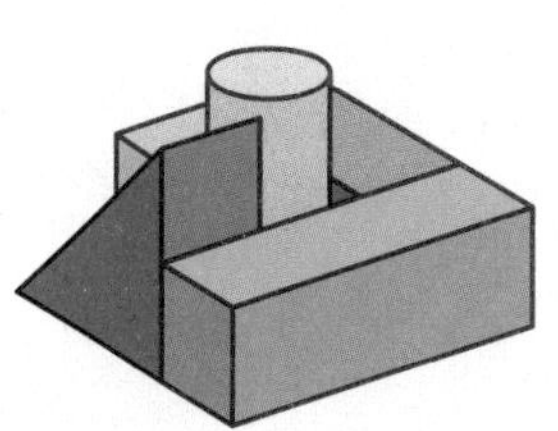

Maintaining concepts and skills

Think and Solve 

a. Use a different color to show each pair of numbers that **add to 10**.

8	5	7	6	3	2	5

b. Circle the leftover number.

c. Use the number you circled to complete this equation.

☐ + ☐ = 10

d. Write a pair of numbers that are not shown above to complete this equation.

☐ + ☐ = 10

Words at Work

Write two sentences about these **3D objects**. You can use words from the list to help you.

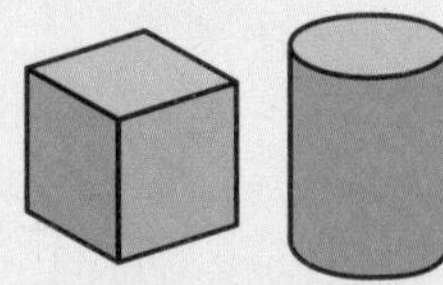

cube
curved
surface
flat
edge
cylinder
same
different

Ongoing Practice **1.** Draw two rectangles that look different.

FROM 1.4.11

2. Read all the clues. Circle the object that matches.

FROM 1.10.11

Clues

- I have four surfaces.
- One surface is a rectangle.
- Only one of my surfaces is curved.

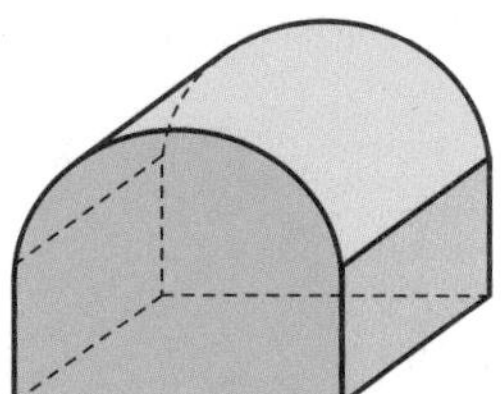 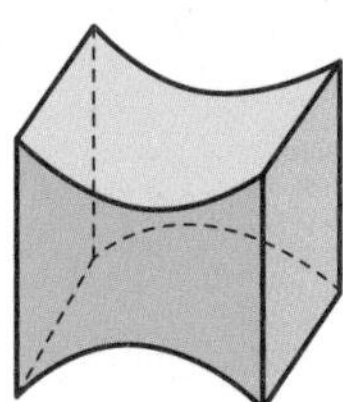 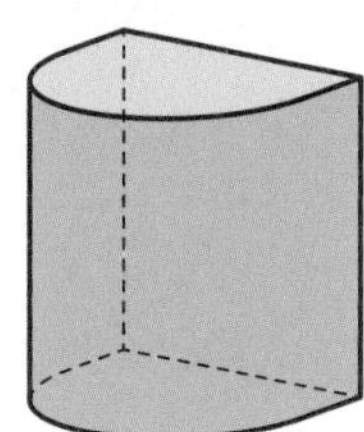 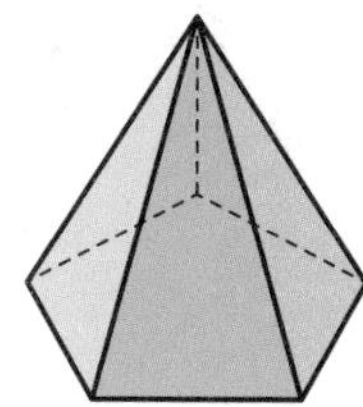

Preparing for Module 11 Draw coins to show the amount on the price tag. Then show the same amount in a different way.

Working Space

11.1 Subtraction: Introducing the think-addition strategy (make-ten facts)

Step In There were 16 stickers on this sheet.

Some of the stickers have been taken off.

How many stickers have been taken off the sheet?

How can you figure out the number of stickers that have been taken without counting each space?

Karen uses a number track to help her thinking.

1	2	3	4	5	6	7	8	9	10	11	12	13	14	15	16

What steps does she take?

Why does she make the first jump to 10?

What is the difference?

Karen uses addition to figure out the difference. She thinks 7 + __ = 16.

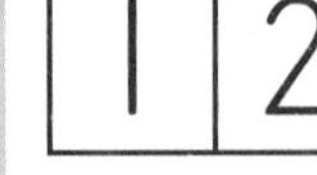

Step Up **1.** Complete the equations. Draw jumps above the number track to show your thinking.

a. 15 – 9 = ___

1	2	3	4	5	6	7	8	9	10	11	12	13	14	15

b. 13 – 8 = ___

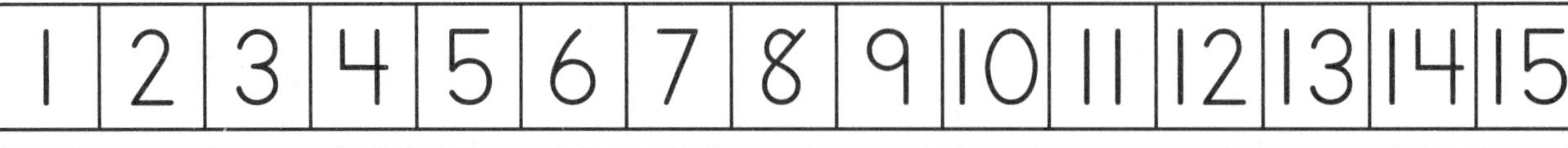

1	2	3	4	5	6	7	8	9	10	11	12	13	14	15

2. Figure out the number of dots that are covered. Then complete the facts.

a. 12 - 5 = ___

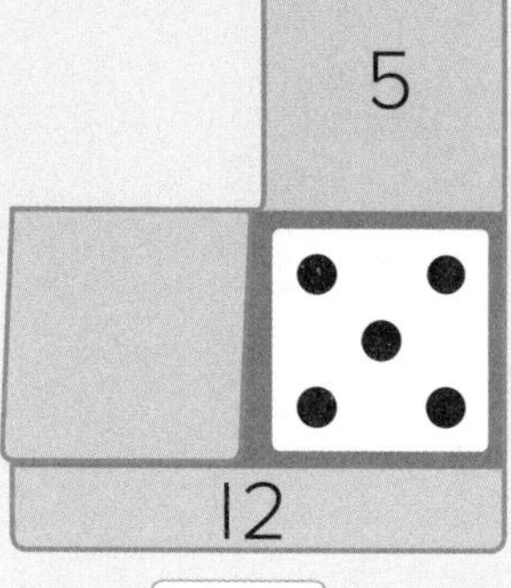

5 + ___ = 12

b. 14 - 9 = ___

9 + ___ = 14

c. 12 - 8 = ___

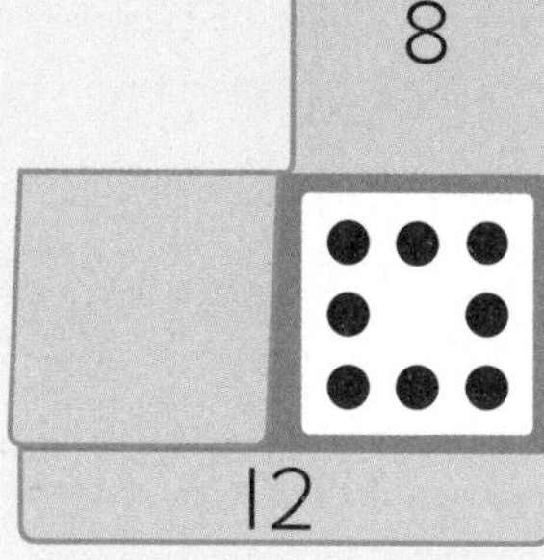

8 + ___ = 12

d. 14 - 8 = ___

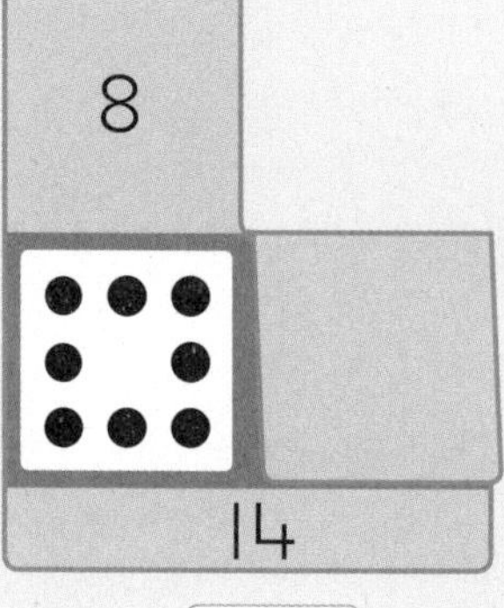

8 + ___ = 14

e. 13 - 5 = ___

5 + ___ = 13

f. 15 - 6 = ___

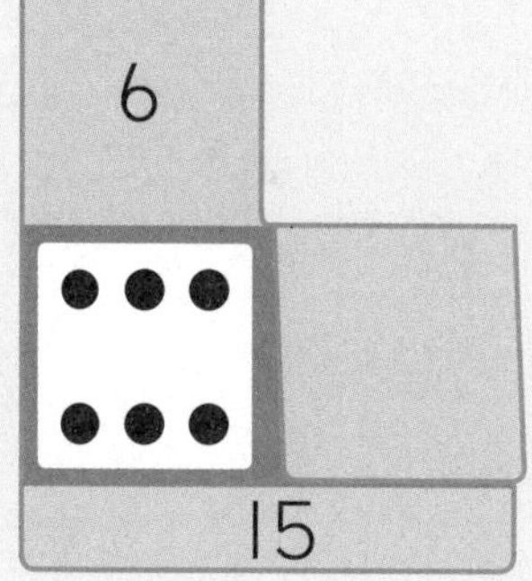

6 + ___ = 15

Step Ahead Complete the equations. Then circle the facts you solved by thinking about a double.

a. 17 - 8 = ___

b. 14 - 6 = ___

c. 14 - 5 = ___

d. 15 - 8 = ___

11.2 Subtraction: Reinforcing the think-addition strategy (make-ten facts)

Step In **There are 15 bees in total.**

Some of the bees are flying around the hive. The rest of the bees are working inside the hive.

How many bees are working inside the hive?

Complete these facts to match.

6 + ☐ = 15   15 - 6 = ☐

Did you use addition or subtraction to figure out the answer?

What strategy would you use to figure out 13 – 8?

Step Up **1.** Draw dots to figure out the missing part. Then complete the addition and subtraction facts to match.

a. 12 dots in total	**b.** 15 dots in total
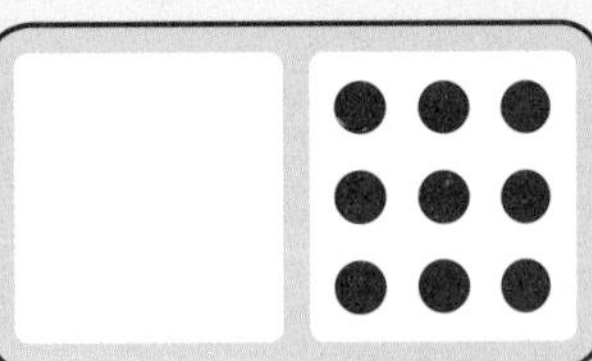	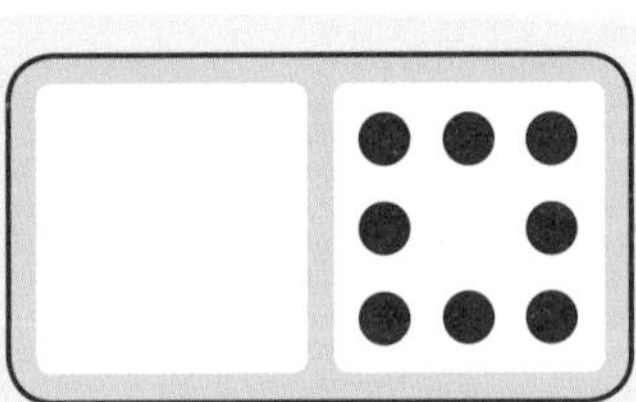
12 - 9 = ☐	15 - 8 = ☐
think	think
9 + ☐ = 12	8 + ☐ = 15

2. Figure out the number of dots that are covered. Then complete the facts.

a. 14 dots in total

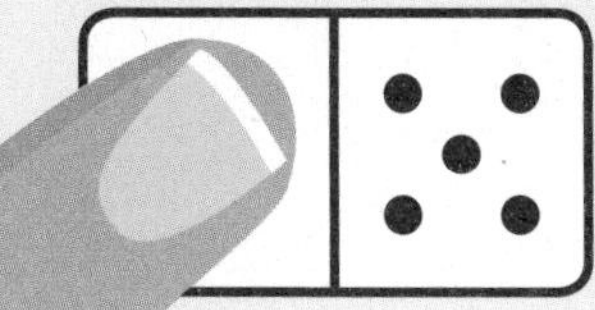

14 - 5 = ___

5 + ___ = 14

b. 16 dots in total

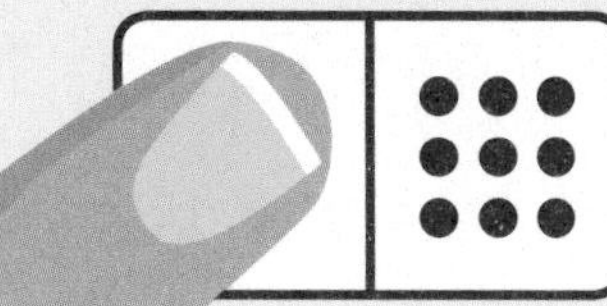

16 - 9 = ___

9 + ___ = 16

c. 12 dots in total

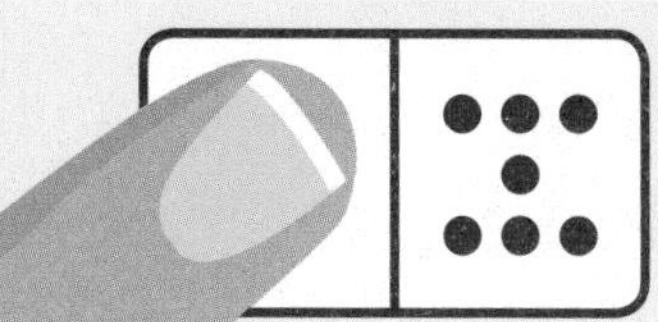

12 - 7 = ___

7 + ___ = 12

d. 11 dots in total

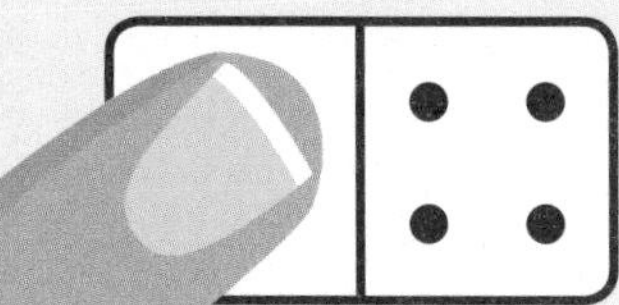

11 - 4 = ___

4 + ___ = 11

e. 13 dots in total

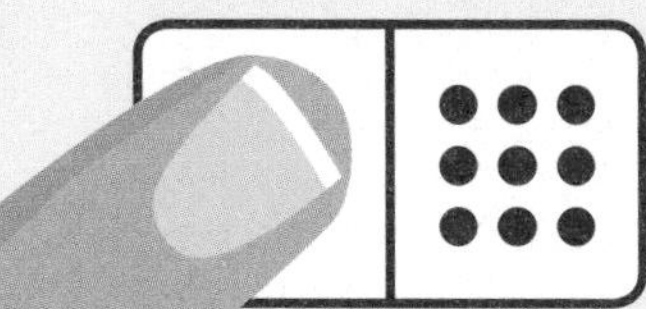

13 - 9 = ___

9 + ___ = 13

f. 17 dots in total

17 - 9 = ___

9 + ___ = 17

3. Complete these facts.

a. 12 - 8 = ___

b. 13 - 7 = ___

c. 14 - 6 = ___

d. 15 - 7 = ___

e. 17 - 8 = ___

f. 13 - 4 = ___

Step Ahead Write the missing numbers.

a. 14 - ___ = 6

b. ___ - 5 = 8

c. 15 - ___ = 6

11.2 Maintaining concepts and skills

Computation Practice

Ramon was in the garden. He found something that had no legs and lots of teeth. What did he find?

★ Complete these equations. Then find each total in the puzzle below and color the matching letter.

10 + 27 = ☐	66 + 20 = ☐	10 + 19 = ☐
47 + 20 = ☐	10 + 51 = ☐	23 + 20 = ☐
20 + 55 = ☐	18 + 20 = ☐	10 + 64 = ☐
35 + 10 = ☐	10 + 42 = ☐	38 + 20 = ☐

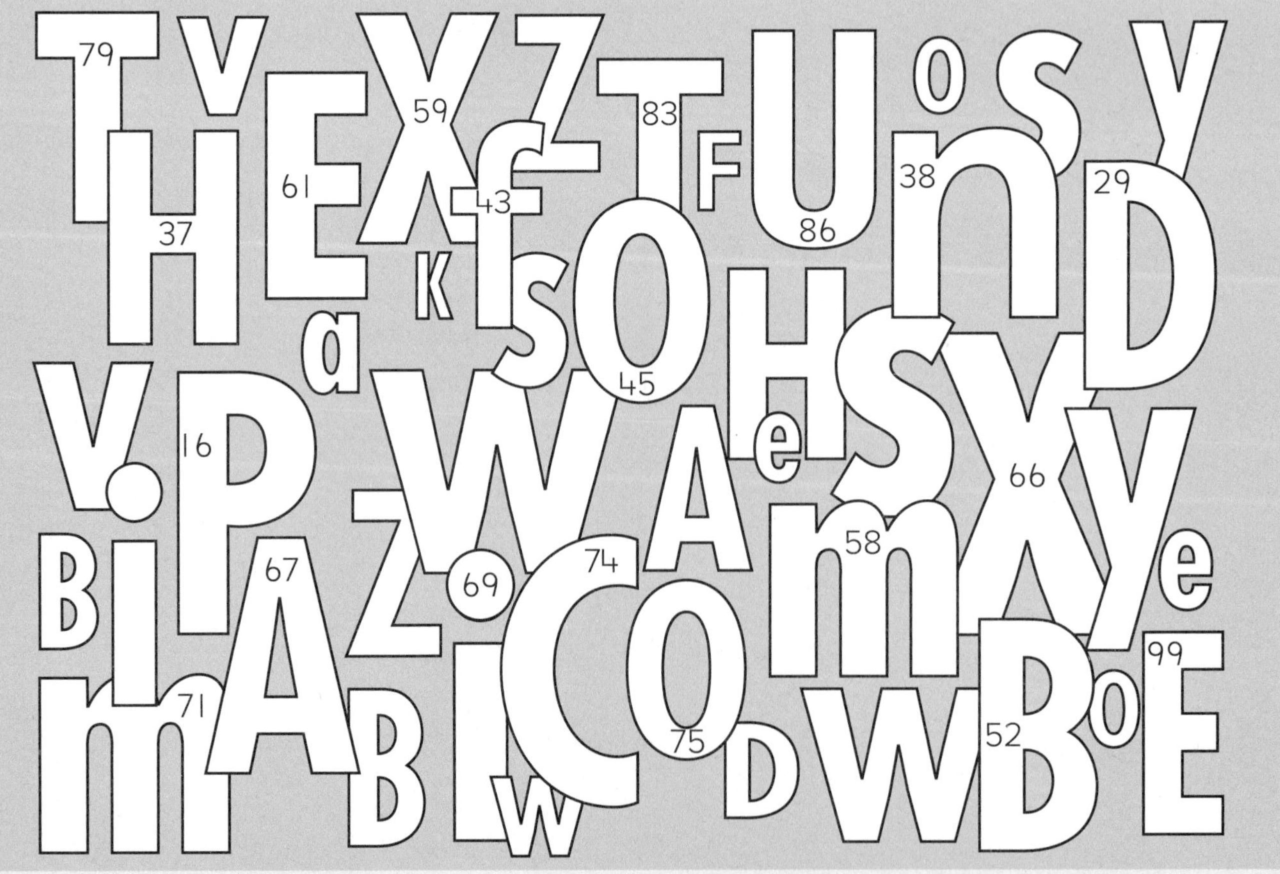

Ongoing Practice

1. Color some of the pictures. Then write the two subtraction facts to match.

a.

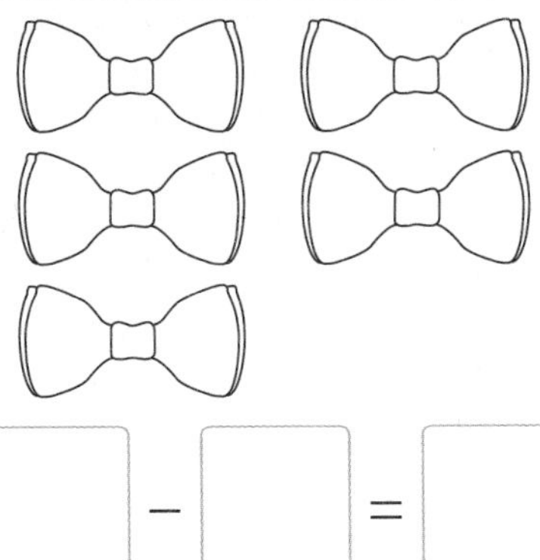

☐ – ☐ = ☐

☐ – ☐ = ☐

b.

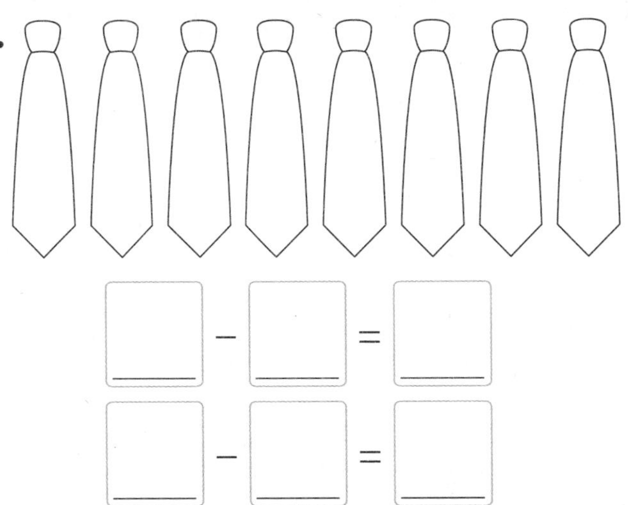

☐ – ☐ = ☐

☐ – ☐ = ☐

FROM 1.10.2

2. Complete these facts. Draw jumps above the number track to show your thinking.

a. 14 – 9 = ☐

1	2	3	4	5	6	7	8	9	10	11	12	13	14	15

b. 15 – 8 = ☐

1	2	3	4	5	6	7	8	9	10	11	12	13	14	15

FROM 1.11.1

Preparing for Module 12

Read each clue. Write the numeral to match.

a. two ones
five tens

b. three tens
zero ones

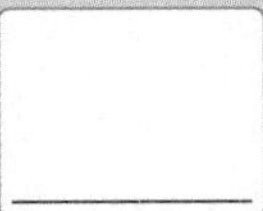

c. seven ones
zero tens

Step In **There are 15 cars in a race.**

Some of the drivers are male.
The rest of the drivers are female.

Write an equation to show how many drivers could be male and female. There is more than one equation.

15 = ☐ + ☐

15 cars start the race, but only 7 cars finish it.
How many cars did not finish the race?

Write an equation to figure out the number of cars that did not finish the race.

What strategy did you use to find the answer?

I started at 7 and jumped to 10.
I then jumped from 10 to 15. I added the jumps (3 + 5) to find the answer.

Step Up 1. Write the answers. Then write **C**, **D**, or **M** in each circle to show the strategy you used to figure out the answer.

Strategies

Ⓒ count-on or -back
Ⓓ doubles
Ⓜ make-ten

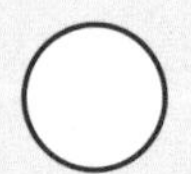 7 - 2 = 	◯ 8 + 4 = ☐	
◯ 13 - 8 = ☐	◯ 7 + 5 = ☐	◯ 17 - 8 = ☐
◯ 7 + 9 = ☐	◯ 11 - 2 = ☐	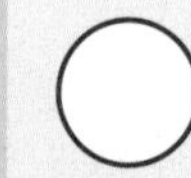 12 - 3 = ☐

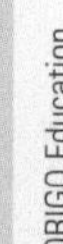

2. Write the answers on the race track.

start

9 - 3 = ____

4 + 5 = ____

9 + 3 = ____

11 - 5 = ____

12 - 4 = ____

2 + 8 = ____

8 + 7 = ____

6 - 6 = ____

4 + 7 = ____

9 - 8 = ____

8 - 0 = ____

9 + 6 = ____

3 + 5 = ____

11 - 9 = ____

finish

Step Ahead Write three different subtraction facts that each have a difference of 5.

a. ____ - ____ = 5

b. ____ - ____ = 5

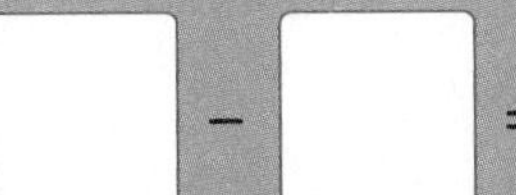

c. ____ - ____ = 5

Addition/subtraction: Solving word problems (all facts)

Step In **Julia collects trading cards.**

The cards are put in a page of plastic sleeves and kept in a folder.

How many cards fit on each page?

Can you figure out the total without counting all the card spaces?

There are four cards in each row.
That is 4 + 4 + 4.

What subtraction fact could you write to show the cards that are missing on the page?

____ – ____ = ____

Ang has the same pages for his cards. He has one page filled with cards, and one page with seven cards missing. How many cards does he have in total?

Step Up **1.** Solve each problem. Show your thinking.

a. Gloria has 3 packets of cards. Each packet has 6 cards. How many cards does she have in total?

____ cards

b. Terri has 4 fewer cards than Reece. Terri has 9 cards. How many cards does Reece have?

____ cards

2. Solve each problem. Show your thinking.

a. Rita has 6 more cards than Ben. He has 4 cards. How many cards does Rita have?

_____ cards

b. Lisa is given 7 fish cards. She now has 15 cards in total. How many cards did she have before?

_____ cards

c. Ruben has 11 cards. Some cards show fish and some show birds. How many cards might be in each group?

_____ fish _____ birds

d. Liam has 6 bird cards, 3 dog cards, and 4 fish cards. His friend has 10 cards. How many cards does Liam have in total?

_____ cards

Step Ahead

Write your own word problem using each of these numbers. 14 6 8

____

____

____

____

11.4 Maintaining concepts and skills

Think and Solve  Write a number to make each balance picture true.

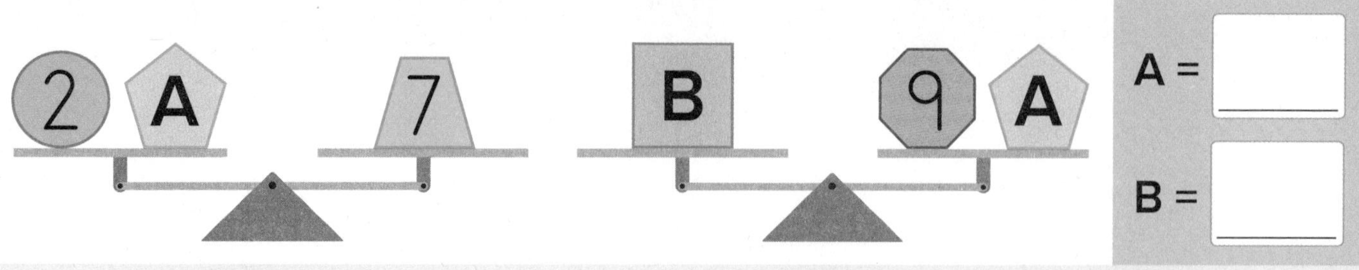

A = ______

B = ______

Words at Work Zoe and Dwane each have some coins. Dwane has 4 cents more than Zoe. They have a total of 20 cents.

a. Draw a picture to show the coins each person could have.

b. Write about how you figured it out.

Ongoing Practice

1. The number in the circle is the total. Write the missing number. Then write one addition fact and one subtraction fact to match.

FROM 1.10.5

a.

___ + ___ = 8

___ − ___ = ___

b.

___ + ___ = ___

___ − ___ = ___

c.

___ + ___ = ___

___ − ___ = ___

2. Draw dots to figure out the missing part. Then complete the addition and subtraction facts to match.

FROM 1.11.2

a. 15 dots in total

15 − 9 = ___

think

9 + ___ = 15

b. 14 dots in total

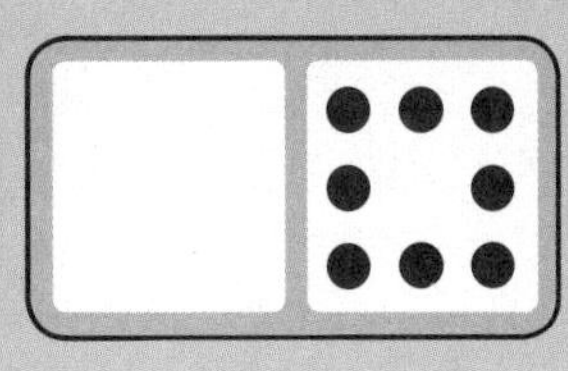

14 − 8 = ___

think

8 + ___ = 14

Preparing for Module 12

Write the missing numbers on this track.

Algebra: Counting in steps of two

Step In How many pairs of shoes do you see?

What is a quick way to figure out the total number of shoes?

Step Up 1. Draw jumps of two. Color the numbers you land on.

a.

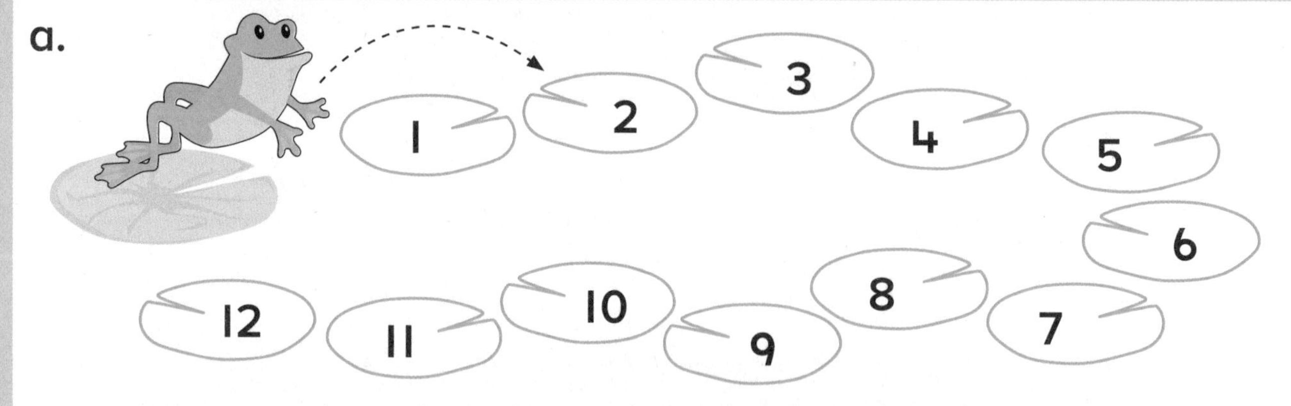

b.

2. Draw jumps of two. Color the numbers you land on.

a.

1 2 3 4 5 6 7 8 9 10 11 12 13 14

b.

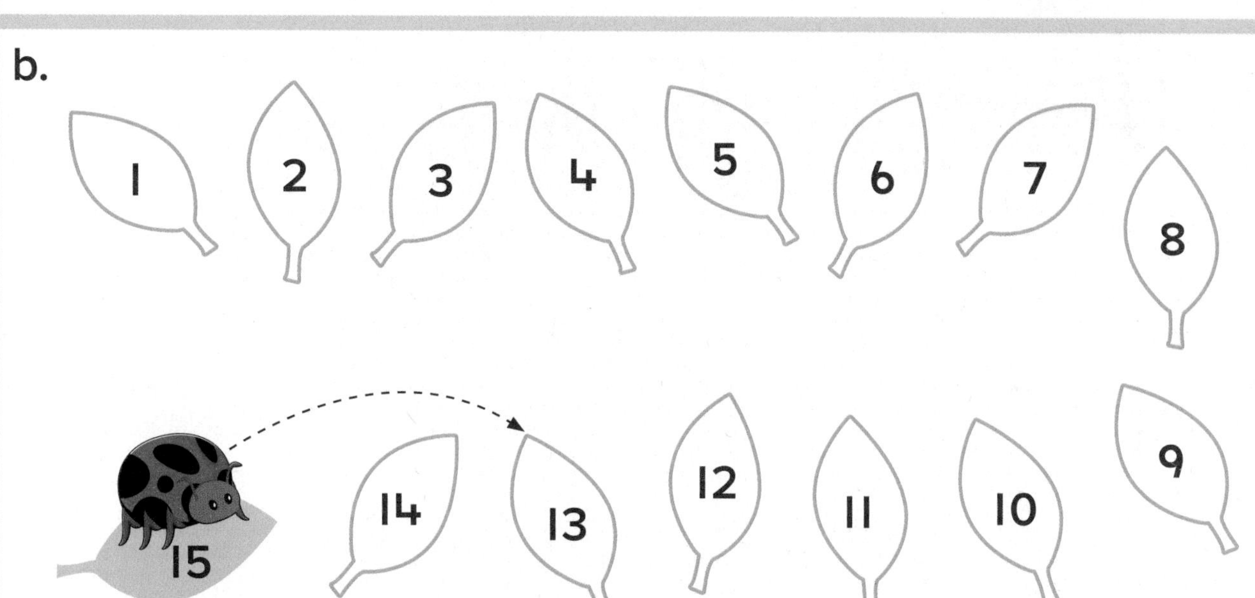

Step Ahead These number patterns were made with jumps of two. Write the missing numbers.

a.

b.

c.

d.

11.6 Algebra: Counting in steps of five and ten

Step In **Look at the number track below.**

How many fives can you find? Which numbers have a five?
How many zeros can you find? Which numbers have a zero?

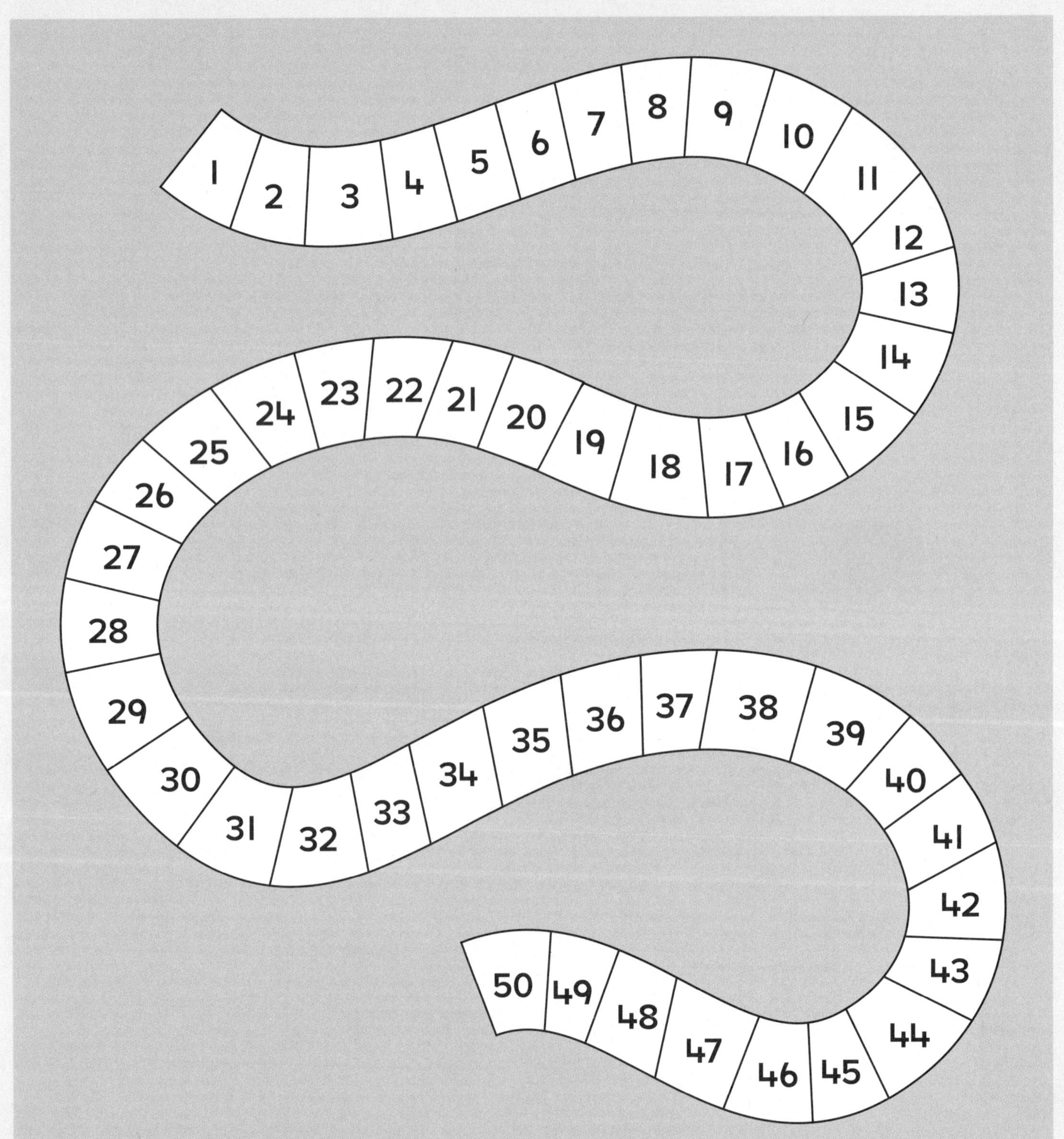

Step Up Use the number track on page 410 to help you complete these.

1. a. Start at 10. Draw ● on the numbers you say when you count by tens.

   b. Write the numbers you say when you count by tens.

   10 ___ ___ ___ ___

   c. Look at the numbers you wrote. Write about a pattern you see.

2. a. Start at 5. Draw ○ on the numbers you say when you count by fives.

   b. Write the numbers you say when you count by fives.

   c. Look at the numbers you wrote. Write about a pattern you see.

Step Ahead Imagine the number track on page 410 went to 99.

a. Write the numbers you would say if you kept counting by tens.

50 ___ ___ ___ ___

b. Write the numbers you would say if you kept counting by fives.

50 ___ ___ ___ ___ ___ ___ ___ ___ ___

Maintaining concepts and skills

Computation Practice

How is a baby like a basketball player?

★ Complete the equations. Then write each letter above its matching total at the bottom of the page.

37 + 10 = ____ i	56 + 10 = ____ r	49 + 20 = ____ a
39 + 20 = ____ n	58 + 10 = ____ w	25 + 10 = ____ t
74 + 10 = ____ b	23 + 10 = ____ p	29 + 20 = ____ e
66 + 20 = ____ l	43 + 10 = ____ h	55 + 20 = ____ d
67 + 10 = ____ y		

Some letters appear more than once.

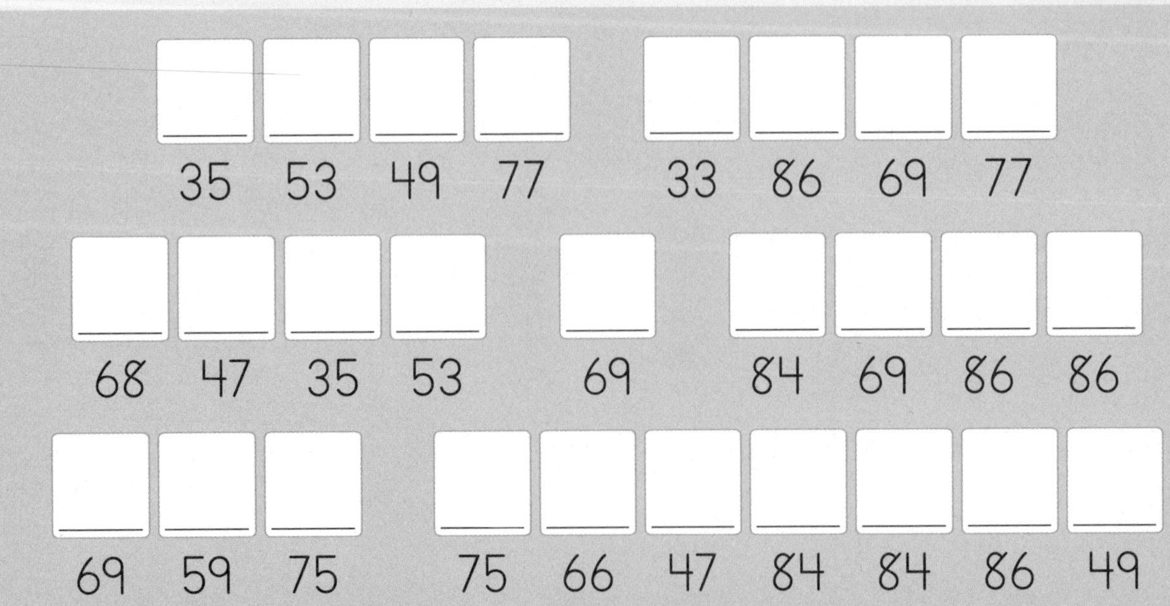

Ongoing Practice

1. Figure out the **difference** between each pair of cube trains. Then complete the equation.

a.

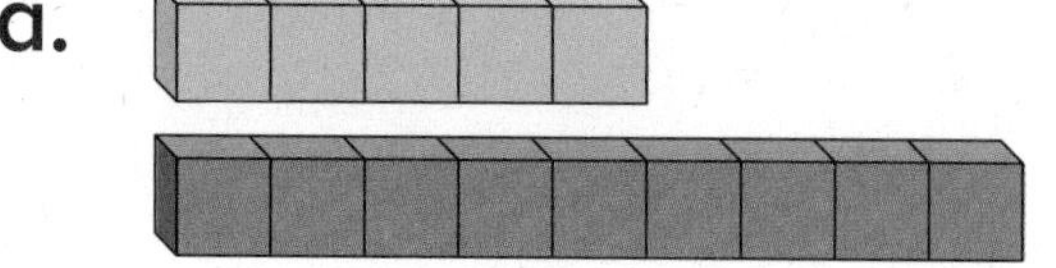

The difference is ___

so 9 – 5 = ___

b.

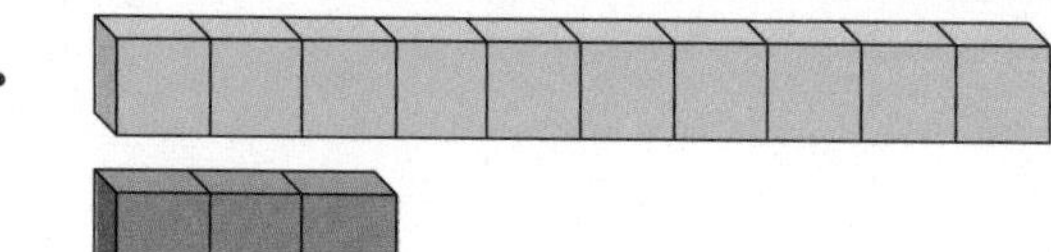

The difference is ___

so 10 – 3 = ___

FROM 1.10.6

2. Complete the equations. Then write **C**, **D**, or **M** in each circle to show the strategy you used to figure out the answer.

Strategies

Ⓒ count-on or -back

Ⓓ doubles

Ⓜ make-ten

FROM 1.11.3

◯ 9 - 2 = ___	◯ 9 + 4 = ___	
◯ 14 - 8 = ___	◯ 6 + 5 = ___	◯ 17 - 9 = ___
◯ 7 + 8 = ___	◯ 11 - 3 = ___	◯ 8 + 2 = ___

Preparing for Module 12

Complete the equations. You can draw jumps above the number track to help you.

1	2	3	4	5	6	7	8	9	10	11	12	13	14	15

a. 5 - 2 = ___	b. 3 - 1 = ___	c. 9 - 2 = ___
d. 12 - 3 = ___	e. 8 - 3 = ___	f. 15 - 2 = ___

11.7 Algebra: Exploring growing and shrinking patterns

Step In **This is a growing pattern. Draw the next picture.**

How would you describe this pattern to another student?

This is a shrinking pattern. Draw the next picture.

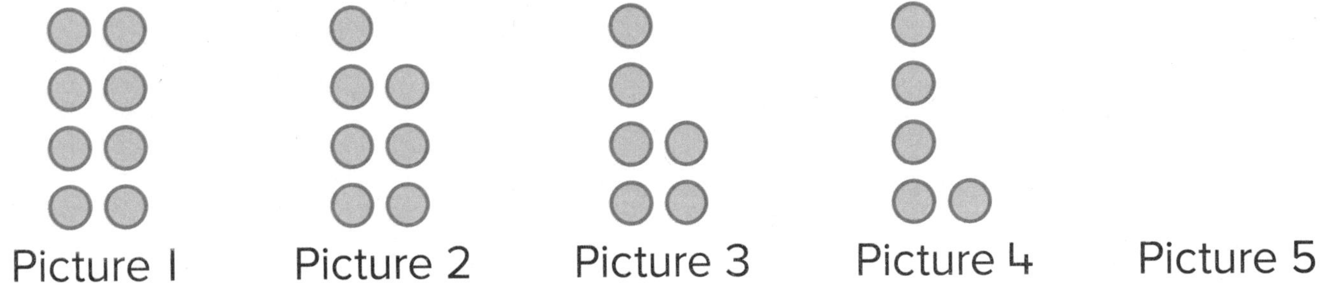

What will the next picture look like? How do you know?

Look at this number pattern. Is this a growing or shrinking pattern? How do you know?

What is a shrinking pattern that uses numbers?

Step Up 1. Draw the next picture in this pattern.

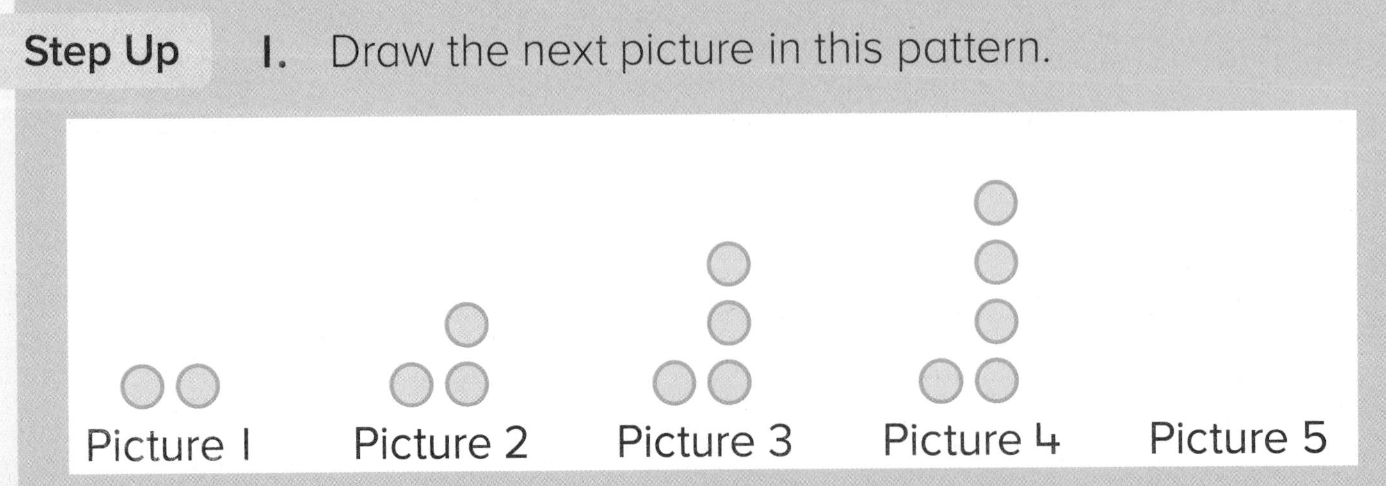

2. Draw the missing picture in each pattern.

a.

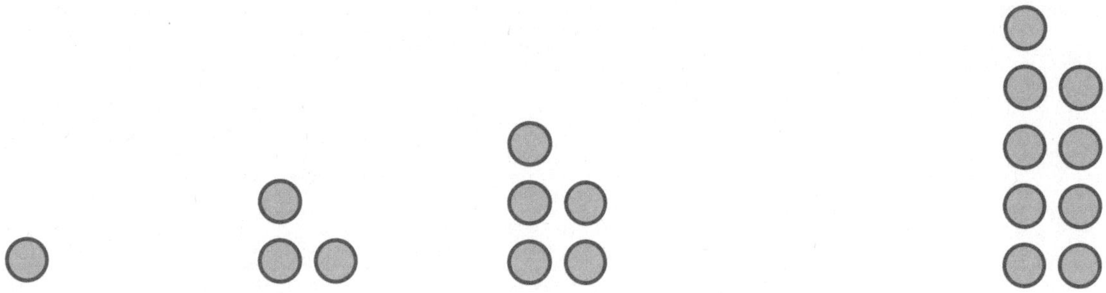

Picture 1 | Picture 2 | Picture 3 | Picture 4 | Picture 5

b.

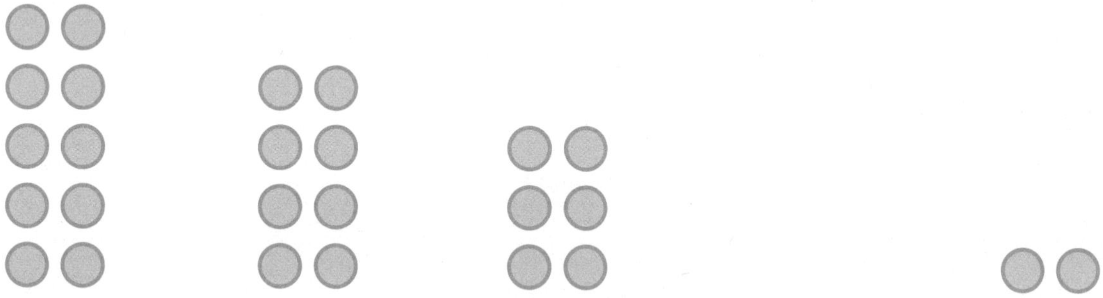

Picture 1 | Picture 2 | Picture 3 | Picture 4 | Picture 5

3. Write the missing numbers in each pattern.

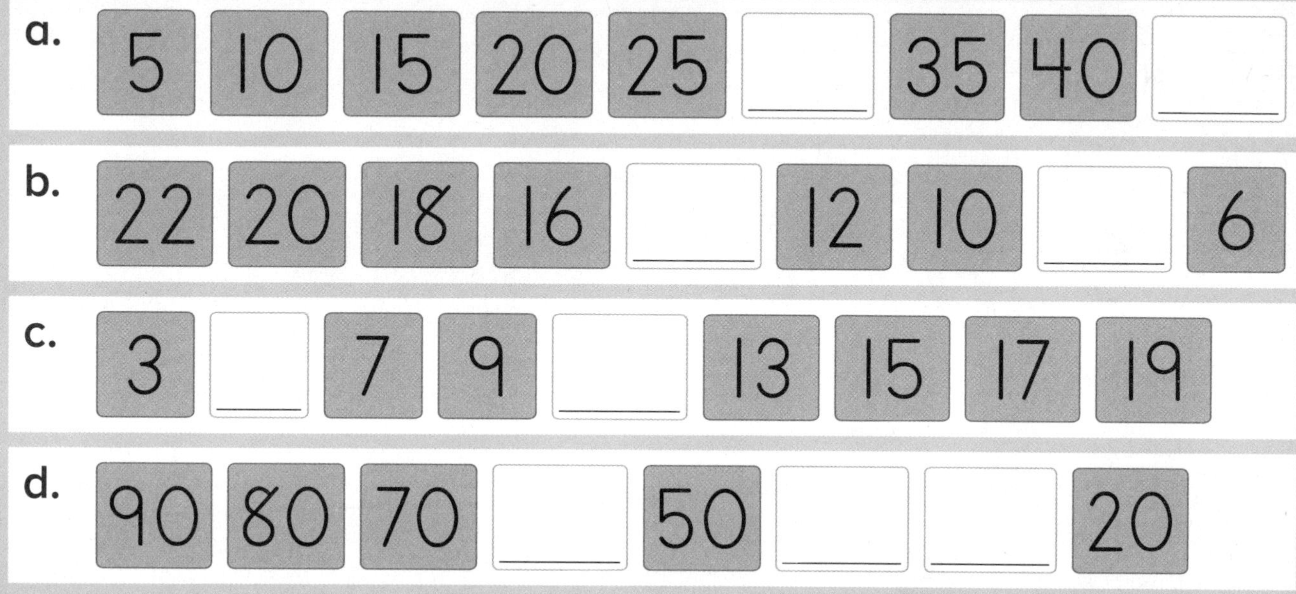

Step Ahead Write numbers to show a different **growing** number pattern.

___ ___ ___ ___ ___ ___ ___ ___

11.8 Money: Relating dimes and pennies

Step In How many dimes could you trade for these pennies?

I can trade 10 pennies for 1 dime.

How many pennies could you trade for 3 dimes? How do you know?

How many dimes could you trade for 50 pennies? How do you know?

Step Up 1. Circle together the pennies you could trade for one dime. Then write the number of pennies left over.

a.

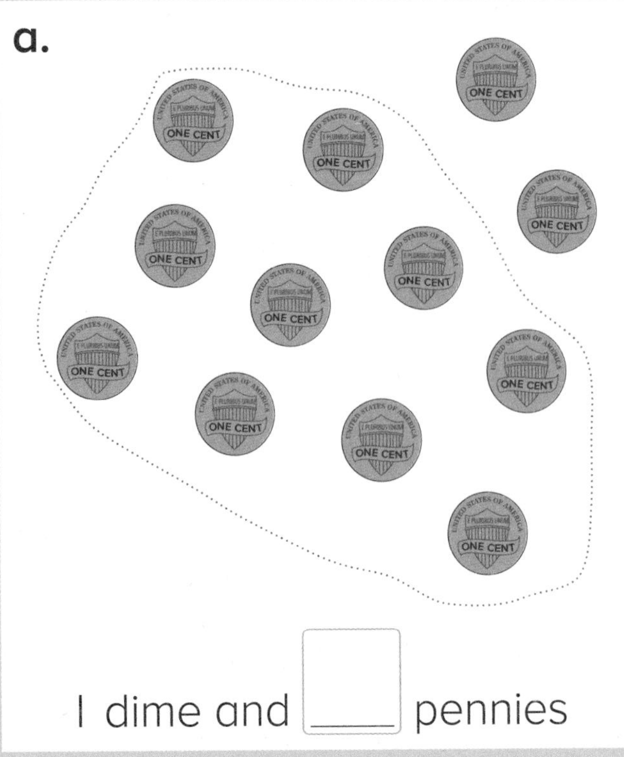

1 dime and ___ pennies

b.

1 dime and ___ pennies

2. Circle together the pennies you could trade for dimes. Then write the total number of dimes and pennies after the trade.

a.

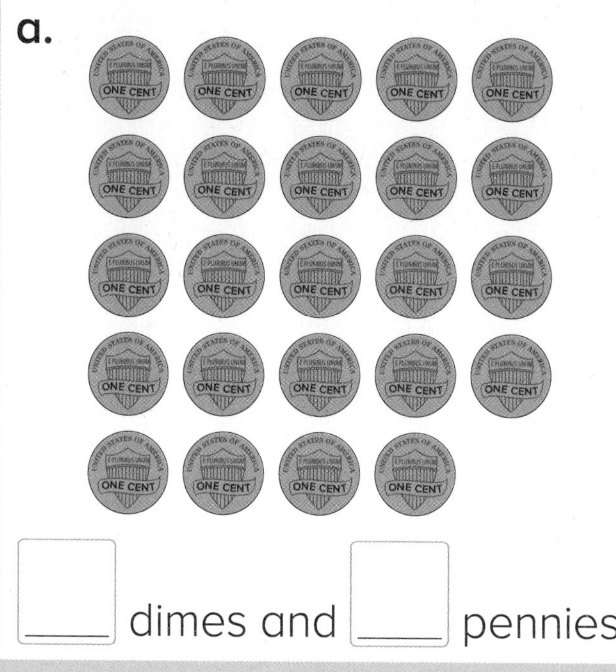

____ dimes and ____ pennies

b.

____ dimes and ____ pennies

3. Write the number of pennies you could trade for these.

a. 9 dimes make the same amount as ____ pennies.

b. 7 dimes make the same amount as ____ pennies.

c. ____ pennies makes the same amount as 6 dimes and 7 pennies.

Step Ahead Draw more coins to pay the **exact** amount for the toy.

11.8 Maintaining concepts and skills

Think and Solve  What is my lucky number?

- It is **greater** than 20.
- It is **less** than 30.
- It is a number you say when you start at 5 and **count by fives**.

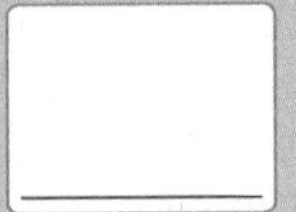

Words at Work

Choose and write a word from the list to complete each sentence below. Some words are used more than once. Some words are not used.

five
count
ten
growing
steps
two
shrinking
repeating

a. If you start at 2 and ____________ in steps of ____________ to ten, you will say 2, 4, 6, 8, 10.

b. If you start at 10 and count in ____________ of ____________ to fifty, you will say 10, 20, 30, 40, 50.

c. You will say the number 35, if you start at 5 and ____________ in steps of five.

d. The numbers 1, 2, 3, 4, 5, 6, 7 show a pattern that is ____________ by one.

e. The numbers 51, 41, 31, 21, 11 show a pattern that is ____________ by ten.

Ongoing Practice

1. Figure out how much **more** money is needed to pay the price. Draw jumps on the number track to show your thinking.

a.
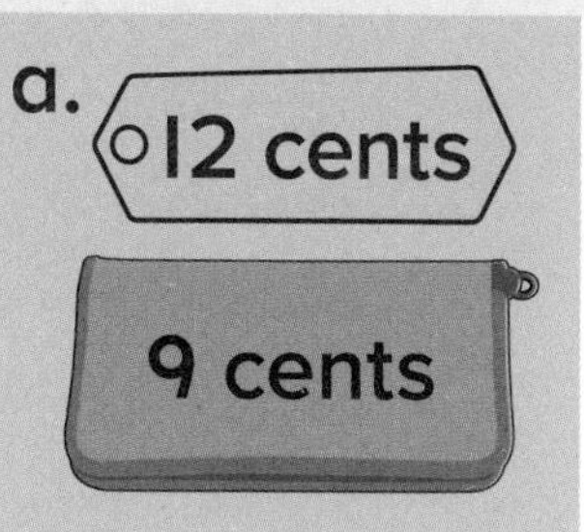

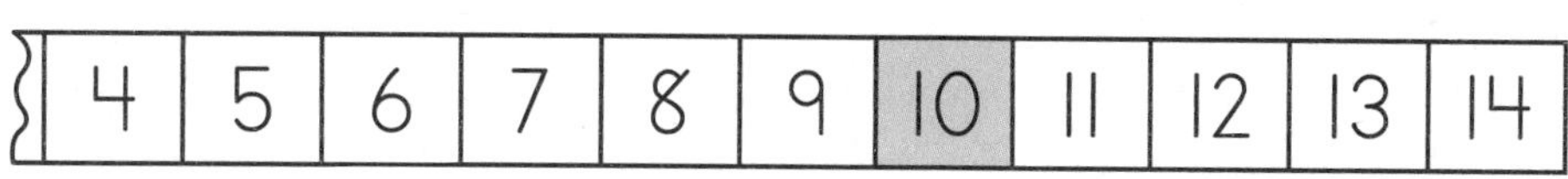

Amount needed is ____ cents

b.
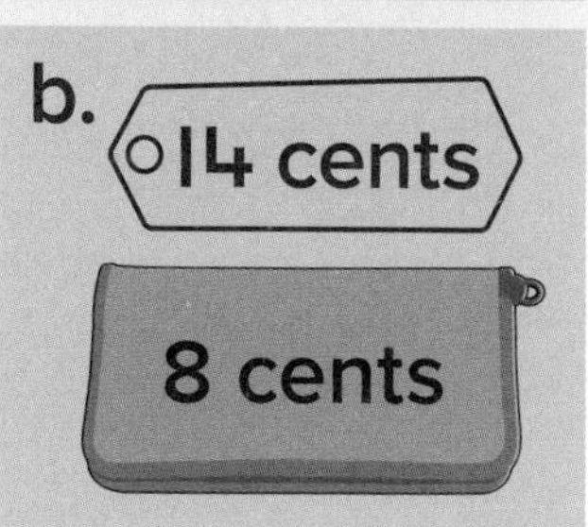

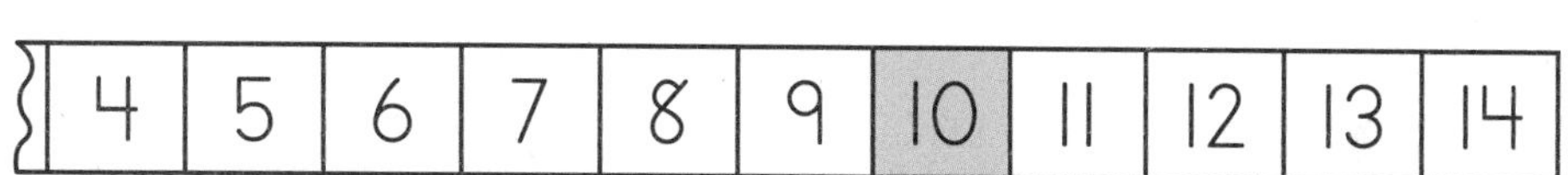

Amount needed is ____ cents

FROM 1.10.8

2. Write the missing numbers in each pattern.

a. 15 20 25 30 35 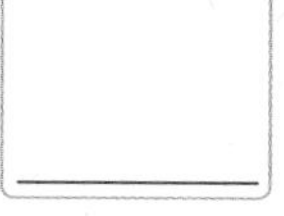 45 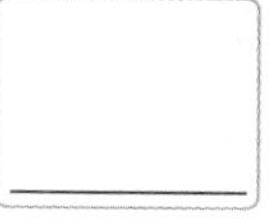

b. 90 80 70 ____ ____ 40 ____ 20

c. 44 46 48 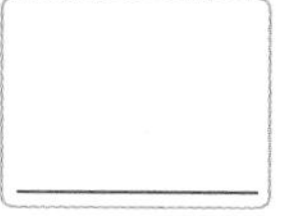 ____ 54 56 58

FROM 1.11.7

Preparing for Module 12

Complete each equation.
Cross out blocks to show your thinking.

a.
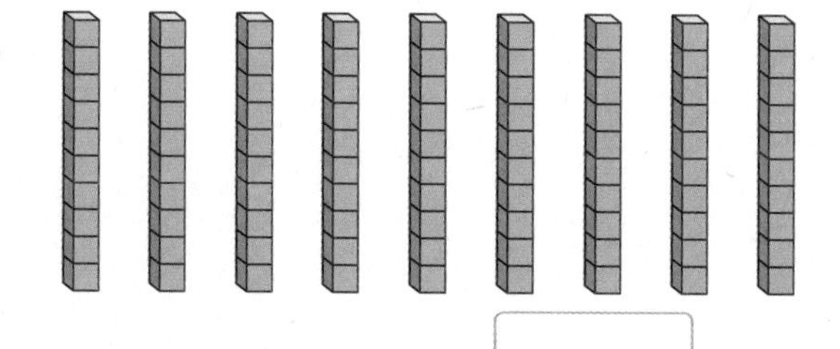

$90 - 30 =$ ____

b.
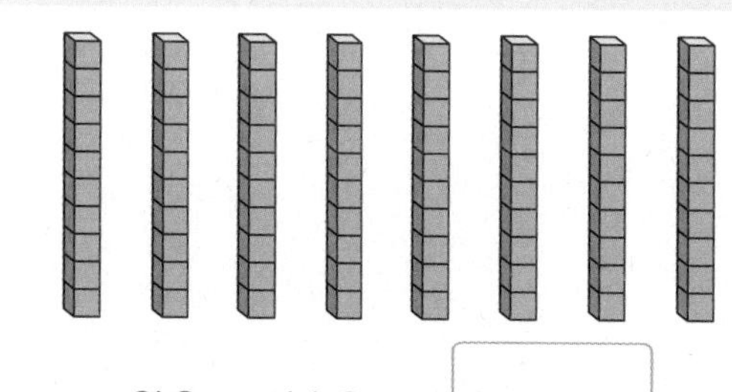

$80 - 40 =$ ____

Money: Relating all coins

Step In

Look at these coins.

What is the name of the small coin?
What is the name of the large coin?

How many pennies could you trade for one quarter?
How do you know?

How many nickels could you trade for one quarter?
How do you know?

One quarter is the same value as 25 cents, so that is 25 pennies.

How can you figure out the number of nickels you could trade for 2 quarters?

Step Up

I. Circle together the nickels you could trade for I quarter. Then write the number of nickels left over.

a.

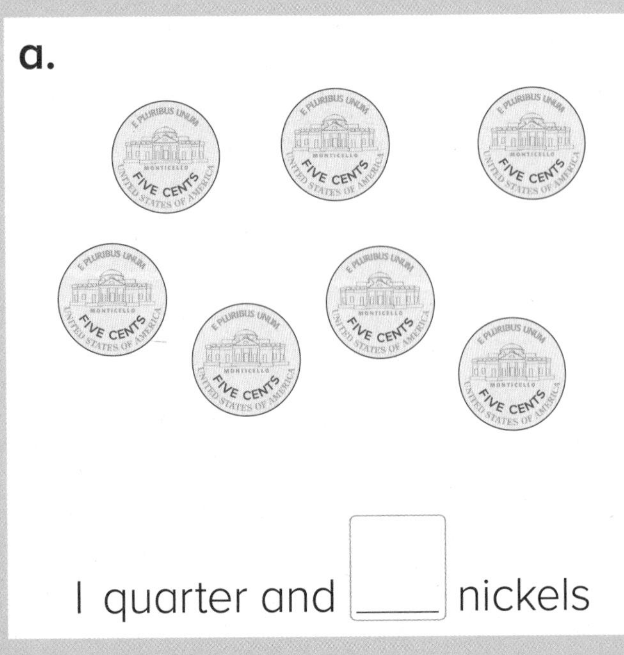

I quarter and ____ nickels

b.

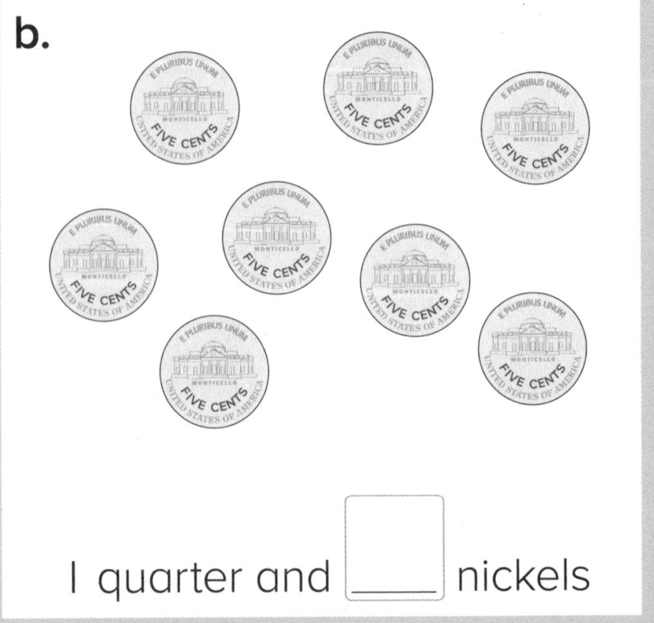

I quarter and ____ nickels

2. Circle together the coins you could trade for quarters. Then write the total number of coins after the trade.

a.

____ quarters and ____ nickels

b.

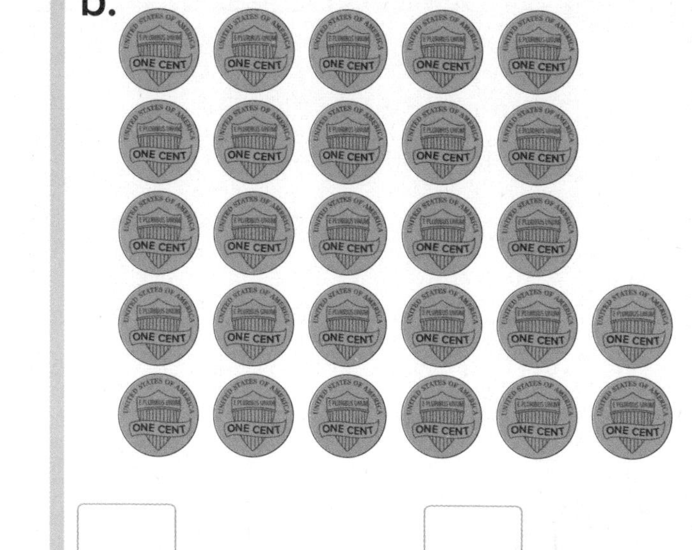

____ quarter and ____ pennies

3. Write the missing numbers.

a. 6 nickels make the same amount as ____ pennies.

b. ____ nickels make the same amount as 2 quarters.

c. 8 nickels make the same amount as ____ dimes.

Step Ahead Look at the collection of dimes. Then draw the nickels you could trade for the same amount.

dimes	nickels

11.10 Money: Determining the value of a collection of coins

Step In **Look at these pennies.**

How many cents are there?
How do you know?

I counted by twos.
That is 10 cents.

How could you count these nickels to figure out the total value?

I counted by fives.
That is 60 cents.

How could you count these dimes to figure out the total value?

I counted by tens.
That is 80 cents.

Step Up **1.** Count by twos. Write the total amount.

_____ cents

2. Count by fives. Write the total amount.

_____ cents

3. Use skip counting to figure out the total amount.

a.

ONE DIME ONE DIME ONE DIME ONE DIME ONE DIME ONE DIME

FIVE CENTS FIVE CENTS

ONE CENT ONE CENT ONE CENT ONE CENT

______ cents

b.

ONE DIME ONE DIME

FIVE CENTS FIVE CENTS FIVE CENTS FIVE CENTS FIVE CENTS FIVE CENTS FIVE CENTS FIVE CENTS FIVE CENTS

ONE CENT ONE CENT

______ cents

c.

ONE DIME ONE DIME ONE DIME ONE DIME

FIVE CENTS FIVE CENTS FIVE CENTS FIVE CENTS FIVE CENTS

ONE CENT ONE CENT ONE CENT ONE CENT ONE CENT ONE CENT ONE CENT ONE CENT

______ cents

Step Ahead Color coins to show 50 cents in two different ways.

Maintaining concepts and skills

Computation Practice

What is as big as an elephant but weighs nothing?

- ★ Complete these equations.
- ★ Write each letter in the box above its matching answer at the bottom of the page.

22 + 20 = ____	n	29 + 1 = ____	h	6 − 2 = ____	s
10 + 16 = ____	o	10 + 33 = ____	e	5 − 3 = ____	a
16 + 20 = ____	t	8 − 3 = ____	h	8 − 1 = ____	d
23 + 10 = ____	p	9 − 1 = ____	a	20 + 19 = ____	w
10 + 39 = ____	n	20 + 28 = ____	e	9 − 3 = ____	s
12 + 10 = ____	l	7 − 4 = ____	a		

8 42   48 22 43 33 30 3 49 36 ' 4

6 5 2 7 26 39

Ongoing Practice

1. Color the ⬭ beside **each** statement that describes this 3D object.

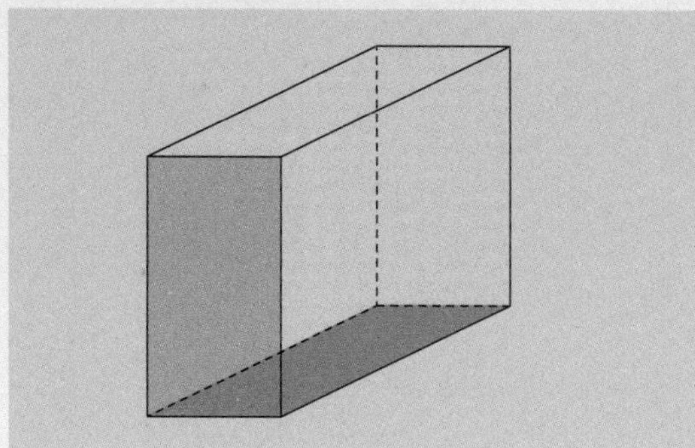

⬭ It can roll.

⬭ It can stack.

⬭ It has all flat surfaces.

⬭ It has two curved surfaces.

FROM 1.10.10

2. Circle together the coins you could trade for quarters. Then write the total number of coins after the trade.

FROM 1.11.9

____ quarters and ____ nickels

Preparing for Module 12

Circle the glass that is holding **less** water.

a.

b.

Money: Paying with coins

Step In **What coins could you use to pay the exact price for this item?**

What is the fewest number of coins you could use? How do you know?

Could you use only dimes? Could you use only nickels?

What are some other ways you could pay for the item?

The symbol for cent is ¢.

Step Up 1. Color the coins you could use to pay the **exact** price for each item.

a.

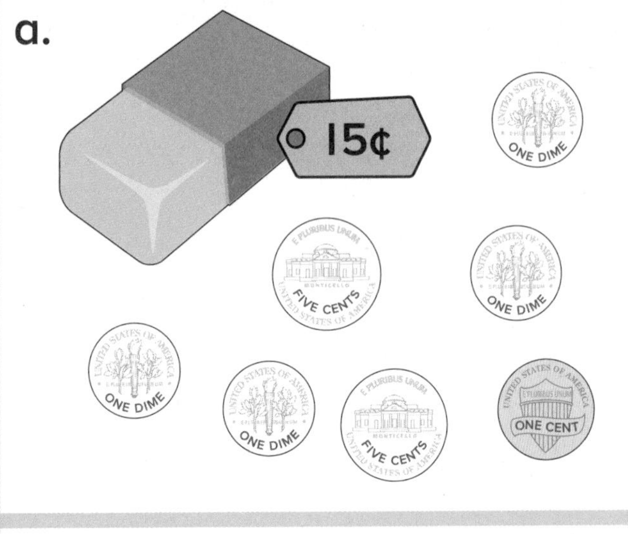

b.

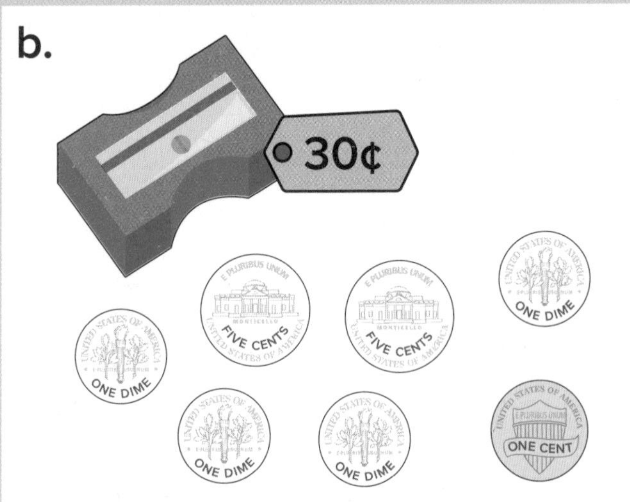

c.

d.

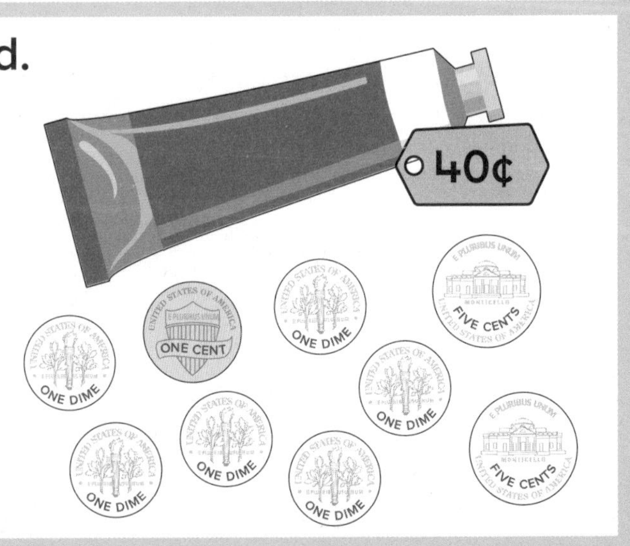

2. Cut out and paste the coins you could use to pay the **exact** amount for each item.

a.

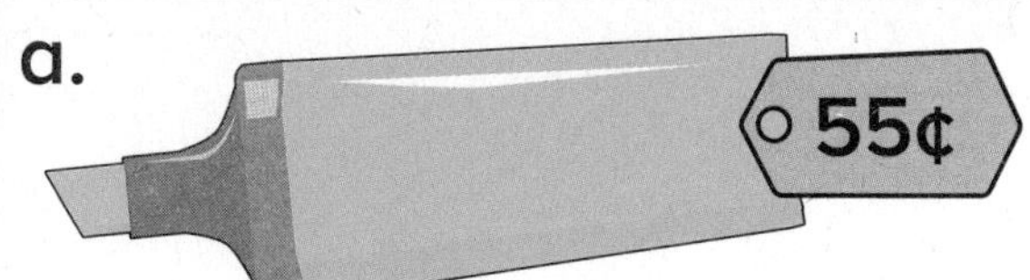

b.

c.

d.

Step Ahead Chayton used **five** coins to pay the exact price of this card. Cut out and paste the coins he used.

11.12 Money: Relating dollars, dimes, and pennies

Step In How many dimes could you trade for these pennies?

What is the name of this **bill**?
What is the value of this **bill**?

How many pennies could you trade for this bill? How do you know?

How many dimes could you trade for this bill? How do you know?

100 pennies can be traded for 1 dollar, so 10 dimes can be traded for 1 dollar.

The symbol for dollar is $.

Step Up 1. Circle together the dimes you could trade for 1 dollar. Then write the total amount.

a.

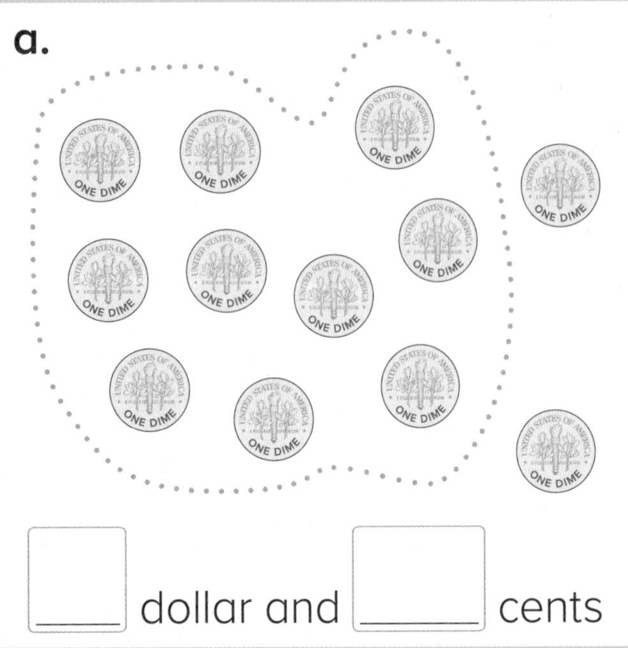

☐ dollar and ☐ cents

b.

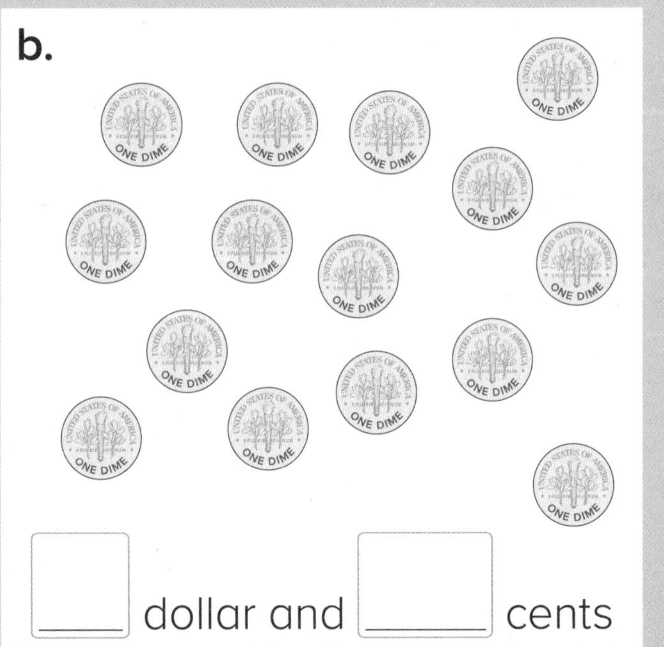

☐ dollar and ☐ cents

2. Circle together the coins you could trade for one dollar. Then write the total amount.

a.

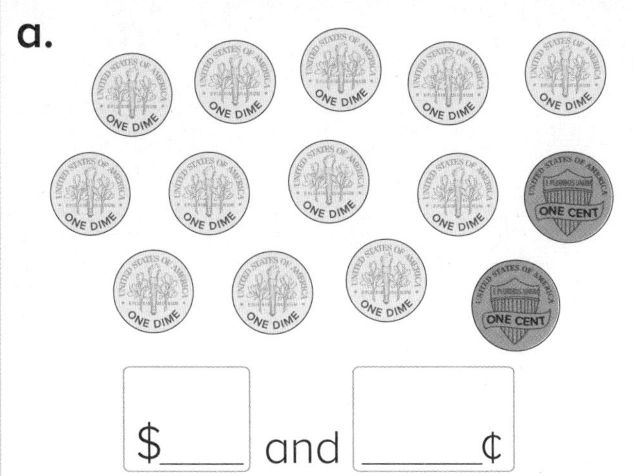

$____ and ______¢

b.

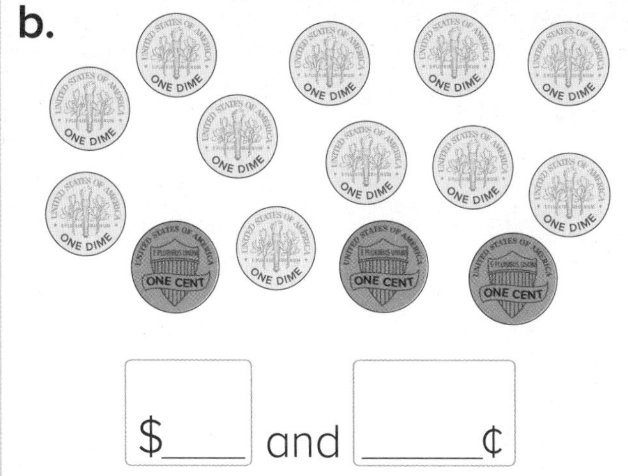

$____ and ______¢

c.

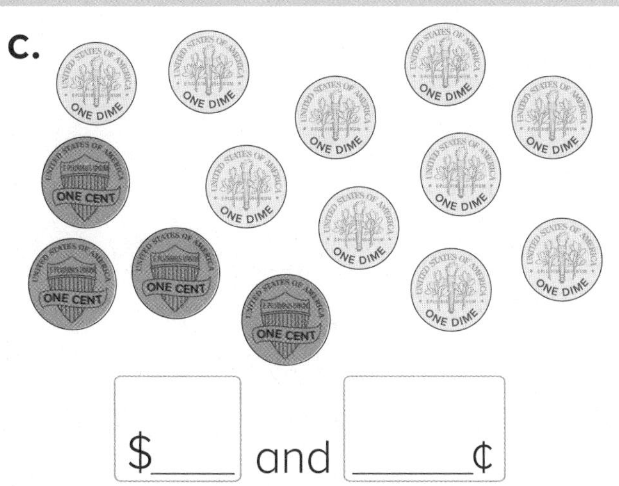

$____ and ______¢

d.

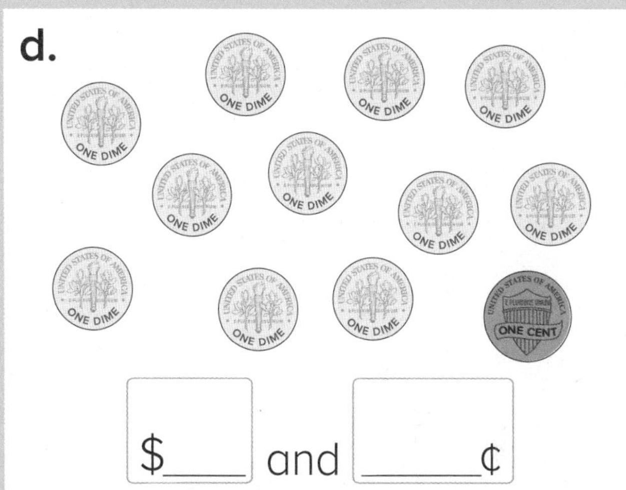

$____ and ______¢

3. Write these amounts as dollars and cents.

a. 126 cents is the same value as ____ dollar and ______ cents.

b. 105 cents is the same value as ____ dollar and ______ cents.

Step Ahead Color the purse that shows **exactly** one dollar.

9 pennies 1 dime	90 pennies 10 dimes	90 pennies 1 dime

Maintaining concepts and skills

Think and Solve

Add the parts.

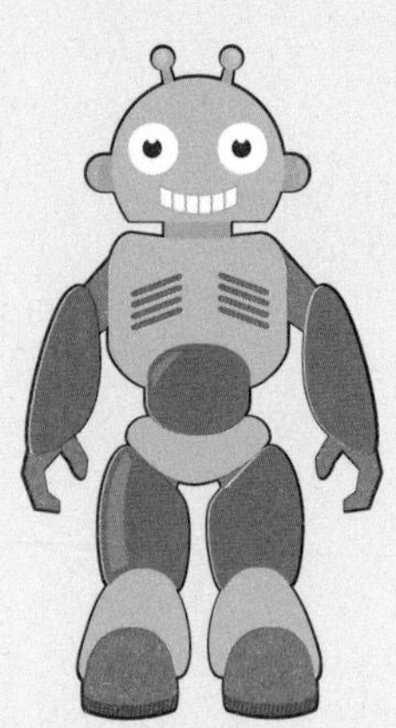

How much does this robot cost? $_____

Words at Work

Write the answer for each clue in the grid.
Use words from the list.

Clues Across

1. There are __ quarters in one dollar.
3. Two nickels have the same __ as one dime.
4. One dollar can be traded for 10 __.

Clues Down

1. __ nickels make one quarter.
2. 100 __ is the same value as one dollar.

five
cents
value
dollar
one
dimes
four
nickels

1				
				2
3				
4				

Ongoing Practice **1. a.** What 2D shapes were used to make this 3D object?

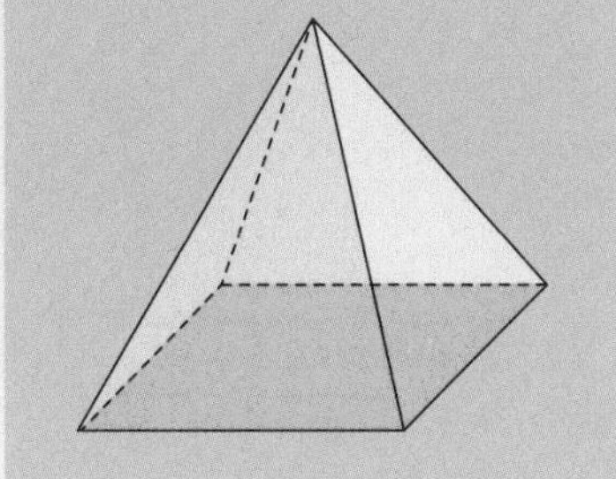

b. How many surfaces does it have? ___

FROM 1.10.10

2. Count by tens. Write the total amount.

a.

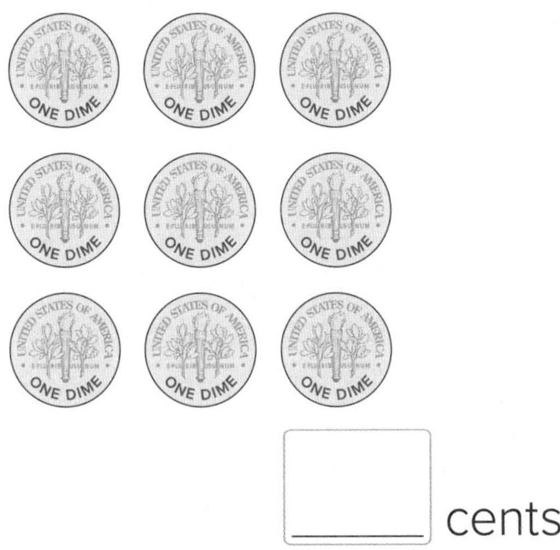

___ cents

b.

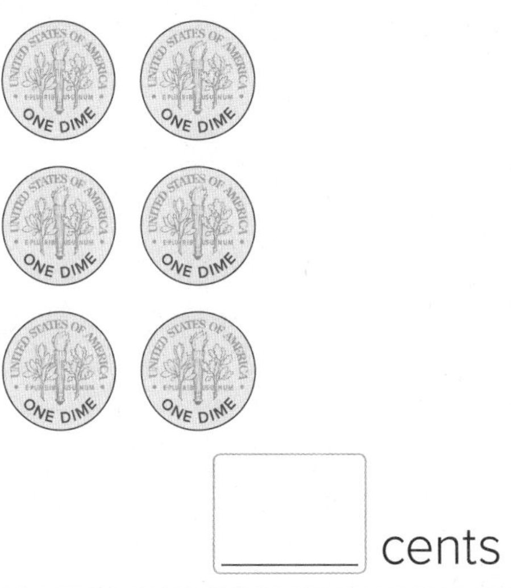

___ cents

FROM 1.11.10

Preparing for Module 12 Circle the toy that is **heavier**.

a.

b.

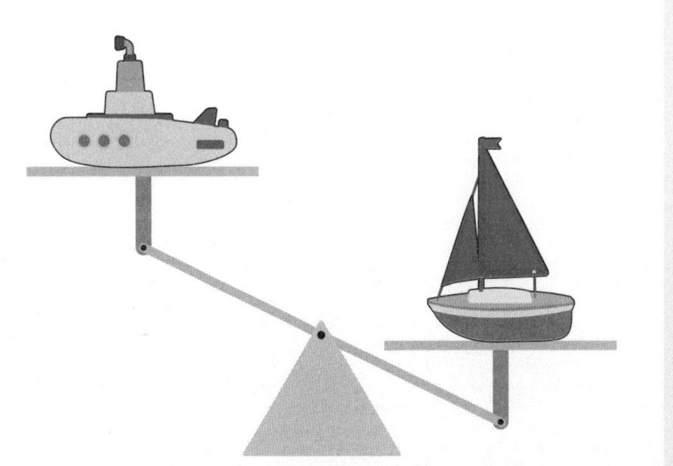

Working Space

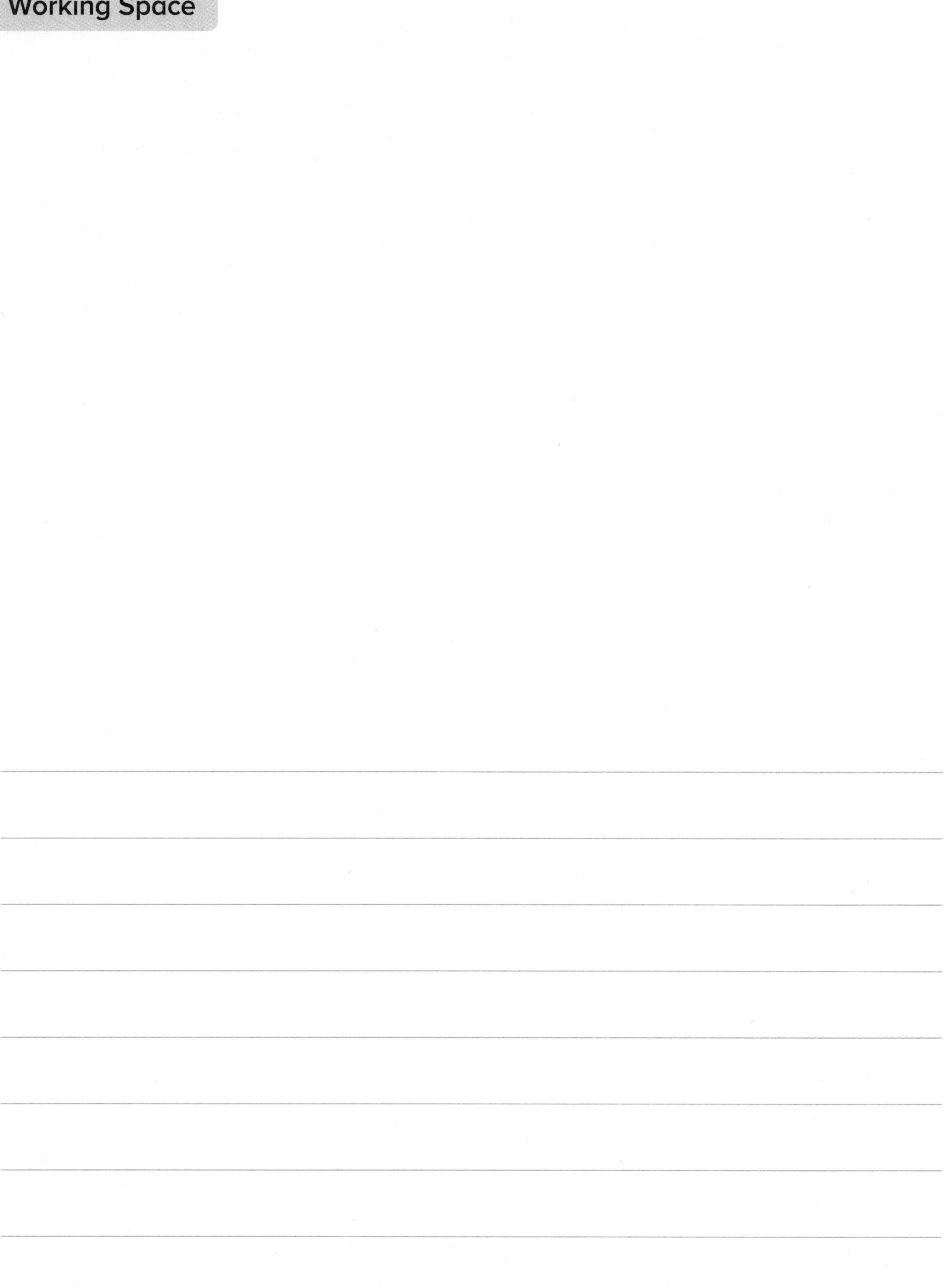

Number: Working with place value (hundred chart)

Step In **Look at the hundred chart below.**

Run your finger along all the numbers that have 6 in the ones place.

Run your finger along the numbers that have 6 in the tens place.

What do you notice?

1	2	3	4	5	6	7	8	9	10
11	12	13	14	15	16	17	18	19	20
21	22	23	24	25	26	27	28	29	30
31	32	33	34	35	36	37	38	39	40
41	42	43	44	45	46	47	48	49	50
51	52	53	54	55	56	57	58	59	60
61	62	63	64	65	66	67	68	69	70
71	72	73	74	75	76	77	78	79	80
81	82	83	84	85	86	87	88	89	90
91	92	93	94	95	96	97	98	99	100

Color any two numbers on the hundred chart.

What digits are written in the tens place and the ones place?

Which of your numbers is greater?

Are your numbers greater than 50? How do you know?

Step Up Use the hundred chart on page 434 to help you complete these.

1. Read the clue then write the matching number.

a. I have 2 in the tens place and 5 in the ones place.	b. I have four ones and three tens.	c. I have 9 in the ones place and 2 in the tens place.
____	____	____

2. a. Write all the numbers that have an 8 in the **tens** place.

____ ____ ____ ____ ____ ____ ____ ____ ____ ____

b. What do you notice about these numbers on the chart?

____

3. a. Write all the numbers that have an 8 in the **ones** place.

____ ____ ____ ____ ____ ____ ____ ____ ____ ____

b. What do you notice about these numbers on the chart?

____

Step Ahead

a. Look at the hundred chart on page 434. Write all the **two-digit** numerals that have the same digit in the tens and ones places.

____ ____ ____ ____ ____ ____ ____ ____ ____

b. What pattern do you see?

____

12.2 Number: Solving puzzles (hundred chart)

Step In **Color three numbers greater than 10 on this hundred chart.**

Each number should be in a different row.

1	2	3	4	5	6	7	8	9	10
11	12	13	14	15	16	17	18	19	20
21	22	23	24	25	26	27	28	29	30
31	32	33	34	35	36	37	38	39	40
41	42	43	44	45	46	47	48	49	50
51	52	53	54	55	56	57	58	59	60
61	62	63	64	65	66	67	68	69	70
71	72	73	74	75	76	77	78	79	80
81	82	83	84	85	86	87	88	89	90
91	92	93	94	95	96	97	98	99	100

What things do you know about your numbers?

Which number has the greatest number of ones?

Which number has the greatest number of tens?

Which number is the greatest?

Which number is the least?

How many numbers are greater than 40?

Step Up Use the hundred chart on page 436 to solve these number puzzles.

1. Read the clues. Write the matching two-digit number.

a. I have 7 in my tens place and 3 in my ones place. ____

b. I am greater than 44 but less than 46. ____

c. I am between 33 and 39. You say me when you start at 5 and count by fives. ____

d. I am in the same row as 56. You say me when you start at 10 and count by tens. ____

2. Write all the two-digit numbers that match these clues.

a. I am less than 43 and I have 4 tens.
____ ____ ____

b. I am greater than 69 and have 8 in the ones place.
____ ____ ____

c. I am greater than 84. You say me when you start at 50 and count by fives.
____ ____ ____

d. I have the same number of tens and ones. I am between 40 and 70.
____ ____ ____

Step Ahead Choose and write one number greater than 10. Write clues about your number. ____

____

____

____

Computation Practice

What do you call a baby whale?

- ★ Complete the equations.
- ★ Write each letter in the box above its matching total at the bottom of the page.

7 + 5 = ___	a	8 + 9 = ___	t
3 + 4 = ___	i	5 + 3 = ___	i
9 + 11 = ___	u	6 + 5 = ___	l
8 + 7 = ___	t	2 + 4 = ___	s
6 + 8 = ___	l	7 + 6 = ___	r
6 + 4 = ___	e	3 + 1 = ___	t
7 + 9 = ___	q		

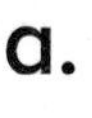

Ongoing Practice

1. Figure out the number of dots that are covered. Then complete the facts.

a. 12 − 7 = ____

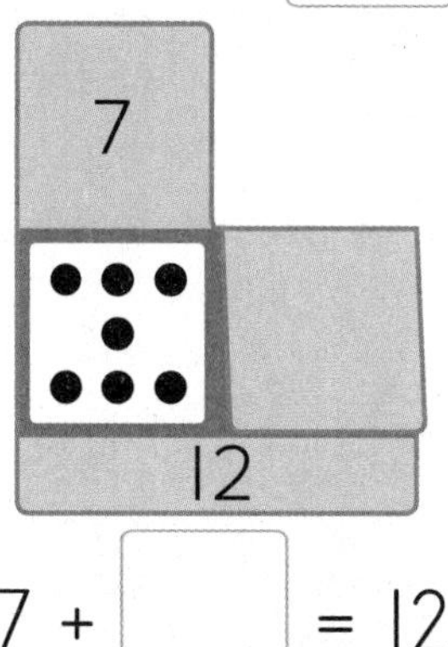

7 + ____ = 12

b. 15 − 9 = ____

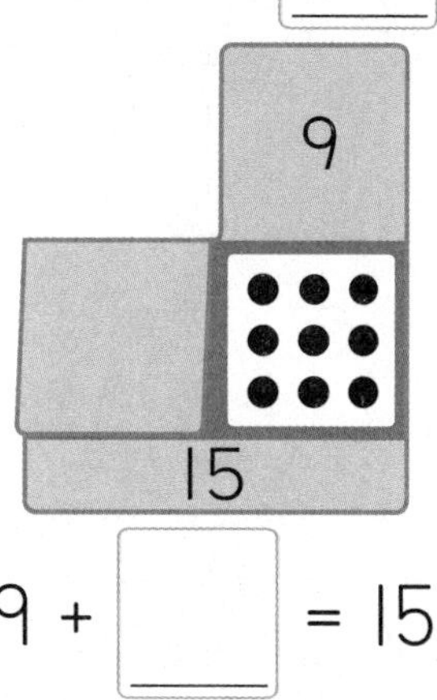

9 + ____ = 15

c. 13 − 8 = ____

8 + ____ = 13

FROM 1.11.1

2. Think about the numbers on a hundred chart. Read each clue then write the matching numeral.

a. I have 3 ones and 5 tens.

b. I have 7 in the tens place and 2 in the ones place.

c. I have 4 tens and zero ones.

FROM 1.12.1

Preparing for Next Year

Compare the numbers in the charts. Circle the words that are true.

a.

Tens	Ones
8	1

is greater than

is less than

Tens	Ones
1	8

b.

Tens	Ones
7	6

is greater than

is less than

Tens	Ones
8	3

12.3 Number: Exploring the counting sequence to 120

Step In **Look at this number chart.**

61	62	63	64	65	66	67	68	69	70

Start at 70. Count on in steps of 10. What numbers do you say?
Where will you write these numbers on the chart? How do you know?
Write the numbers on the chart.

Think about the numbers that come just before the numbers you wrote.
What digit will be in the ones place of each number? How do you know?
Write these numbers on the chart.

Start at 70. Count on in steps of 5.
Write these numbers on the chart.
What digit will be in the ones place of each number **just after**?
How do you know? Write these numbers on the chart.

Start at 70. Count on in steps of 2.
Write these numbers on the chart.
What digit will be in the ones place of each number **just before**?
How do you know?

Step Up 1. Complete the chart on page 440.

2. Write the number that comes **just before** each of these.

a. ____ 120 b. ____ 105 c. ____ 119

3. Write the number that comes **just after** each of these.

a. 117 ____ b. 110 ____ c. 108 ____

4. Write the numbers missing from these number chart pieces.

a.

111			

b.

	107		

c.

112				116			119	

Step Ahead a. Circle in blue the numbers you say when you start at 100 and count on in steps of 5.

b. Circle in red the numbers you say when you start at 100 and count on in steps of 2.

102	110	105	120	115	118

c. Write what you notice about the numbers that are circled in both red and blue. What are two other numbers you would circle with both colors?

____

____

____

Subtraction: Extending the count-back strategy

Step In **Look at this part of a number track.**

50	51	52	53	54	55	56	57	58	59	60	61

Imagine you were standing on 58 and made one jump back to 56.
How can you show your jump on the number track?

You could draw an arrow like this.

50	51	52	53	54	55	56	57	58	59	60	61

What equation could you write to show what you did?

☐ – ☐ = ☐

What other jumps could you make on this part of the number track?
What equations could you write to show what you did?

Step Up **1.** Complete the equations.

a. 29 - 1 = ☐

b. 34 - 1 = ☐

c. 36 - 1 = ☐

2. Complete the equations. Draw jumps on the number track to help you.

51	52	53	54	55	56	57	58	59	60	61

a. 54 - 2 = ☐

b. 57 - 2 = ☐

c. 61 - 3 = ☐

74	75	76	77	78	79	80	81	82	83	84

d. 75 - 1 = ☐

e. 78 - 2 = ☐

f. 82 - 3 = ☐

88	89	90	91	92	93	94	95	96	97	98

g. 91 - 3 = ☐

h. 95 - 3 = ☐

i. 98 - 2 = ☐

3. Write the missing numbers.

a. ☐ - 2 = 65

b. ☐ - 1 = 47

c. ☐ - 3 = 71

Step Ahead Use a number track above to help you solve this problem.

Selena has 95 cents.
Jamar has 2 cents less than Selena
Ruth has 3 cents less than Jamar.
Connor has one cent more than Ruth.

How much money does Connor have?

☐ cents

Maintaining concepts and skills

Think and Solve

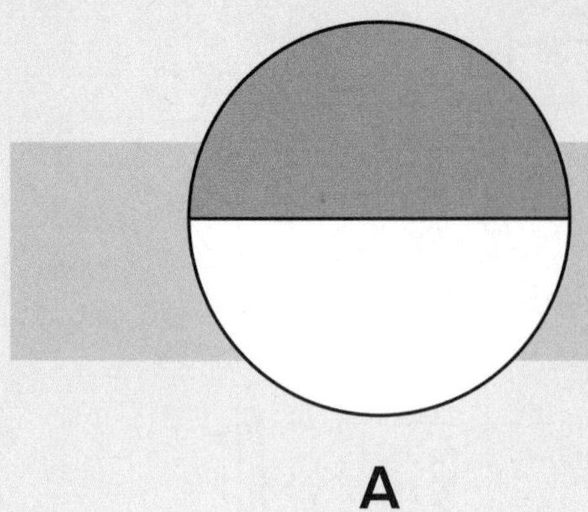

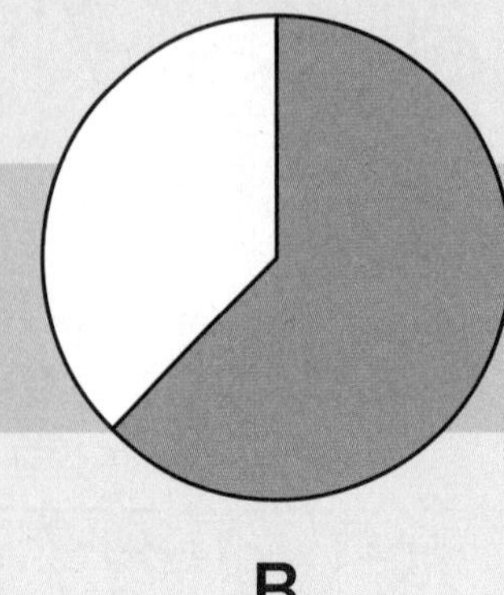

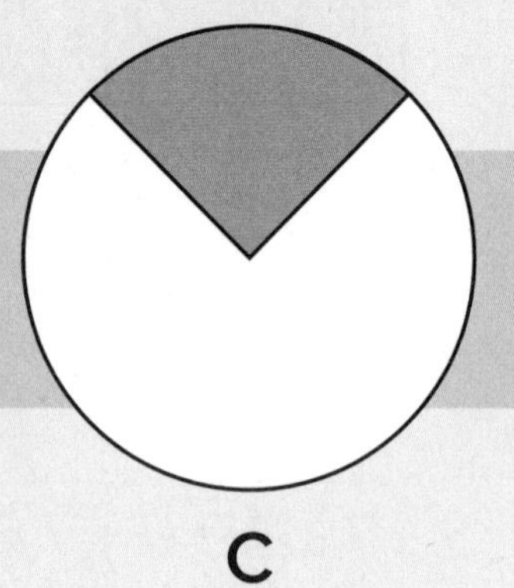

A B C

a. Which circle is one-half purple? ____

b. Which circle is **less** than one-half purple? ____

c. Which circle is **more** than one-half purple? ____

Words at Work

Write clues to match the number **85**.
You can use words from the list to help you.

count by
tens place
ones place
number
less than
greater than
starts with
ends with

Ongoing Practice

1. Figure out the number of dots that are covered. Then complete the facts.

FROM 1.11.2

a. 14 dots in total

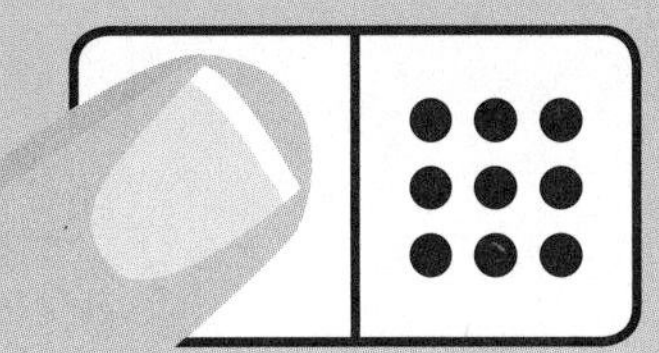

14 - 9 = ☐

9 + ☐ = 14

b. 13 dots in total

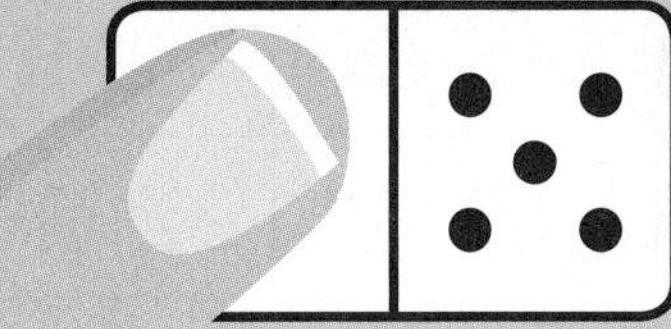

13 - 5 = ☐

5 + ☐ = 13

c. 15 dots in total

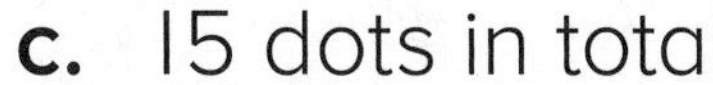

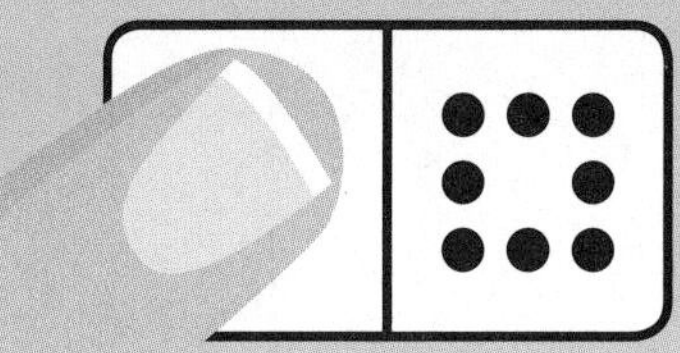

15 - 8 = ☐

8 + ☐ = 15

2. Figure out these number puzzles.

FROM 1.12.2

a. I am between 65 and 75. I have 2 ones.

b. I am less than 20 but greater than 10. I have 7 ones.

c. I have the same number of tens and ones. I am between 40 and 50.

Preparing for Next Year

Circle the number. Then write the number of ones that are not circled.

a. Circle 60 fingers.

 not circled

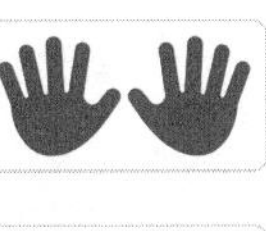

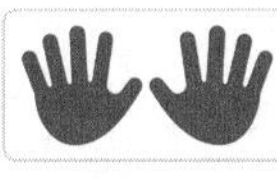
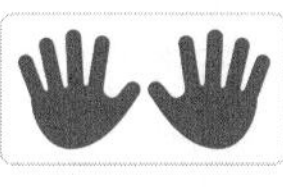

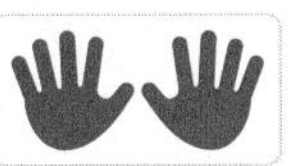
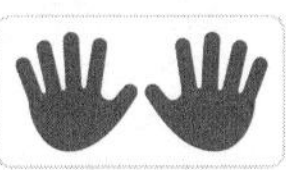
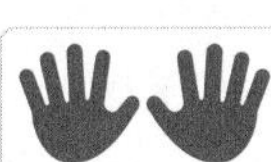
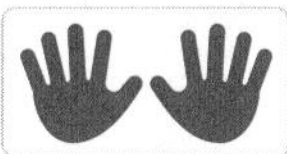
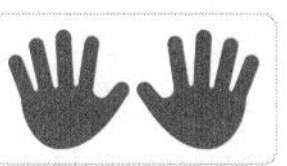

b. Circle 20 fingers.

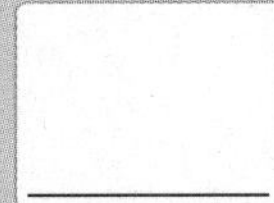 not circled

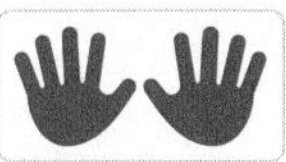
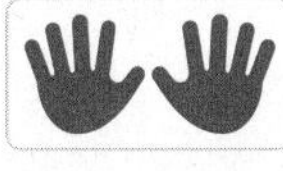
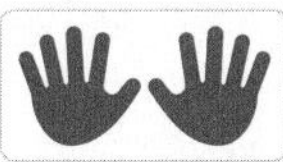
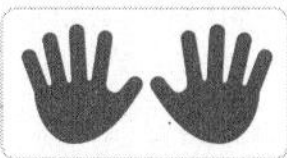

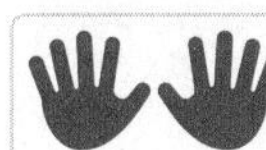
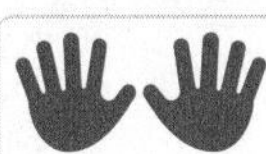
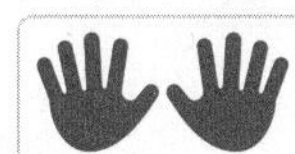
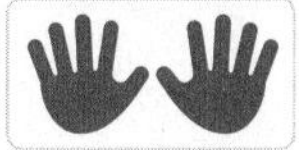

12.5 Subtraction: Exploring patterns

Step In Look at these numbers.

1	2	3	4	5	6	7	8	9	10
11	12	13	14	15	16	17	18	19	20
21	22	23	24	25	26	27	28	29	30
31	32	33	34	35	36	37	38	39	40
41	42	43	44	45	46	47	48	49	50

What number is 2 less than 45? How do you know?

What number is 1 less than 38? How do you know?

What is different about all the numbers that have 4 in the ones place?

Step Up 1. Write the missing numbers.

a.	b.	c.
5 - 1 = ____	18 - 2 = ____	4 - 3 = ____
15 - 1 = ____	28 - 2 = ____	14 - 3 = ____
25 - 1 = ____	38 - 2 = ____	24 - 3 = ____
35 - 1 = ____	48 - 2 = ____	34 - 3 = ____
45 - 1 = ____	78 - 2 = ____	64 - 3 = ____
95 - 1 = ____	88 - 2 = ____	84 - 3 = ____

2. Think about the numbers **between 1 and 50**.

a. Write all the numbers that have 6 in the ones place.

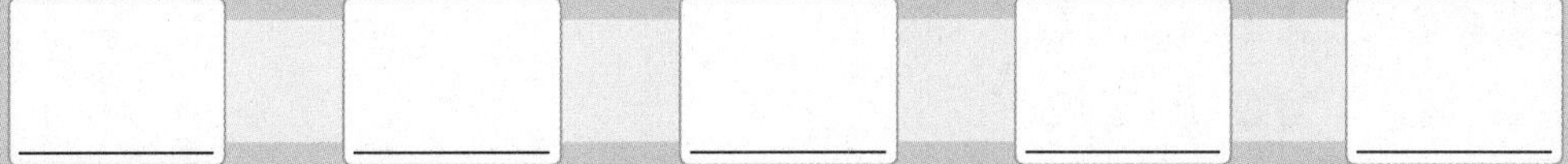

b. Write the numbers that are **2 less** than the numbers you wrote.

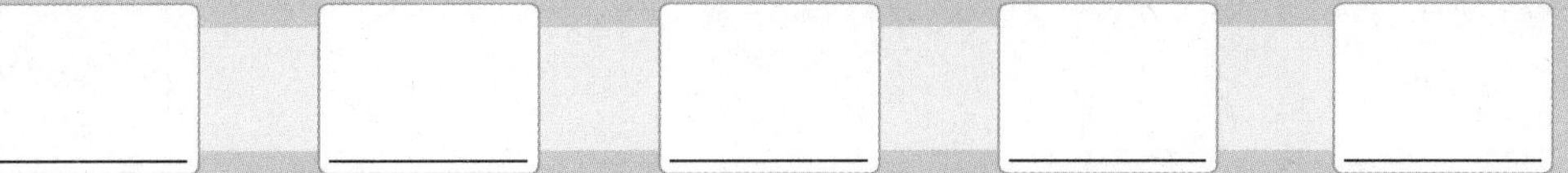

3. Think about the numbers **between 50 and 100**.

a. Write all the numbers that have 9 in the ones place.

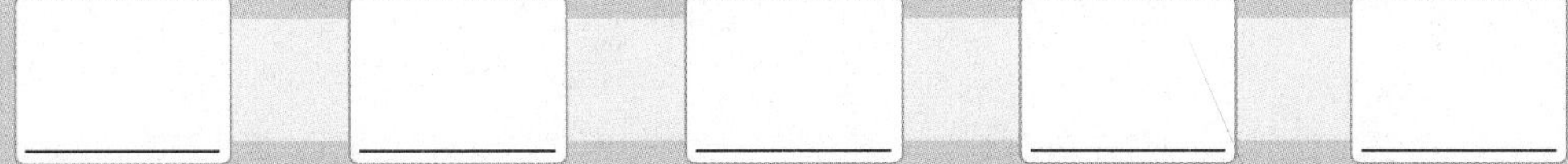

b. Write the numbers that are **2 less** than the numbers you wrote.

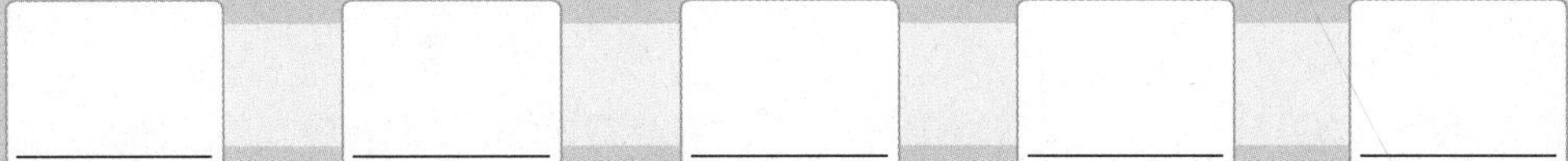

4. Write numbers **between 11 and 50** to complete these to show different equations.

a. ☐ - 3 = ☐

b. ☐ - 2 = ☐

c. ☐ - 1 = ☐

Step Ahead

Dorothy had 65 cents. She spent 3 cents. Vishaya had 66 cents. She lost 2 cents. Jacob had 67 cents. He gave away 3 cents.

Who had the least money left over? Write equations to show your thinking.

12.6 Subtraction: Multiples of ten from any two-digit number (hundred chart)

Step In **Look at this part of a hundred chart.**

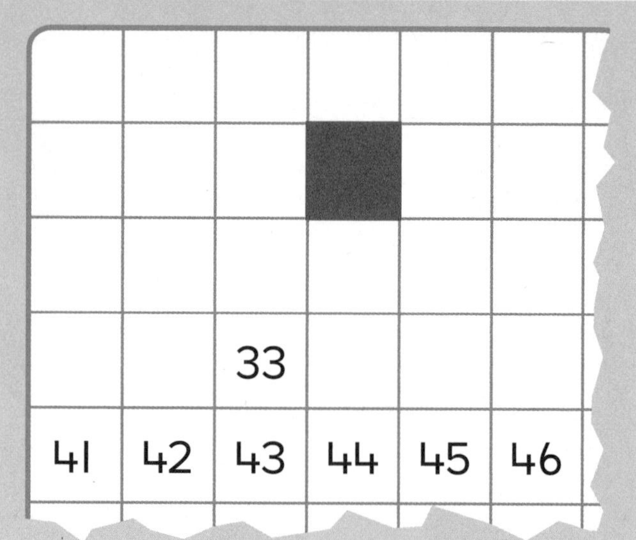

How can you figure out what number is behind the shaded tile?

I would start at 44 and count back in steps of 10 to the shaded tile.

How many steps of 10 is that?

What equation could you write to match? ____ – ____ = ____

What other way could you subtract numbers like these?

Step Up **1.** Complete the equations. You can draw arrows on this part of a hundred chart to help.

1	2	3	4	5	6	7	8	9	10
11	12	13	14	15	16	17	18	19	20
21	22	23	24	25	26	27	28	29	30
31	32	33	34	35	36	37	38	39	40
41	42	43	44	45	46	47	48	49	50
51	52	53	54	55	56	57	58	59	60

a. 34 - 10 = ____

b. 41 - 30 = ____

c. 59 - 50 = ____

2. Complete the equations. Use this chart to help.

41	42	43	44	45	46	47	48	49	50
51	52	53	54	55	56	57	58	59	60
61	62	63	64	65	66	67	68	69	70
71	72	73	74	75	76	77	78	79	80
81	82	83	84	85	86	87	88	89	90
91	92	93	94	95	96	97	98	99	100

a. 73 - 20 = ____

b. 94 - 40 = ____

c. 85 - 30 = ____

d. 94 - 10 = ____

e. 78 - 30 = ____

f. 61 - 20 = ____

3. Figure out and write each difference.

a. 52 - 50 = ____

b. 33 - 20 = ____

c. 88 - 30 = ____

d. 99 - 60 = ____

e. 67 - 30 = ____

f. 56 - 20 = ____

Step Ahead

Write **+10**, **+20**, **−10**, or **−20** to make the number trails true.

a. 25 → ____ → 45 → ____ → 35 → ____ → 55

b. 74 → ____ → 64 → ____ → 74 → ____ → 54

Maintaining concepts and skills

Computation Practice

★ Complete the equations as fast as you can.

start

9 - 2 = ___

8 - 4 = ___

10 - 8 = ___

6 - 4 = ___

9 - 6 = ___

8 - 7 = ___

5 - 3 = ___

7 - 5 = ___

6 - 0 = ___

7 - 1 = ___

9 - 5 = ___

10 - 3 = ___

8 - 6 = ___

5 - 2 = ___

7 - 4 = ___

10 - 4 = ___

7 - 2 = ___

9 - 1 = ___

4 - 3 = ___

9 - 0 = ___

finish

Ongoing Practice

1. Draw jumps of two.
Color the numbers you land on.

FROM 1.11.5

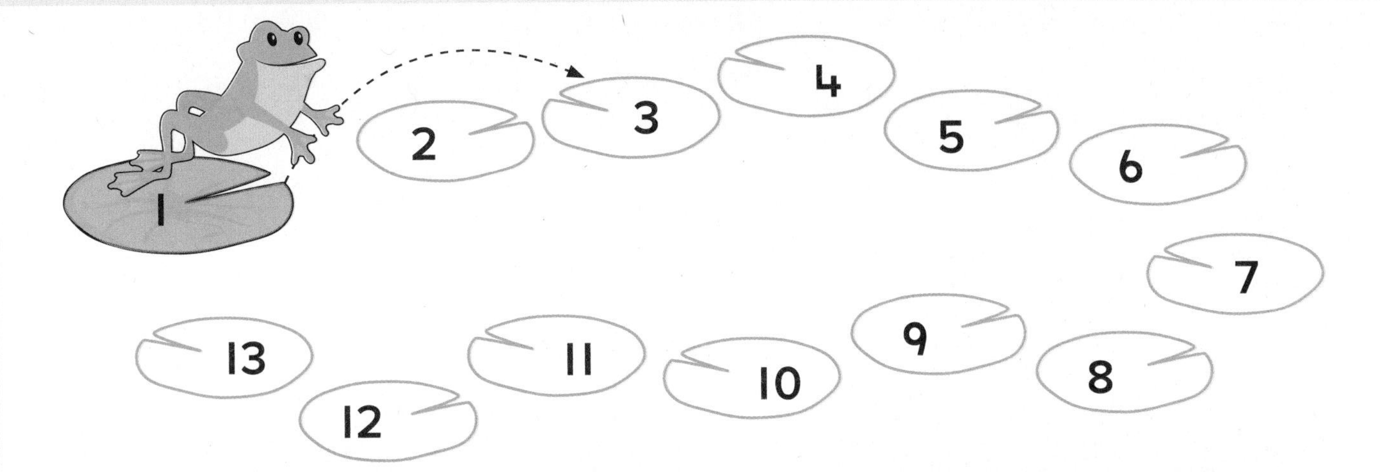

2. Write the answers. Use the number track to help you.

FROM 1.12.4

61	62	63	64	65	66	67	68	69	70	71

a. 63 - 2 = ____

b. 68 - 1 = ____

c. 65 - 3 = ____

d. 70 - 2 = ____

e. 69 - 3 = ____

f. 71 - 2 = ____

Preparing for Next Year

Color blocks to match the number shown on each expander.

a.

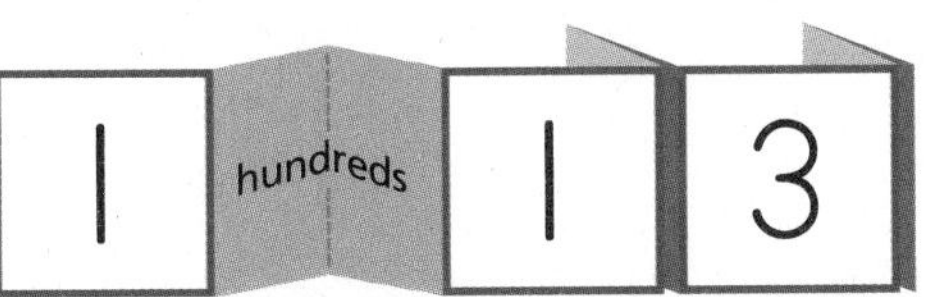

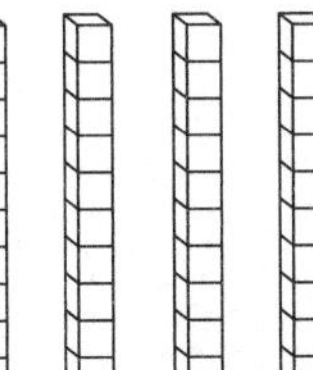

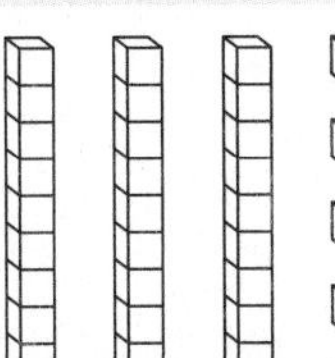

b.

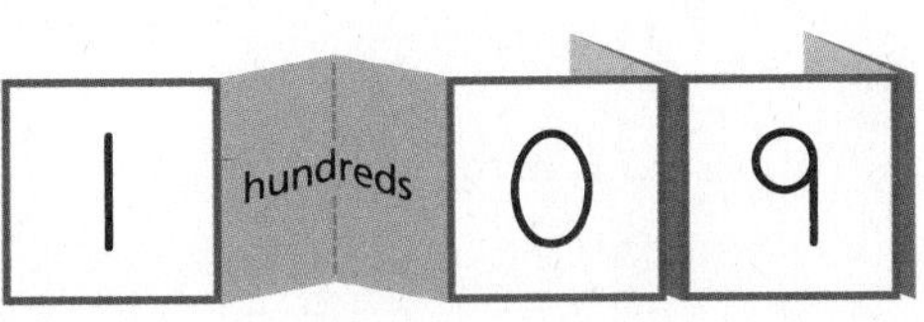

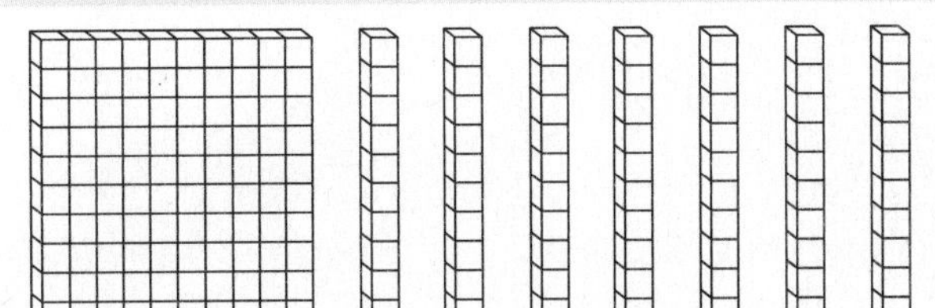

12.7 Subtraction: 1, 2, 3 or 10, 20, 30 from any two-digit number (hundred chart)

Step In **Look at this part of a hundred chart.**

1	2	3	4	5	6	7	8	9	10
11	12	13	14	15	16	17	18	19	20

What happens to the numbers as you move from right to left?

What happens to the numbers as you move back a row?

Look at this part of the same hundred chart.
What numbers are missing? How do you know?

35

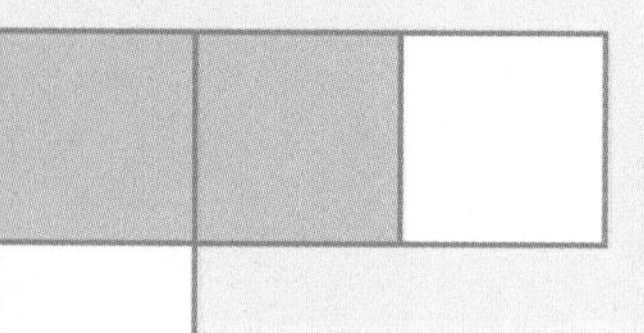

Look at this piece of the hundred chart.
What numbers could you write in the white spaces?
How do you know?

Step Up 1. Complete the equations. Use the chart to help.

a. 43 – 2 = ______

b. 37 – 10 = ______

c. 25 – 3 = ______

21	22	23	24	25	26	27	28	29	30
31	32	33	34	35	36	37	38	39	40
41	42	43	44	45	46	47	48	49	50
51	52	53	54	55	56	57	58	59	60

d. 29 – 20 = ______

e. 53 – 1 = ______

f. 51 – 30 = ______

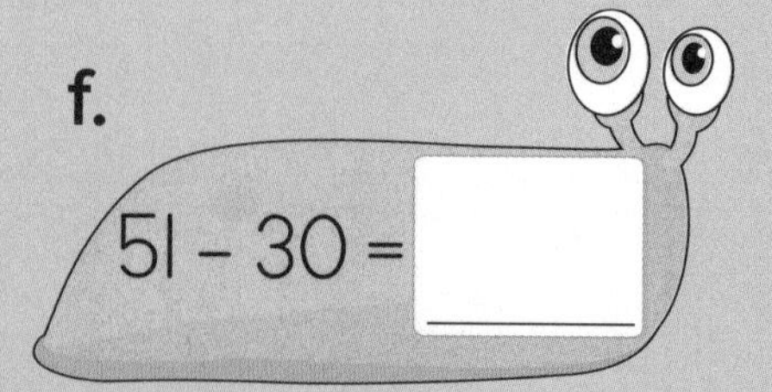

2. Figure out and write the answers.

a. 72 – 10 = ____

b. 65 – 2 = ____

c. 58 – 20 = ____

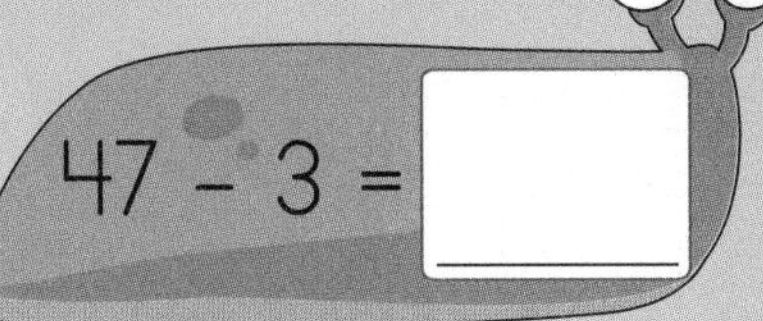

d. 47 – 3 = ____

e. 76 – 20 = ____

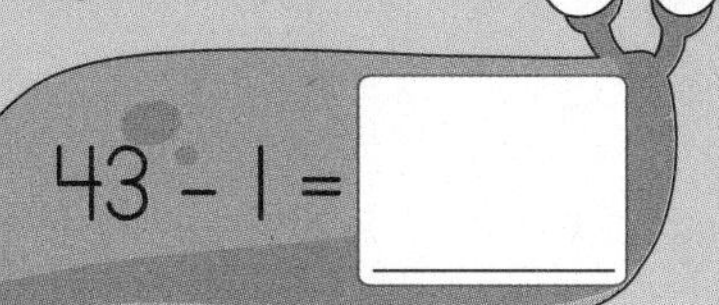

f. 43 – 1 = ____

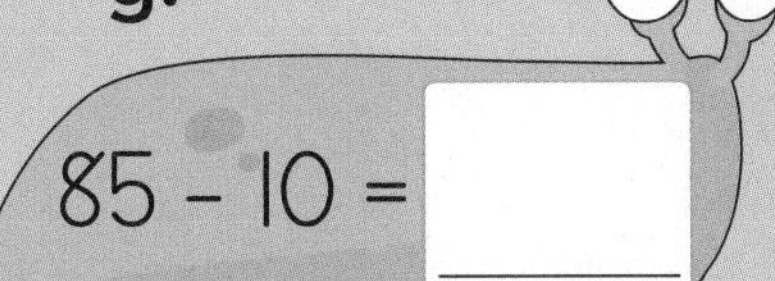

g. 85 – 10 = ____

h. 35 – 1 = ____

i. 57 – 2 = ____

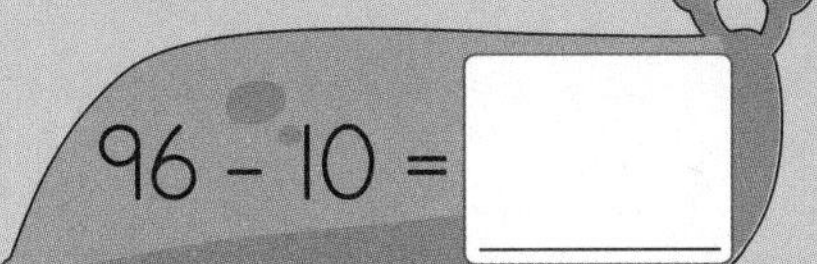

j. 96 – 10 = ____

k. 39 – 10 = ____

l. 69 – 20 = ____

Step Ahead Write the missing numbers along the trail.

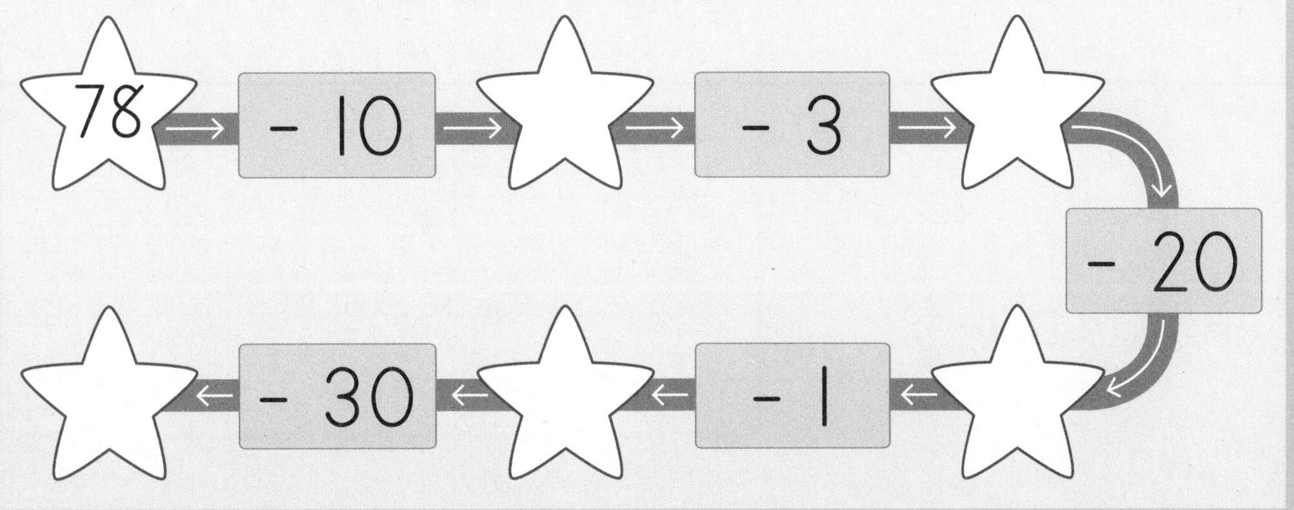

12.8 Subtraction: Two-digit numbers (hundred chart)

Step In **Look at this part of a hundred chart.**

How would you move the counter to subtract 20?

How would you move the counter to subtract 1?

How would you move the counter to subtract 21?

Does it matter if you subtract the ones before the tens?

1	2	3	4	5	6
11	12	13	14	15	16
21	22	23	24	25	26
31	32	33	34	35	36
41	42	43	44	45	46

Step Up **1.** Draw arrows on this hundred chart to show how you figure out each equation. Then write the answers.

a. 36 - 12 = ____

b. 89 - 21 = ____

c. 75 - 31 = ____

d. 34 - 13 = ____

e. 49 - 33 = ____

f. 64 - 12 = ____

g. 27 - 21 = ____

h. 95 - 32 = ____

1	2	3	4	5	6	7	8	9	10
11	12	13	14	15	16	17	18	19	20
21	22	23	24	25	26	27	28	29	30
31	32	33	34	35	36	37	38	39	40
41	42	43	44	45	46	47	48	49	50
51	52	53	54	55	56	57	58	59	60
61	62	63	64	65	66	67	68	69	70
71	72	73	74	75	76	77	78	79	80
81	82	83	84	85	86	87	88	89	90
91	92	93	94	95	96	97	98	99	100

2. Write the number at the end of each part of hundred chart. Then complete the matching equation.

a.

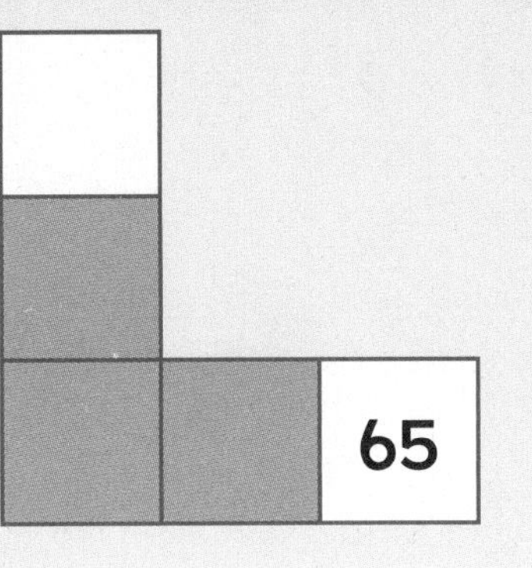

= ______

b.

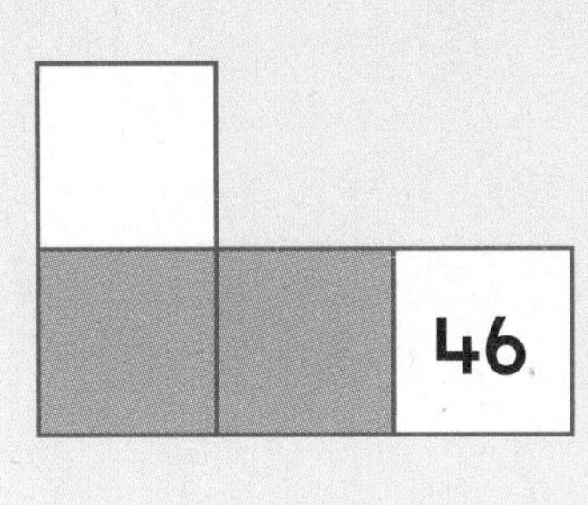

______ – ______ = ______

c.

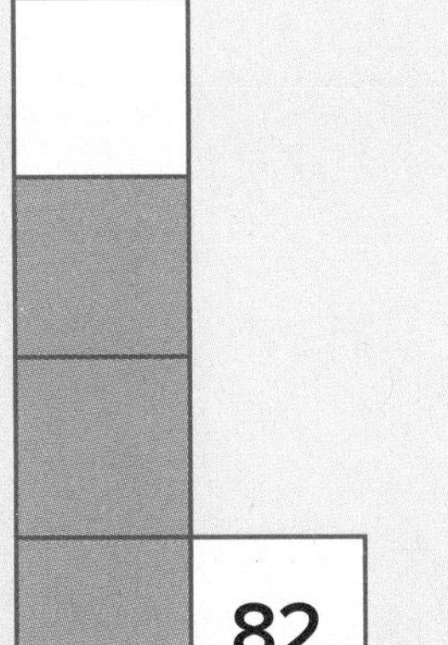

______ – ______ = ______

d.

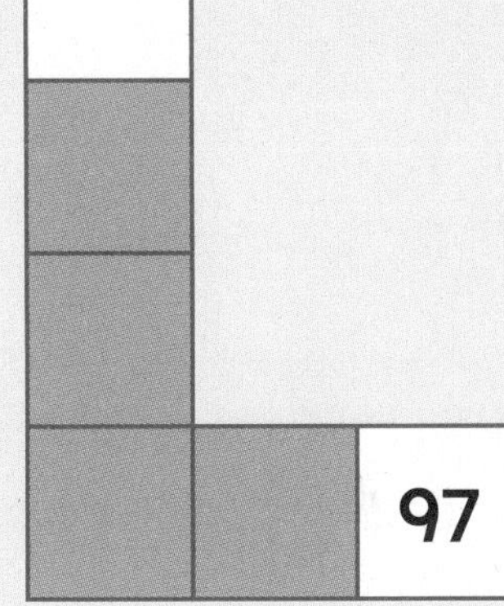

______ – ______ = ______

Step Ahead

This is part of a hundred chart. Write the numbers that should be shown in the white boxes.

						37			
	42								
51									
							68		

Maintaining concepts and skills

Think and Solve

Write a number to make each balance picture true.

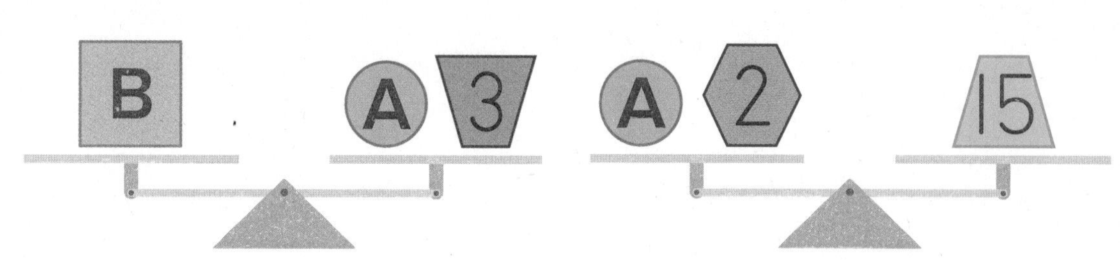

A = ______

B = ______

Words at Work

What is **subtraction**? You can use words from the list to help you.

- less
- equals
- take away
- count back
- walk away
- left over
- subtract
- count on
- difference

Ongoing Practice **1.** Draw the missing picture in each pattern.

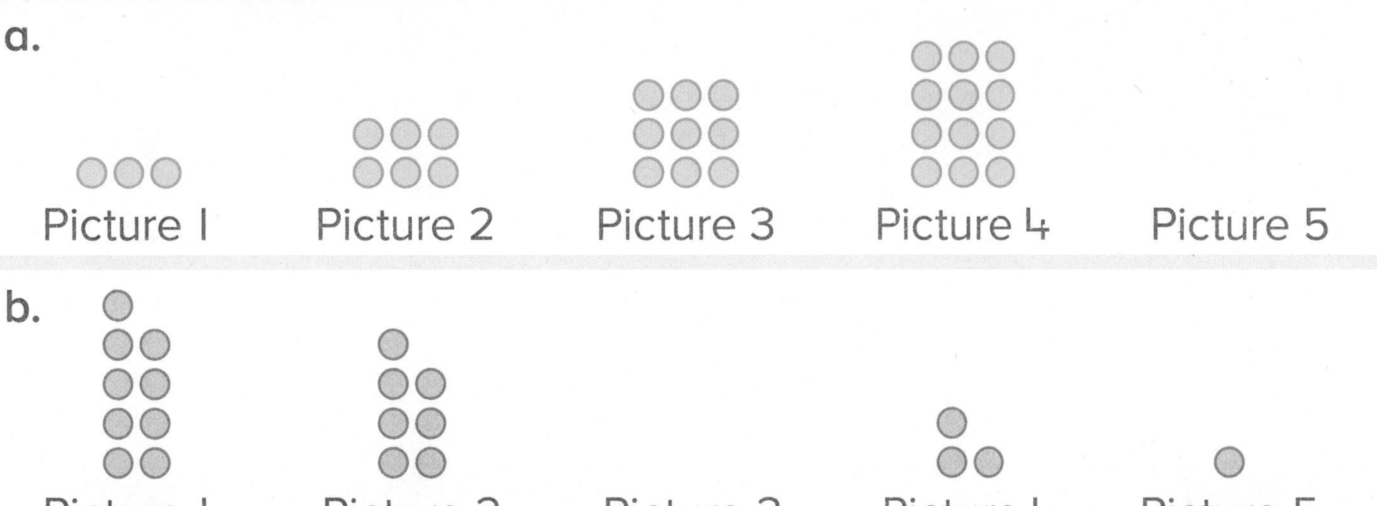

FROM 1.11.7

2. Write the differences. You can use this chart to help.

a. 84 - 30 = ____

b. 76 - 2 = ____

c. 98 - 40 = ____

d. 87 - 3 = ____

51	52	53	54	55	56	57	58	59	60
61	62	63	64	65	66	67	68	69	70
71	72	73	74	75	76	77	78	79	80
81	82	83	84	85	86	87	88	89	90
91	92	93	94	95	96	97	98	99	100

FROM 1.12.7

Preparing for Next Year Look at the blocks. Write the matching number on the expander. Then complete the number name.

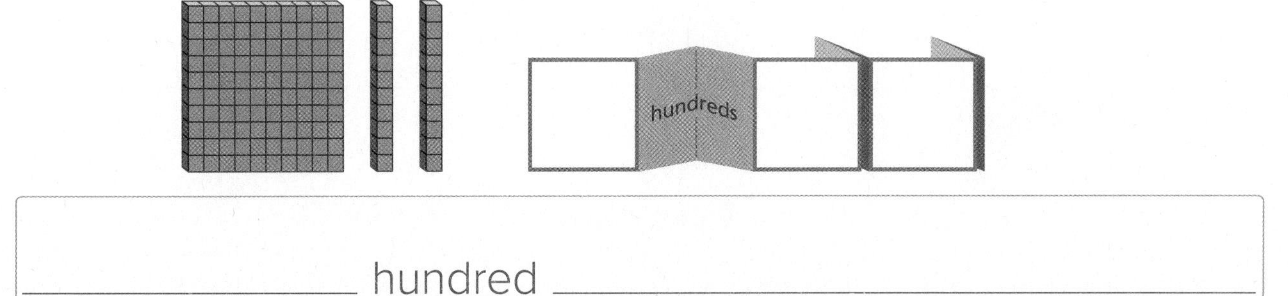

____ hundred ____

12.9 Capacity: Making direct comparisons

Step In

Each of these bottles is full of water. Which bottle holds the most water?

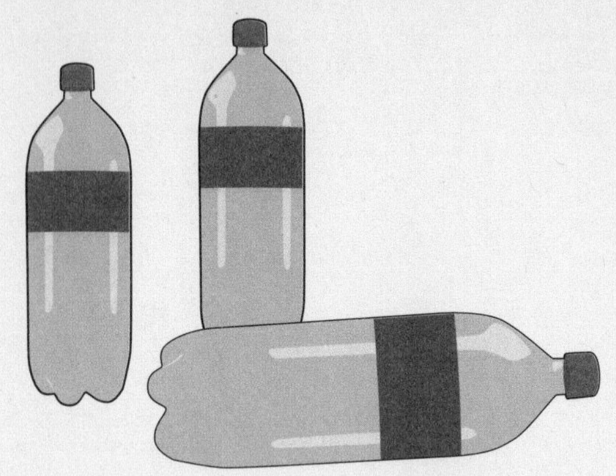

How could you order these bottles by the amount of water that they each hold?

Two of these water bottles have the same **capacity**.

Capacity tells the amount of liquid that a container can hold.

Step Up

1. Circle the containers that would hold **less** water than this pitcher.

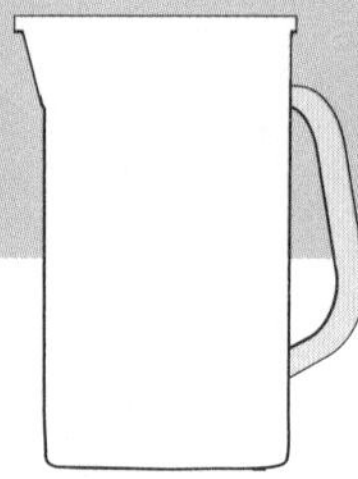

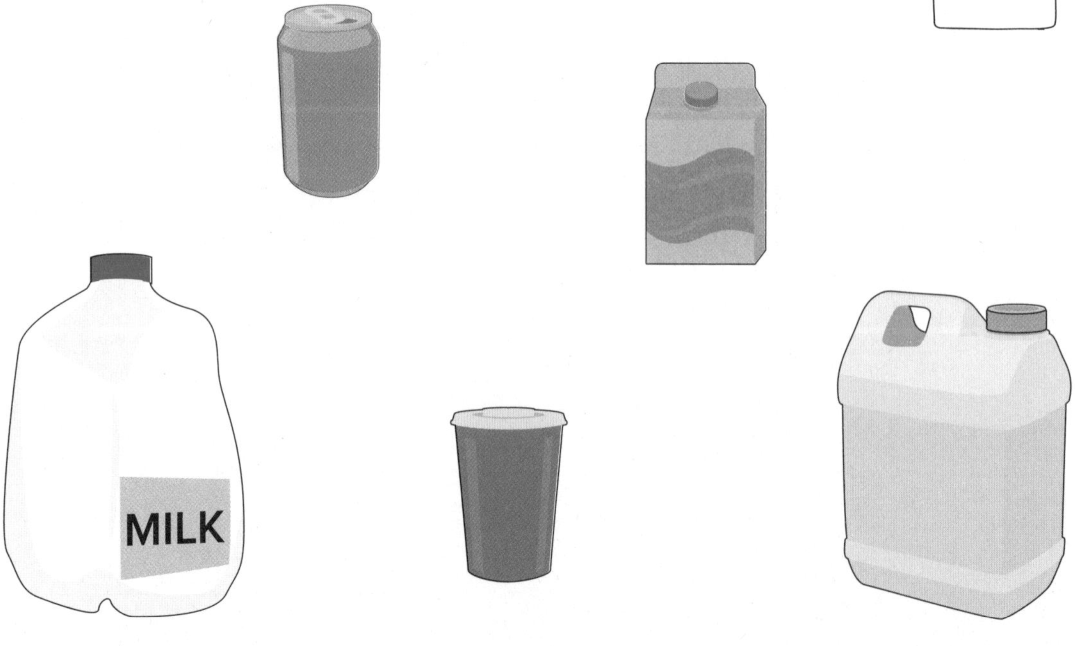

MILK

2. Circle the container with the **greater** capacity.
Circle both containers if the capacity looks the **same**.

a.

b.

c.

d.

e.

f.

Step Ahead

This bottle has been squashed.
Has the amount of water that
the bottle can hold changed?
Share your thinking with another student.

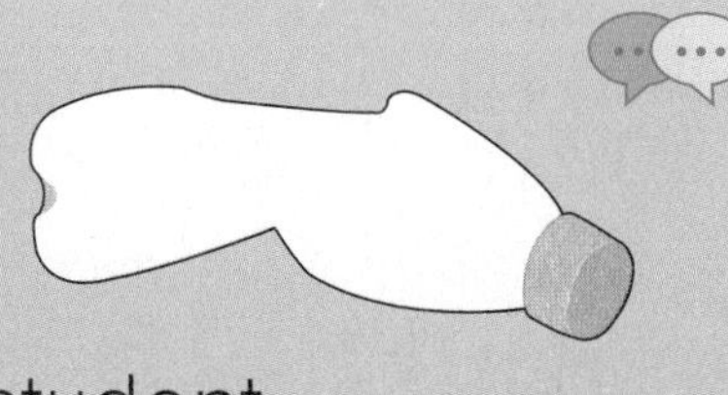

Capacity: Measuring with non-standard units

Step In **Look at these containers.**

How could you use the scoop to figure out the capacity of each container on the table?

How could you record the results?

What else could you use to measure the capacity of each container?

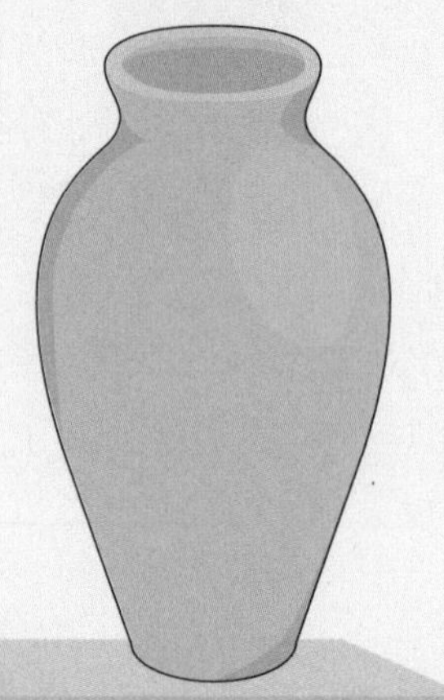

Step Up I. Write the number of scoops for each container.

Container	Number of Scoops of Rice
a.	____ scoops
b.	____ scoops
c.	____ scoops
d.	____ scoops

2. Write the number of scoops for these containers.

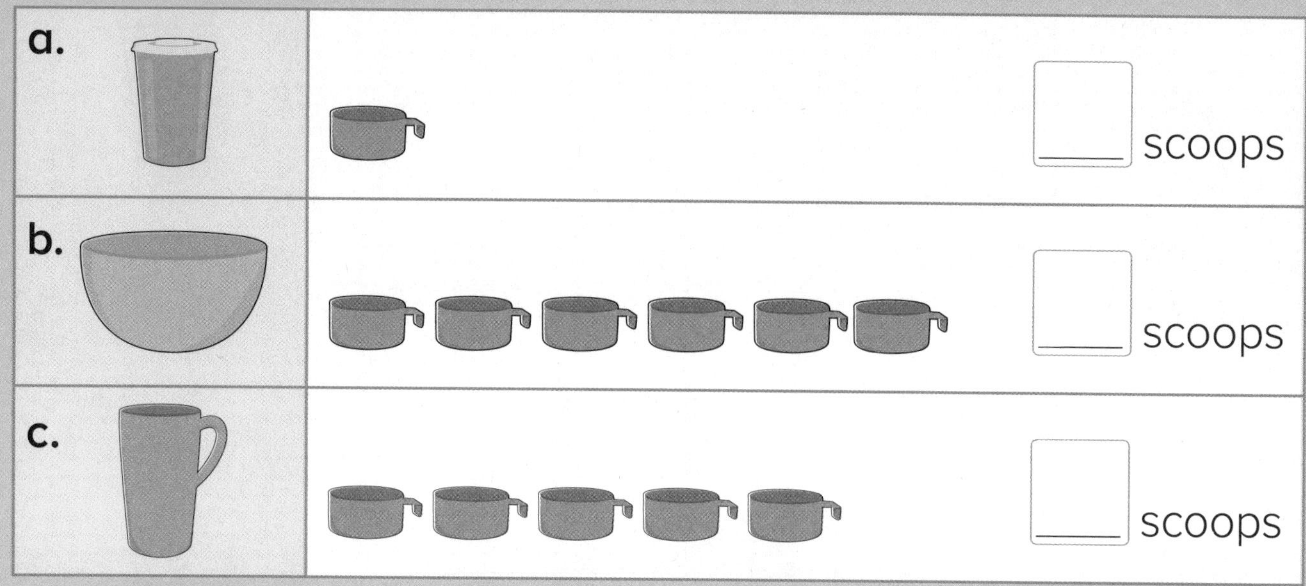

3. Compare these containers from Questions 1 and 2.
For each pair, circle the container that can hold more.

Step Ahead Look at the containers in Questions 1 and 2.

a.
Color the ⬭ beside the number of scoops it would take to fill two mugs.

⬭ 5 ⬭ 8 ⬭ 6 ⬭ 10

b.
Color the ⬭ beside the number of scoops it would take to fill two containers.

⬭ 2 ⬭ 6 ⬭ 5 ⬭ 3

Maintaining concepts and skills

Computation Practice

What is the best way to catch a fish?

★ Complete the equations. Then write each letter above its matching answer at the bottom of the page. Some letters appear more than once.

32 - 3 = ___	h	77 - 2 = ___	i
23 - 2 = ___	u	65 - 1 = ___	s
47 - 1 = ___	m	55 - 3 = ___	v
51 - 3 = ___	o	91 - 2 = ___	a
84 - 2 = ___	y	88 - 1 = ___	n
29 - 1 = ___	w	44 - 3 = ___	e
66 - 3 = ___	r	41 - 2 = ___	t

29 89 52 41 64 48 46 41 48 87 41

39 29 63 48 28 75 39 39 48 82 48 21

Ongoing Practice

1. Circle together the pennies you could trade for dimes. Then write the total number of dimes and pennies after the trade.

FROM 1.11.8

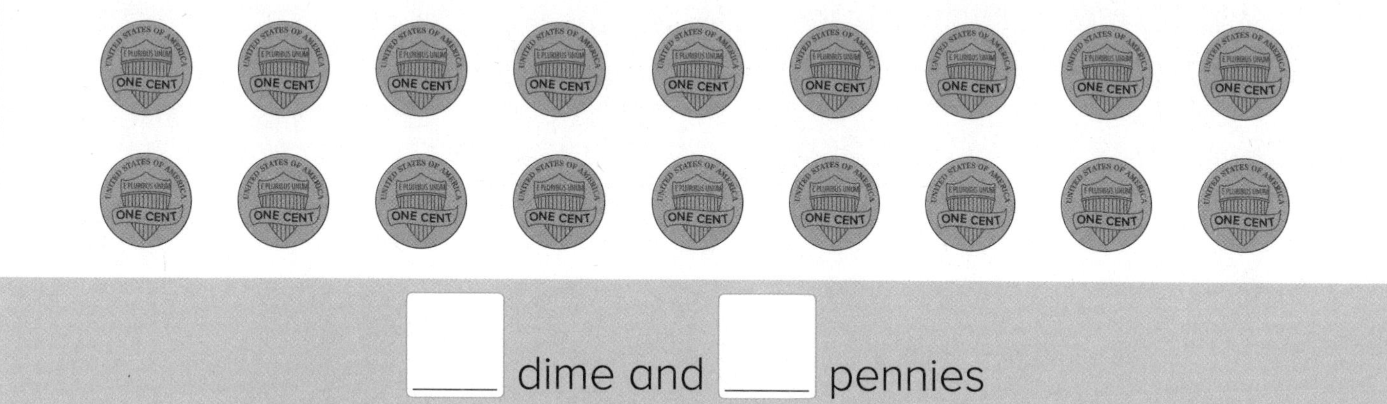

____ dime and ____ pennies

2. Write the number of scoops of rice for each container. Then circle the container that holds the most.

FROM 1.12.10

Container	Number of Scoops of Rice
a.	____ scoops
b.	____ scoops
c.	____ scoops

Preparing for Next Year

Figure out the total. Write the addition fact.

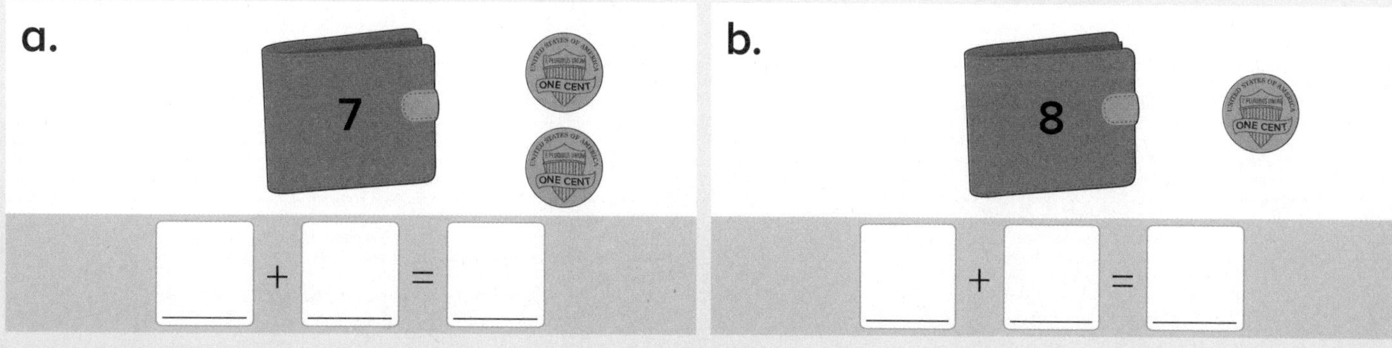

a. ____ + ____ = ____

b. ____ + ____ = ____

12.11 Mass: Making direct comparisons

Step In What do you know about the mass of each grocery item in this picture?

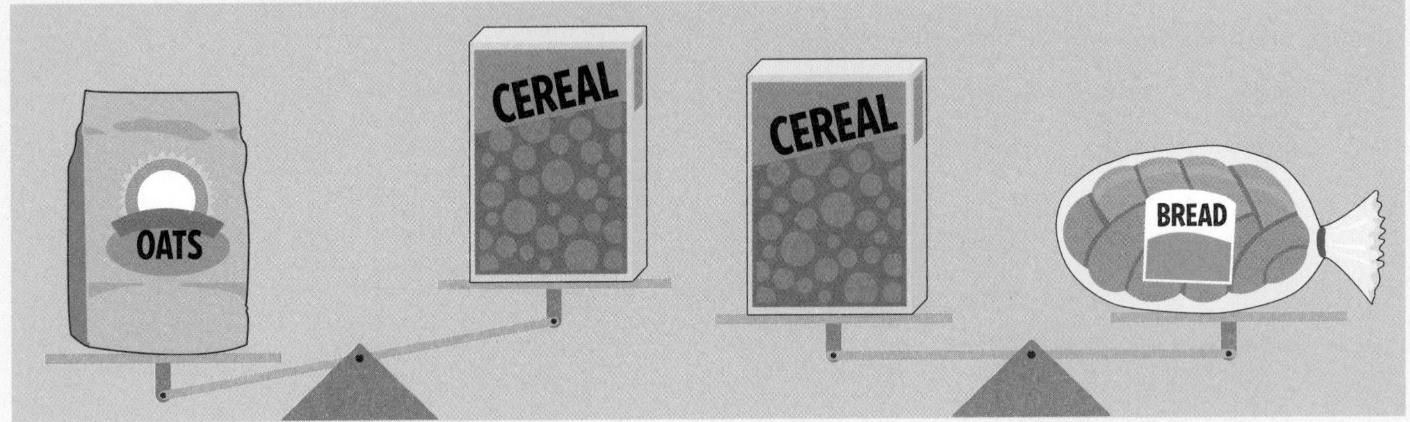

How could you compare the mass of the bread and the oats?

Write **bread** and **oats** on this pan balance to show your thinking.

The bread and cereal have the same mass. The oats are heavier than the cereal.

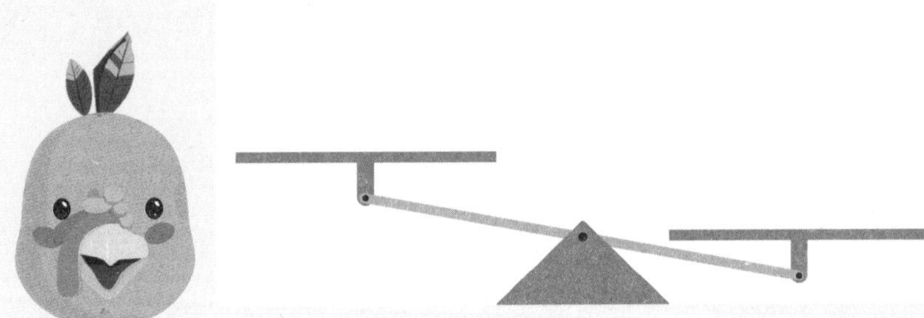

Step Up 1. Look at each picture. Write **more** or **less** to complete each sentence.

a.

The sugar weighs ____________ than the flour.

b.

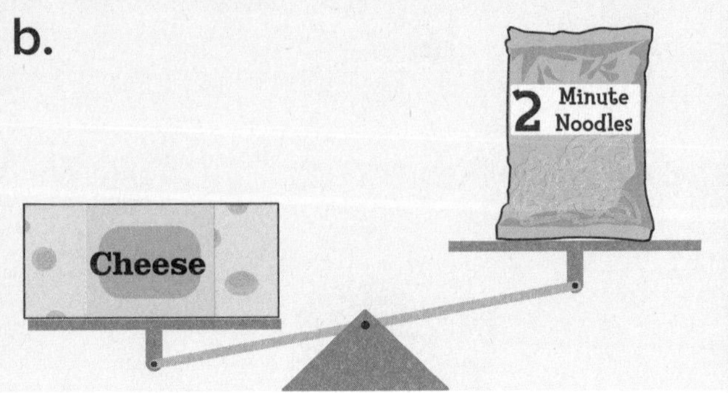

The noodles weigh ____________ than the cheese.

2. Look at each picture. Write **more than**, **the same as**, or **less than** to compare the mass.

a.

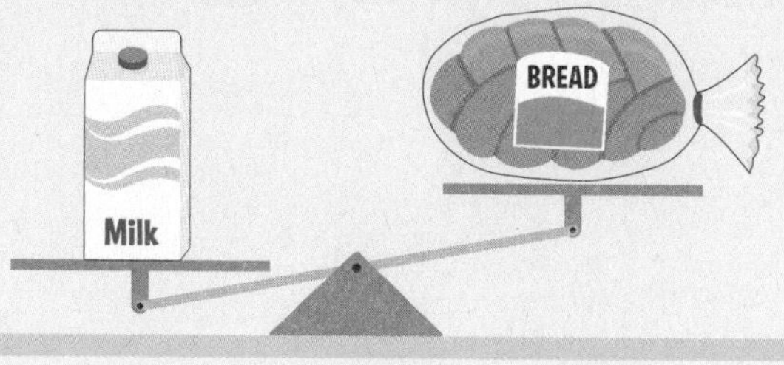

Milk

BREAD

The bread weighs

____

the milk.

b.

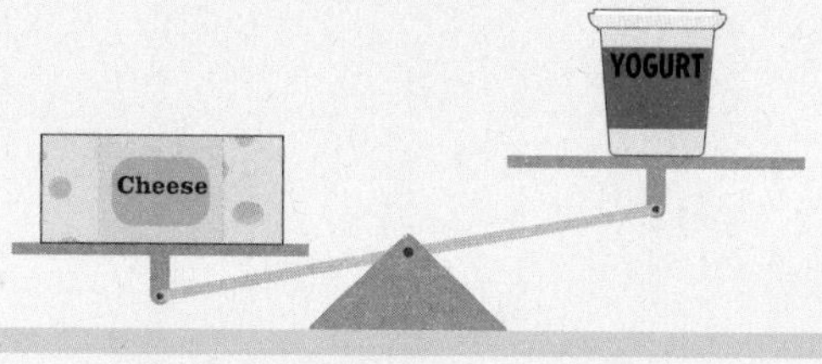

Cheese

YOGURT

The cheese weighs

____

the yogurt.

c.

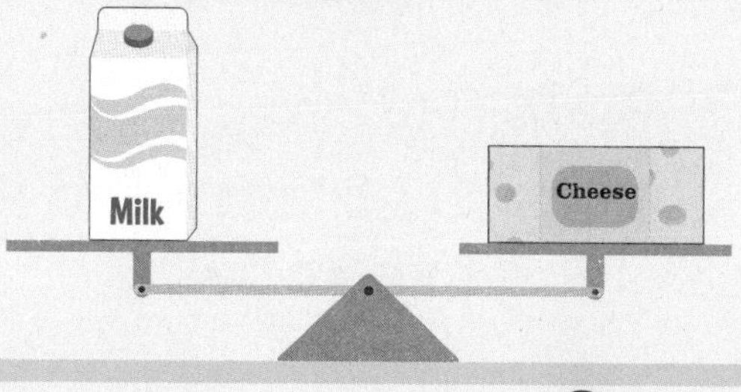

Milk

Cheese

The milk weighs

____

the cheese.

d.

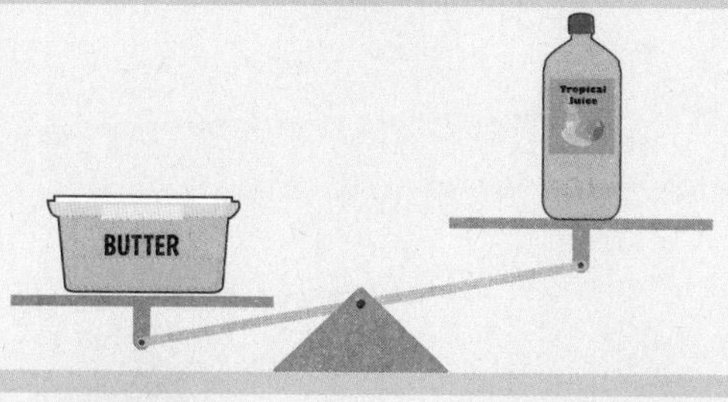

BUTTER

Tropical Juice

The juice weighs

____

the butter.

e.

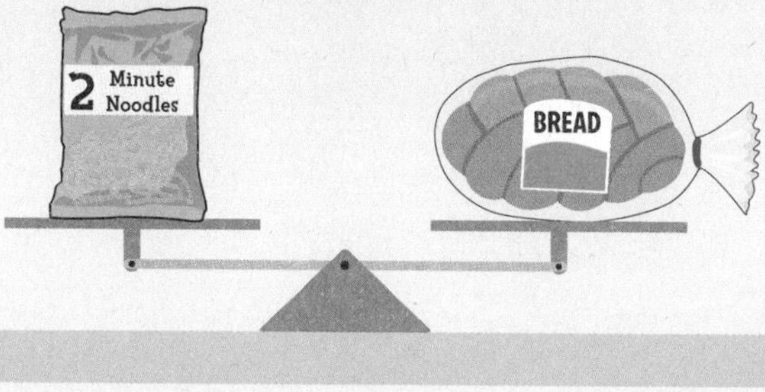

2 Minute Noodles

BREAD

The noodles weigh

____

the bread.

Step Ahead Look at the balance pictures above. Write **yogurt** and **milk** on this pan balance to make it true.

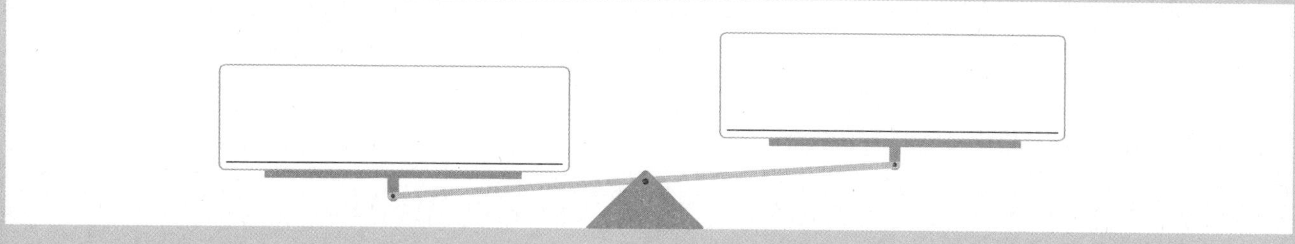

Mass: Measuring with non-standard units

Step In Does the ball weigh more or less than 10 cubes? How do you know?

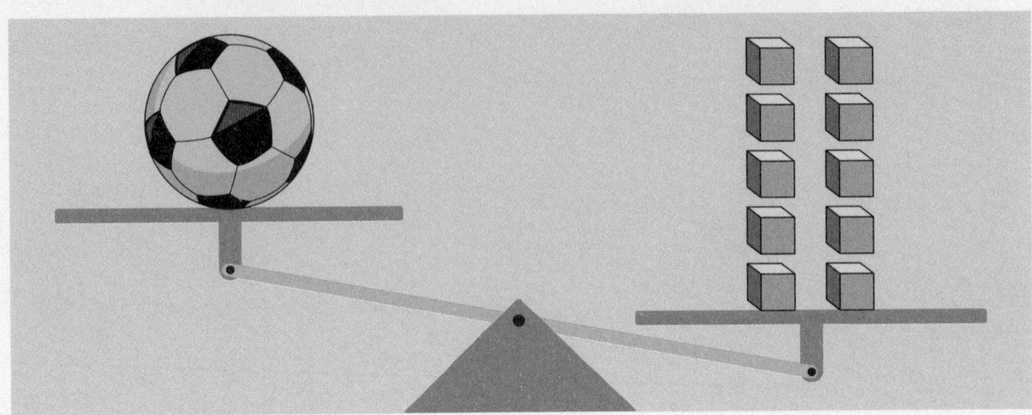

Imagine the ball and the cubes had the same mass.
What would the balance look like? How could you balance the ball?
Would you add more cubes or take some of the cubes away?

Step Up 1. Look at the balance. Color the ⬭ beside the words that best describe the mass of the toy.

a.

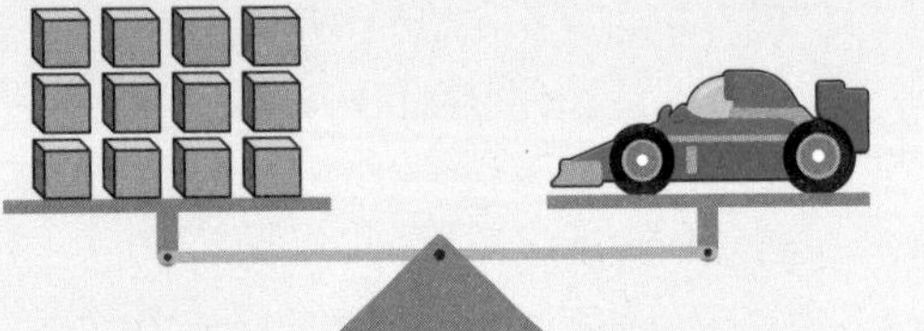

- ⬭ more than 12 cubes
- ⬭ fewer than 12 cubes
- ⬭ balances 12 cubes

b.

- ⬭ more than 10 cubes
- ⬭ fewer than 10 cubes
- ⬭ balances 10 cubes

c.

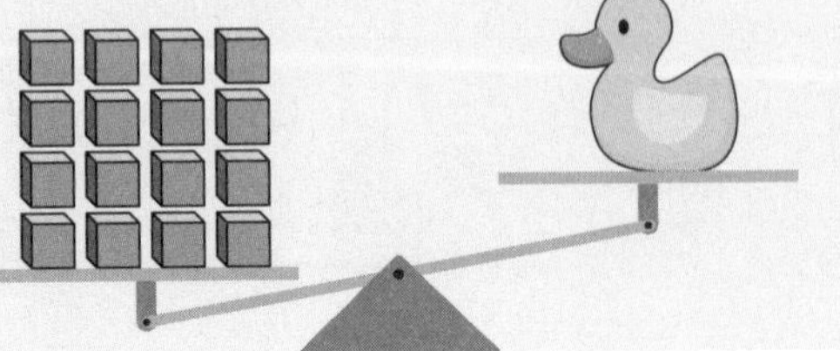

- ⬭ more than 16 cubes
- ⬭ fewer than 16 cubes
- ⬭ balances 16 cubes

d.

- ⬭ more than 9 cubes
- ⬭ fewer than 9 cubes
- ⬭ balances 9 cubes

2. Write the number of cubes in each space. Color the ⬭ beside the words that best describe the mass of the toy.

a.

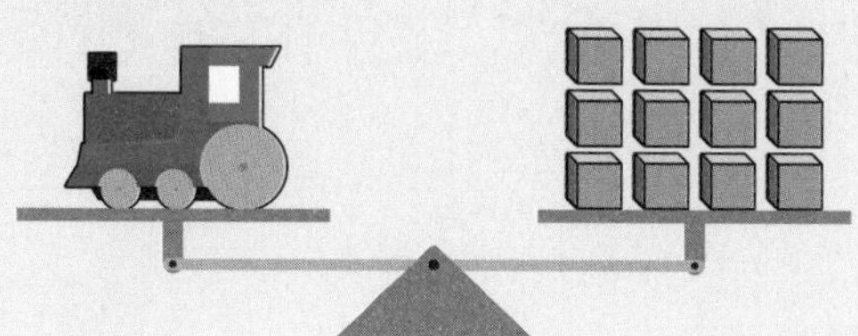

⬭ more than ____ cubes

⬭ fewer than ____ cubes

⬭ balances ____ cubes

b.

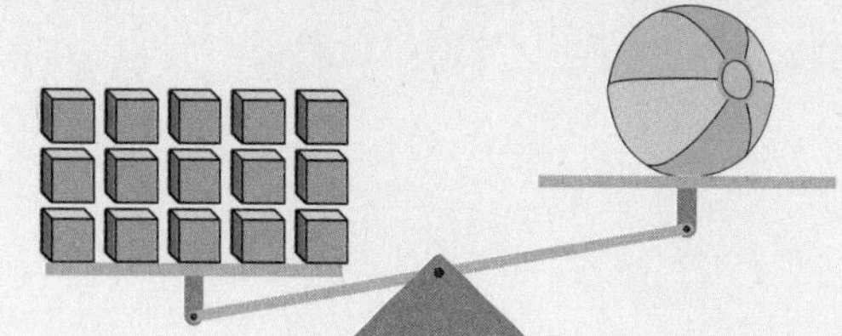

⬭ more than ____ cubes

⬭ fewer than ____ cubes

⬭ balances ____ cubes

c.

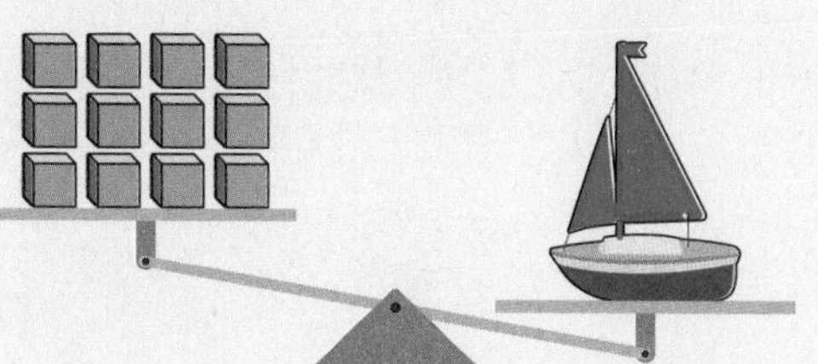

⬭ more than ____ cubes

⬭ fewer than ____ cubes

⬭ balances ____ cubes

d.

⬭ more than ____ cubes

⬭ fewer than ____ cubes

⬭ balances ____ cubes

Step Ahead

How many cubes might this toy weigh?
Write three possible answers.

____ cubes

____ cubes

____ cubes

Maintaining concepts and skills

Think and Solve  Read the clues. Use the letters to answer.

Clues

G holds more than **D**.

E holds less than **D**.

F holds less than **E**.

a. Which cylinder holds the **most**? 

b. Which cylinder holds the **least**? 

Words at Work Choose and write words from the list to complete the sentences below. One word is not used.

capacity
mass
heavier
holds less
lighter
holds more

a. ____________ tells the amount something weighs.

b. A small cup ____________ than a milk bottle.

c. A pumpkin is ____________ than a ones block.

d. A bathtub ____________ than a cup.

e. ____________ tells the amount a container can hold.

Ongoing Practice

1. Color the coins you would use to pay the **exact** amount for each item.

FROM 1.11.11

a.

b.

2. Write the number of cubes. Then color the ⬭ beside the words that best describe the mass of the piece of fruit.

FROM 1.12.12

a.

- ⬭ more than ______ cubes
- ⬭ fewer than ______ cubes
- ⬭ balances ______ cubes

b.

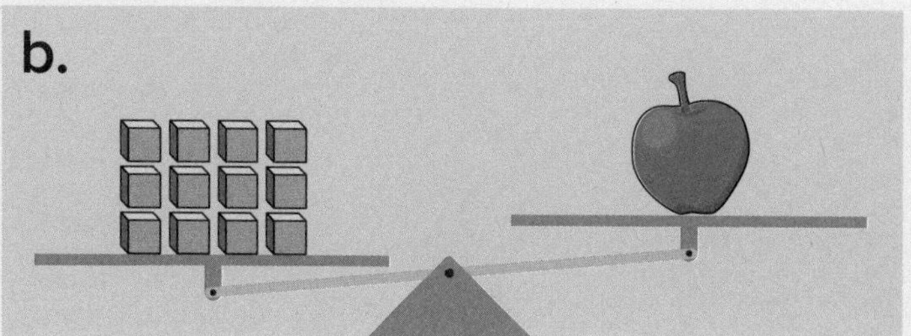

- ⬭ more than ______ cubes
- ⬭ fewer than ______ cubes
- ⬭ balances ______ cubes

Preparing for Next Year

Write the addition fact.
Then write the turnaround fact.

a.

____ + ____ = ______

____ + ____ = ______

b.

____ + ____ = ______

____ + ____ = ______

c.

____ + ____ = ______

____ + ____ = ______

Working Space

Working Space

2D shape

A **two-dimensional (2D) shape** has straight sides, curved edges, or straight sides and curved edges. For example:

 triangle	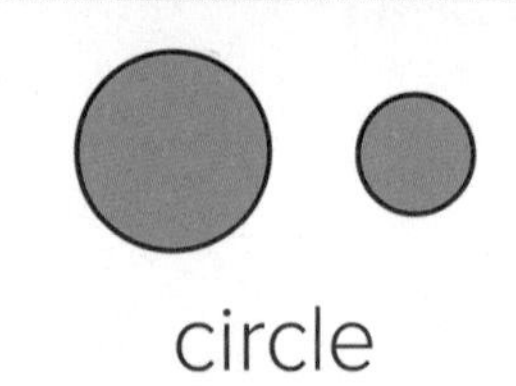 circle	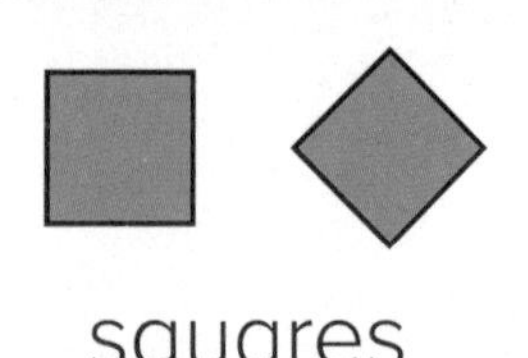 squares	 other shapes

3D object

A **three-dimensional (3D) object** has flat surfaces, curved surfaces, or flat and curved surfaces. For example:

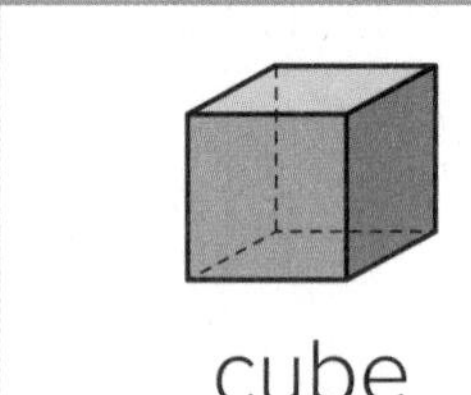 cube	 sphere	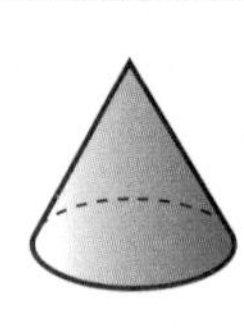 cone	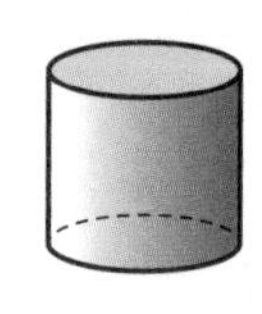 cylinder

Addition

Addition is finding the total when two or more parts are known. When adding, another word for total is **sum**.

Part	+	**Part**	=	**Total**
2	+	3	=	5

Capacity

Capacity tells the amount a container can hold. For example, a cup **holds less** than a juice bottle.

Common fraction

Common fractions describe equal parts of one whole.

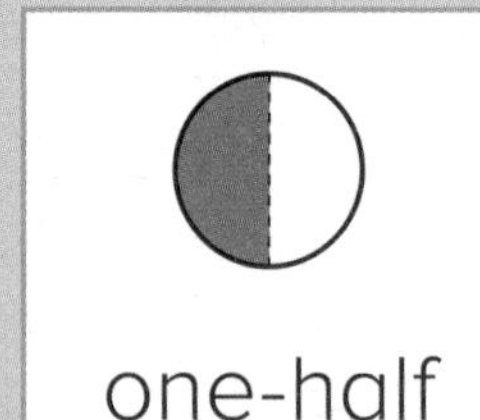
one-half

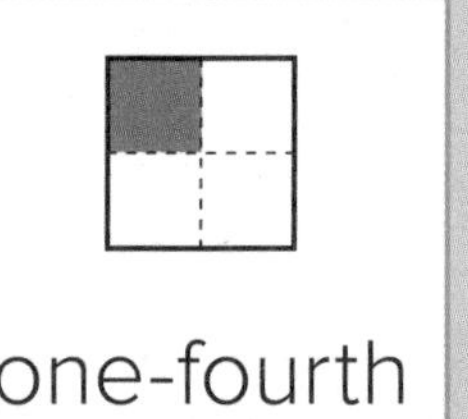
one-fourth

Comparing

When read from left to right, the symbol > means **is greater than**.
The symbol < means **is less than**.
For example: 2 < 6 means 2 **is less than** 6

Equals

2 and 3 **balances** 5
2 and 3 **is equal to** 5
2 + 3 = 5

Equation

An **equation** is a number sentence that uses the equals symbol.
For example: 7 + 8 = 15

Fact family

A **fact family** includes an addition fact, its turnaround fact, and the two related subtraction facts. For example:

4 + 2 = 6
2 + 4 = 6
6 − 4 = 2
6 − 2 = 4

Mass

Mass tells the amount something weighs.
For example, a cat **weighs more** than a mouse.

Mental computation strategies for addition

These are strategies you can use to figure out a mathematical problem in your head.

Count-on	*See* 2 + 8	*think* 8 + 1 + 1
	See 58 + 24	*think* 58 + 10 + 10 + 4
Doubles	*See* 7 + 7	*think* double 7
	See 25 + 26	*think* double 25 plus 1 more
	See 35 + 37	*think* double 35 plus 2 more
Make-ten	*See* 9 + 4	*think* 9 + 1 + 3
	See 38 + 14	*think* 38 + 2 + 12
Place-value	*See* 32 + 27	*think* 32 + 20 + 7

Mental computation strategies for subtraction

These are strategies you can use to figure out a mathematical problem in your head.

Count-back *See* 9 – 2 *think* 9 – 1 – 1
See 26 – 20 *think* 26 – 10 – 10

Think-addition *See* 17 – 9 *think* 9 + 8 = 17 so 17 – 9 = 8

Number

Number tells "how many." For example, there are nine blocks in this group.

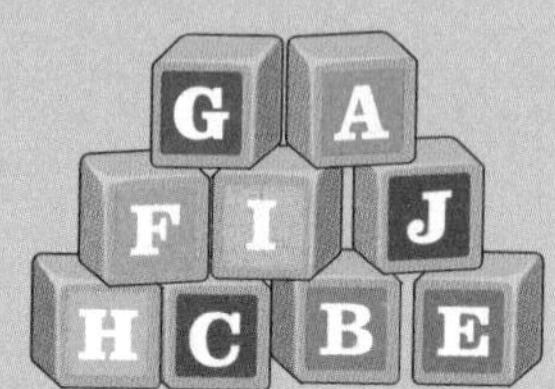

Number facts

Addition facts are all the addition equations that show two one-digit numbers being added. Addition facts can be written with the total at the start or at the end.

For example: 2 + 3 = 5 or 3 = 1 + 2

Subtraction facts are all the subtraction equations that are related to the addition facts.

For example: 5 – 2 = 3 or 3 – 2 = 1

Numeral

A **numeral** is the symbol for a number.

Related subtraction facts

Each subtraction fact has a **related** fact.

For example: 7 – 4 = 3 and 7 – 3 = 4

Subtraction

Subtraction is finding a part when the total and one part are known.

Total	−	Part	=	Part
5	−	2	=	3
Part	+	___	=	Total
2	+	___	=	5

Tally

A **tally** is a single mark used to record the number of times something occurs. A gate tally is a mark used to group every five tallies. For example:

||||

four tally marks

Turnaround fact

Each addition fact has a related **turnaround fact**.

For example: 2 + 3 = 5 and 3 + 2 = 5